Keeping the Link

Ethernet Installation and Management

Martin A.W. Nemzow

McGraw-Hill Book Company

New York   St. Louis   San Francisco   Auckland   Bogotá
Caracas   Colorado Springs   Hamburg   Lisbon
London   Madrid   Mexico   Milan   Montreal
New Delhi   Oklahoma City   Panama   Paris
San Juan   São Paulo   Singapore
Sydney   Tokyo   Toronto

Library of Congress Cataloging-in-Publication Data

Nemzow, Martin A.W.
  Keeping the link.

  Bibliography: p.
  Includes index.
  1. Ethernet (Local area network system) I. Title.
TK5105.8.E83N46   1988   004.6'8   88-8881
ISBN 0-07-046302-6

1234567890   DOC/DOC   8921098

ISBN 0-07-046302-6

Printed and bound by R.R. Donnelley & Sons Company.

For more information about other McGraw-Hill materials,
call 1-800-2-MCGRAW in the United States. In other
countries, call your nearest McGraw-Hill office.

Love to Carol Eve Weingrod for enduring my long hours away from her.

This book would not have been without the support from friends, associates, and industry experts who supplied both encouragement, technical information, documentation, and some of the photographs within.

Special thanks to Melinda Thedens and Mickey Smith.

Contents

Preface

Data communications and Ethernet networks are often promoted as a "competitive weapon" and the means to solve computer problems and lower data processing expenses. Such approaches often misfire unless the network is carefully and intelligently administered. Networks are complex in all phases, from design to organization, from execution to daily operation and maintenance. A well-run network can match the promise of Ethernet and furnish an organization with a powerful strategy that outstrips competition.

This book presents the practical knowledge needed to design, build, grow, and maintain an Ethernet communication network for most vendor equipment, whether Apollo, Apple, Altos, Bridge, Convergent, DEC, DG, Hewlett-Packard, IBM, Sun, Xerox, or many others. This book is designed primarily to answer questions facing an Ethernet network manager and his or her team. The specifications of the IEEE 802 committee and the ISO network standard are used as a base for definition of key terms because most vendors try to adhere to these standards. Vendor Ethernet documentation is expanded and explained, and its practical ramifications are discussed. In addition, the nuts and bolts of planning for installation and cabling, capacity planning, physical maintenance, and statistical tracking are presented for the busy network administrator. Concise and specific illustrations and descriptions prepare even the novice for all stages of network administration, and clarify the ambiguous and sparse vendor Ethernet documentation.

This preface presents the organization of *Keeping the Link*. As an acknowledgment of the reader's limited time, Figure 1 illustrates the design and flow of the knowledge contained within this book.

Chapter 1 presents the network in light of its connective power as a strategic resource in today's competitive resource-limited environment and suggests how to make a persuasive argument for network technology.

Chapter 2 discusses in overview the benefits of networking and describes what Ethernet is, how it works, the variations in Ethernet protocols, and the types of problems that can be encountered in a production environment.

Chapter 3 presents a networking model and the variations in Ethernet. It describes the three standard baseband variations and the rationale supporting many organizations' selection of nonstandardized broadband.

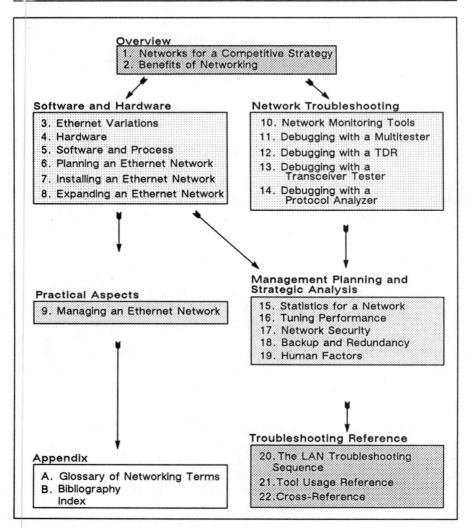

Figure 1 The organization of *Keeping the Link.*

Chapter 4 describes the hardware and the mechanical process of Ethernet. The components of an Ethernet network are described and illustrated to help the reader understand the ingenious simplicity of an Ethernet network.

Chapter 5 explains the Ethernet process. This includes the transmission methodology and the characteristic features of network-level software.

Chapter 6 details the planning procedures for the mechanical components of Ethernet networks, completing what spartan vendor instructions omit. This chapter outlines those issues that an experienced network manager considers before building or expanding an Ethernet network.

Chapter 7 explains the installation procedures for the mechanical components of Ethernet networks, completing what spartan vendor instructions omit. This chapter suggests what steps an experienced network manager takes for testing and benchmarking a newly installed network.

Chapter 8 explains why bridges, fan-out units, gateways, and repeaters are necessary on a large Ethernet, and how these units are installed. Since organizational growth is likely to outstrip the capacity of any original network, bridges, fan-out units, gateways, and repeaters are also presented as solutions to overloaded networks.

Chapter 9 presents practical rules of thumb and suggestions for successfully using Ethernet. The formal IEEE and ISO specifications do little to explain the hows and whys of success and failure with Ethernet, therefore Chapter 9 concentrates on operational management.

Chapter 10 suggests practical tools that test, monitor, and analyze nework status. When the network fails there are various techniques to identify, locate, and repair problems. Some techniques are time-consuming or expensive and some require specialized tools like a multimeter, a time domain reflectometer, a transceiver tester, and a network analyzer. Because each of these tools is indispensable on a large, busy, or critical network, information on to how use them and interpret their results is presented in separate chapters complete with photographs, illustrations, and tables.

Chapter 11 details appropriate steps to verify the correct electrical operation of network hardware using a multimeter. This tool provides a first pass for testing a network. It is often the one tool available to a network manager to solve serious network failures.

Chapter 12 details the usage of a time domain reflectometer and the practical steps to check the conductivity and usability of network cable, connections and cable fittings, and to check for correct installation of taps and repeater hardware. This tool also provides a highly desirable method for benchmark cable installation.

Chapter 13 explains the operation of the transceiver tester, including how to connect and operate it, and how to interpret this tool's results.

Chapter 14 describes the necessity for the network protocol analyzer. The methodology for using this monitor to identify, locate, and isolate suspected network problems is presented in detail.

Chapter 15 calculates the statistics of Ethernet. Ethernet is a *carrier-sense multiple-access with collision detection* (CSMA/CD) process. This means Ethernet transmission is a random process and that many non-mechanical problems are inherently statistical. In order to understand why bottlenecks occur, why Ethernet collisions decrease performance, why a network can fail completely, the mathematics are analyzed and charted.

Chapter 16 builds upon the knowledge from the chapters on installation, configurations, network traffic, and statistics for the purpose of tuning network performance. It also discusses optimal planning, network loads, and alternative solutions for overloaded networks. This single chapter can be invaluable when network trouble occurs, when no solutions are self-evident, and when there appear to be no options for locating network failures.

Chapter 17 discusses security issues, explains why the networking model contains no reference to either data or physical security, why Ethernet is not secure, and what precautions can be taken to protect a network from outside prying and unauthorized access. Because Ethernet is a public network, packets are freely readable by any node workstation. As such, it is dependent on network software, specialized hardware, and judicious management procedures to maintain security.

Chapter 18 explains backup procedures and suggests what hardware, software, or operational procedures can be implemented to produce a nearly fault-tolerant network. Issues and redundancy for the important network services - files storage, printing, tape backup of network data, shutdown of failed segments - are discussed in this chapter.

Chapter 19 illustrates why trained and qualified people are an important resource for network administration. Ethernet depends on people with expertise and experience. Without knowledgeable people, the network will perform below capacity, cause severe operational problems, constrain organization growth, and in extreme cases, even fail to function.

Chapter 20 is a detailed troubleshooting manual that describes techniques to isolate hardware, software, and the common network overloading problems.

Chapter 21 summarizes the contents of this book with an Ethernet tool usage manual. This chapter supplies ideas and information on when to use the multimeter, the TDR, the transceiver tester, and a protocol analyzer to solve network problems.

Chapter 22 iconically describes the network components and then, using tables with four different formats, matches symptoms of common network problems with the possible causes. This information is not available cross-referenced, nor completely accessible from other sources including vendor documentation or the IEEE Ethernet specifications.

Chapter 23 is a glossary with local area network and Ethernet terms defined and cross-referenced by the all-too-common acronyms.

Symbols Used in this Book

®   Segment Repeater

             Segment Bridge

             Segment Gateway

             Coaxial Tap and Transceiver (MAU)

             Transceiver Drop Cable (AUI)

             Network Node

             Designated Network Node

             Cheapernet or Thinnet Coaxial Cable

             Ethernet Coaxial Cable

○   End Connector

●   End Connector with Terminator

○○   End Connectors with Barrel Connector

Part 1

Overview

This section presents an overview of Ethernet networking. The first chapter presents the network in light of its connective power as a strategic resource in today's competitive resource-limited environment and suggests how to make a persuasive argument for network technology. Chapter 2 discusses in overview the benefits of networking and describes what Ethernet is, how it works, the variations in Ethernet protocols, and the types of problems that can be encountered in a production environment.

Chapter 1

Networks for Competitive Strategy

The complex business environment is challenging organizations to discover new ways to gain competitive advantages. In addition to the traditional physical and monetary assets such as equipment, buildings, and cash reserves, an organization has information and networking assets. Although information management is better understood by most private-sector business administrators through the context of the *value chain, market dynamics, distribution channel,* and *price points* than it is through the context of computer technology, networking, management of information systems, or data processing, an organization also can leverage the creative uses of information and networking technology for strategic benefit. The aim of networking strategies is to move an organization to its potential while locking out with aggressive information systems its competitors and providing a *sustainable competitive advantage* which those competitors will find difficult to copy.

There is a continuum of complexity with computer and communication technology. For a small company, networking just the inventory system might be considered a strategic advantage, while a larger company might implement a network to serve all workers at all locations. There is a learning curve attached to information and communication technologies. Even while the key to success is to learn faster and implement sooner than competition, the networking trend is continuing. Each success raises the ante; more complex and intuitive applications of networking are required to sustain a competitive advantage.

This proliferating new communications technology has reshaped the marketplace because it has altered the competitive game for all organizations. Communications have become integral to most computer and business activities. Some organizations will fail to recognize the available opportunities, and others will fail to recognize how to adapt them to the new possibilities in their strategic planning. Technological changes improve the efficiency and enhance implementation of communication. Networking, in particular, is a sophisticated and deliberate strategy that can improve profits, productivity, market share, product distribution, and work environments by facilitating quick decisions, improving information flow and accuracy, and communicating such information and decisions rapidly to those who would benefit from them.

If information and networking technology appear to be strategic solutions, this technology must be applied with foresight, forethought, and a critical understanding of the market. Clearly, the risk is not only to those who try new technology with its potential for clumsy and inefficient results; too many organizations have learned the painful consequences of limiting the reach and coverage of information exchange. The risk is also to those who watch and wait while others succeed first. With the accelerating pace of change, the complexity of technology, and the increasing sophistication of those applying networking technology, there is little ascertainable difference between strategic initiative and a "hare-brained" idea; for a strategy to be effective it must be implemented correctly before the competition understands what that strategy is. Of necessity, effective strategies precede the complete understanding of the applicable technology.

Advantages of Networks

Networks yield significant advantages that can overwhelm a competitor. Networking power can provide better service with fewer resources. It can also provide a medium in a research and development environment for cross-fertilization of ideas. Networking can streamline processes inherently slow or inherently fragile, and automate these processes for higher integrity. While the financial planner is often severely challenged to quantify these benefits in terms acceptable to stockholders, trustees, and bankers, it is proven that networks do generate cost-effective benefits, create significant economies of scale, boost worker productivity, and create unanticipated and imaginative results. Networks thus offer an applicable competitive strategy. The competitive advantages created through networking are summarized in Figure 1.1.

- Higher worker productivity
- Integration of process and information
- Lower installation cost per device or user
- Sharing of expensive resources
- Consolidation of scarce resources
- Creation of critical channels for communications
- Increases in the speed of contact and transactions
- Global access to information
- Higher resource utilization
- R&D discovery
- Interaction between information workers

Figure 1.1 Networks provide competitive advantages over mainframes.

It has been known for years that data processing is a viable competitive tool. Such systems have generated information that managers have applied to pare costs, simplify product design, identify excessive or expensive procedures, locate cost variances, reduce inventory, target customer preferences, and provide strategic product information required to capture market segment. Data processing is most useful in capturing cost, inventory, pricing, and production information. More sophisticated uses of computer networking power have been integrated directly into marketed products and services, and these products and services sell better because of that informational content. While computer-related products—hardware, software, information, publishing, or R&D—are often presented as products and services that strategically benefit from computer networking, many "unlikely" products and services benefit as well by providing wider information exchange and faster response, and by opening new areas and new sources. Examples include airline flights, hospital supplies, air conditioners, and cosmetics.

Networks Create Monopolies

TWA built the APOLLO flight reservation system while American Airlines constructed the SABRE network. These two reservation systems were integrated into the travel agent's selling cycle. They surpassed expectations because they offered precise and readily available information about flight times, seating availability on a selected flight, and connecting links. Once these flight reservations had widely replaced the mediocre travel agent, reinforced the knowledgeable agent, and circumvented other information channels, these systems monopolized the purchasing decisions by preventing travelers from seeing alternatives to TWA and American flights.

Preprinted Flight Schedules	Online Reservation System
Determine Traveler Source and Destination	Determine Traveler Source and Destination
Locate Flight Options: direct flights indirect flights connecting flights Repeat for Each Airline Confirm with Airline Determine Seating Availability Determine Pricing	Query Terminal for: flight times seating availability cost flight plan
Select Option Confirm with Airline Check Alternatives Repeat if Error	Select Option Confirm with Airline

Figure 1.2 Flight reservation purchasing process.

Cost information was filtered at the time of the presentation to the benefit of the airlines and detriment of the traveler. The reservation system bypassed alternative purchasing processes by providing time-critical information otherwise unavailable to the true decision maker, the agent, not the traveler. Figure 1.2 contrasts the functional simplicity of the flight reservation system with more complicated preprinted information schedules.

Networks Focus Distribution Channels

Hospital Supply Corporation of America (HSC) supplied hospitals with free video display terminals and connections to its headquarters. Not only were the connections mechanical, but also administrative. This computer link-up provided hospitals with information on both hospital and HSC inventory levels, product prices, alternative products, and an instantaneous ordering process with known delivery times. Hospitals were able to reduce in-house inventory, pare costs, and uniformly locate better products at better prices.

HSC also was able to plan its own inventory levels with more efficiency and analyze what hospitals needed and when, thus offering automatic deliveries of basic commodities. Competitors of HSC who tried to install terminals for their inventory lines found desk top space lacking, users unwilling to learn a new computer ordering system, and hospital administrations unwilling to cover training costs for small improvements offered by HSC competitors. Once the ordering system was installed and proven successful, competitors lacked a sufficient infrastructure to compete. When these systems were integrated into the daily workings of the hospitals and buying economies were passed along to them, then HSC raised prices and substituted higher priced products for commodity items. This yielded a stunning price advantage for HSC, an advantage that is both legal and sustainable.The influence of the computer purchasing systems in the buying process is presented in Figure 1.3.

- Automate inventory
- Determine product shortages
- Locate new/improved products
- Search for lowest price
- Locate sufficient quantity to complete order
- Order
- Backorder
- Expedite emergency shipments
- Arrange delivery
- Bill
- Return

Figure 1.3 The influence of computerized purchasing.

Networks Improve Information Flow

Fedders, Incorporated, which supplies environmental cooling and heating systems for large commercial and industrial buildings, gave large customers personal computers with software. Architects and building engineers use this software to configure the cooling and heating needs for a planned building. The building engineer transmits this information to Fedders offices for processing, and naturally, the results specify selected Fedders components. Not only are the architects hard-pressed to gather similar specifications from competitors, but Fedders gains early knowledge of building plans. As a result, Fedders vigorously sells components to the contractors before the competition even knows about the proposed building and promotes architectural specification of Fedders equipment at the design stage. Competitors of Fedders, like competitors of HSC, find themselves locked out of similar strategies because of the reluctance of architects to learn and simultaneously use a second and not necessarily superior computer product. Figure 1.4 positions this critical influence of a computer on the architect's decision-making cycle.

- Accept plan
- Design building per architect's concept
- Configure cooling and heating systems
- Determine equipment components and prices
- Search for lowest price
- Accept configuration/redesign
- Verify qualities and performance by vendor
- Select vendor
- Arrange delivery

Figure 1.4 The influence of computers on the architectural design cycle.

Networks Add Value to Products

Cosmetic companies are using computers to learn about potential customers from a data entry questionnaire process at department store counters. The questionnaire seeks such information as skin color and tone, skin dryness, skin problems, specific cosmetic color preferences, clothes style preference, and lifestyle. An "expert system," a computer program that simulates the skills of an expert cosmetologist, generates a report containing details about, and categorizing problems facing, the customer. A salesperson can use this focused and highly personalized information to make a good sale and suggest specific products for the customer.

Often the report contains specific instructions for the customer on product usage. This report sells products more successfully than other methods because the products are bundled into proper combinations and proper quantities. Not incidentally, the sales ticket is often higher. After a successful sale, customer data are sent to headquarters, and customers are contacted periodically by phone or mail, or in person, solicited for reorders, plied with new products that may appeal to them, and tracked for all future purchases. Figure 1.5 demonstrates how an integrated sales system augments the initial buying process, and later the re-marketing programs.

- Determine customer preferences
  - stated
  - subconscious
- Determine customer requirements
- Determine customer criteria for satisfaction
- Determine price ranges for sales ticket
- Determine customer impulse buying habits
- Generate a qualified lead
- Increase average sales ticket

Figure 1.5 Integrated computer systems improve sales procedures.

Information Distribution Supplants Processing

All these computer-aided product sales are billed as "data processing" coups. The technology of the times was extended from corporate support services to front-line product enhancement. Additionally, process information converts the product marketing cycle into a value added at the time of sale. While, in fact, these computer information systems do apply data processing operations, a key component of their success is dependency upon data transmission *networks*. The flight reservation systems coordinate global information over wide area telecommunication networks, the hospital supply ordering system relies upon leased lines to connect hospitals with corporate computers, and both the air conditioning and cosmetic supplier initially used mail delivery of superior customer-supplied information to corporate headquarters for analysis and eventual retargeted marketing. The air conditioning and cosmetic suppliers have since integrated on-site data collection with corporate in-house data processing. In all phases of these processes, a *network* provides data transmission.

The information that made these results feasible was always available but difficult to accumulate in accurate or useful formats. Data processing made data collection possible, and networks made the information readily and easily available; this becomes the strategic advantage. Information that is readily gathered within a focused and familiar content with a clearly identified benefit to the end-users (consumers) is apt to be more accurate than any information gathered from shopping mall or telephone surveys. These data can be passed, without anyone filtering it, directly to the people who process the information and distributed to those who implement products or services.

Ethernet, as a local area network, emphasizes transmission at high speed over short distances; nonetheless, Ethernet also promotes, via the network, the same distributed processing and dissemination as presented in the four examples. All models for Ethernet networks include these stages of data gathering, processing, and dissemination in the definition: a network is a system that interconnects.

Networks are Fundamental to Wall Street

Financiers value information highly. Stock prices represent a forecasted view of the future; it is information. Therefore, effectively, financiers buy and sell information. Not only does information have extraordinary value in terms of identifying takeover targets and estimating the purchase price range for an entire company, or a portion of its capital stock, information has become an important commodity in its own right. As a consequence, financiers are becoming more familiar with the data processing methodology and networking since better information is their competitive advantage.

Information processing and distribution systems provide the data with which the Wall Street brokers and bankers price stocks, anticipate the financial health of a company, and assign value to a company for the purpose of making loans. As price-arbitrage becomes a more readily accepted method for beating the market, brokers and bankers want faster systems, more data, and better integration of the information processing and distribution channels. They need networks to survive.

As an example, the New York Stock Exchange (NYSE) processes during peaks days over 300 million shares representing 500,000 individual transactions. The buying and selling of stock takes place at kiosks within the pit area of the exchange. Increasingly, exchanges are made in block transactions. These transactions are negotiated between buyer and seller in other buildings, in other cities, and need to be 'posted' on the NYSE to provide the transaction price data for other buyers and sellers. A device called the Universal Floor Device Controller (UFDC) routes the data all over the the stock exchange floor, and exports it to ticker-tape machines and information brokers. The UFDC is a network of data entry points, displays, and printers that provides sales confirmations—it automates the outdated brokerage system first introduced in the cattle mercantile exchanges of Chicago in the 1880s. See Figure 1.6.

On October 19, 1987, when the market fell 508 points, the transaction volume exceeded the planned peak by 250 million shares. Some of the panic that day, and on subsequent days, can be directly attributed to delays in the processing and distribution of information. Because there were delays in communicating verbal information in the usual way, by telephone, brokerage firms found it difficult to predict stock prices and execute orders. Because trades failed to occur as rapidly as expected the price information was delayed. Because trade confirmations were delayed or lost as the price dropped, brokers and consumers feared further price decreases and tried to sell more stock. This cycle deepened the panic; it was alleviated when the NYSE management halted trading early each day for two weeks to unburden the data processing facilities before the system was undermined beyond repair. The stock transaction network was saturated with trades, and the solution was to reduce transmission volume and off load the transactions to hours when the exchange was closed.

> - List buy and sell orders
> - Announce transaction prices
> - Print transaction confirmations
> - Calculate transaction volumes
> - Announce bid and ask prices
> - Segregate odd lots
> - Transmit confirmations to brokerage houses
> - Transmit all information to distribution channels
> - Disseminate corporate news and rumors

Figure 1.6 The functions of the Wall Street networks.

Various commissions have since determined that computer trading and its associated networks were a fundamental cause in the market panic; Wall Street now accepts the fundamental importance of data processing and these data transaction networks which bind together the financial fabric. Telephone networks cannot handle the information efficiently or accurately, and confirmation on paper has become a bottleneck as well; computer trading, trade processing, and distribution of transaction prices is now critically dependent on data networks. Not only was the telephone as a transaction medium effectively obsoleted in October 1987, the importance of the computer network was firmly and irrevocably established as the telephone's successor.

Another sign that the financial community is aware of the value of networks is illustrated by an example of a recent takeover. Scandia Airlines (SAS) decided to acquire British Caledonia (BC). The usual first step in a takeover attempt is for the acquiring company to purchase a large block of stock in the target company. This stock represents the power to change the board of directors and make new policy for the target company. In this example, SAS orchestrated a preemptive strike and hired many key British Caledonia data processing (DP) managers and computer programmers prior to purchasing any of BC's stock.

As the APOLLO and SABRE networks demonstrate, information and networking are the key control, management, and marketing tools in today's information-based economy. SAS manipulated the outcome of this takeover because BC was stripped of vital value; other companies which had sought to acquire BC clearly saw that BC was severely weakened by the loss of the DP department. In some ways, this maneuver was the ultimate 'poison pill,' although perpetrated by the aggressor in this case. Future takeover targets might consider the desire of selling a DP department to thwart acquisition.

Ultimately, whether these aggressive tactics are legal and acceptable will be determined by judges and legislators. In the interim, other corporate acquisitions will start with a purchase of corporate information, and the acquisition of the information department and the networks that distribute corporate information.

Strategic Value of Networks

Ethernet provides strategic advantages. There are economic advantages to Ethernet, as well as process and informational improvements. More difficult to justify as advantages are interconnection, intercommunication, and project worker interrelationship. Figure 1.7 outlines these six "I's."

- Influence (economic)
- Integration of process
- Information
- Interconnection
- Intercommunication
- Interrelationship

Figure 1.7 The strategic advantages of Ethernet.

The economic arguments are straightforward. Ethernet is a low cost installation, less expensive than PBX systems utilizing switching networks and modems, that encourages sharing of expensive resources and constructs a critical communications channel. Furthermore, data storage and printing services can be consolidated; data storage is usually cheaper in bulk units, and printing services are usually sporadic so that one printing unit can usually provide adequate service for many users. Peripheral devices, specialized processors, and other services can be shared network-wide with ease of access to yield higher utilization rates and similar shared economies.

Networking provides a major recognized strategic advantage by integrating disparate steps into a continuous cycle. This process improvement is often observed in automated production and manufacturing environments. It is also an advantage where information is gathered, processed, stored, and sold. Networks integrate software design processes, accounts processing, and computer-aided design (CAD) into computer-aided manufacturing (CAM). Electronic and desktop computer-aided publishing (CAP) gathers text and graphic components together in a single place—the computer—and integrates an awkward, time-consuming, and time-constrained process into a streamlined cycle.

This streamlining of design, accounting, production, manufacturing, quality assurance, and ultimately the marketing processes amplifies labor to increase worker productivity. Figure 1.8 shows production cycle steps, typically time-consuming, that are streamlined by networking.

- Plan
- Determine data collection requirements
- Collect data
- Filter and correct data
- Process data
- Generate reports
- Analyze
- Make decisions
- Produce results, develop information products
- Assure quality
- Market
- Sell
- Package and direct for shipment
- Deliver
- Bill
- Analyze the financial results

Figure 1.8 The steps streamlined by Ethernet network integration.

Shared Network Resources

Shared resources is a catch-all phrase that means everybody accesses all the equipment, a concept usually perceived from the resource-rich viewpoint. However, the reverse is also true. A resource not purchased because it is too expensive, too specialized, marginally utilized by a single person or group may be highly desirable when viewed as a global network resource. A marginal resource on a network will be used to capacity, rather than remaining idle and wasted. Processes and methods not otherwise attempted will be tried and perfected because these resources are accessible.

Shared information has value in three ways. The first of these is that information otherwise duplicated is consolidated for data collection, data storage, and processing. Data are inherently inaccurate, but single sources of information tend to be more accurate than succeeding information. As data are duplicated so are their inherent errors multiplied by the number of copies distributed and modified by the processing operations as errors that become second, third, or more generations removed from the original errors. The second value of shared information is that information otherwise difficult to gather becomes readily available for planning, processing, analyzing, and decision-making. It might not otherwise be generated, but because it is available, it will be applied. Two people sharing information may uncover novel possibilities when they chance to meet and discuss their different views of the shared data. The third of the ways that shared information is strategically important concerns its value in innovation, accidental discovery, and incidental research and development.

Business Arguments for a LAN

Communications is an organizational Tower of Babel. The challenge, as senior-level personnel perceive it, is to regain control of data processing, desktop computing, and networking without exceeding already tight budgets. The goals of the network manager and the administration team are to maintain the network, resolve any complaints from the user community, keep pace with the ever-changing technology, and enjoy their work. Since senior management increasingly questions the productivity gains from information technology, a convincing case is necessary.

Local area networks can create order from chaos as Figure 1.9 shows. LANs clearly interconnect a diverse array of machines including personal

- Interconnection
- Integration
- Control
- Economy
- Utility
- Stability
- Strategic value
- Supplemental values (voice and video channels)
- Resource sharing
- Flexibility

Figure 1.9 The business case for networking as provided by Ethernet.

computers, terminals, mainframes and minicomputers, CAD/CAM and CAP equipment, and specialized peripheral devices. A local area network coalesces the information and processing systems into a coherent environment with minimum duplication of resources; therefore, networks enable better management of resources. Additionally, a network streamlines connections, thus making separate or duplicate wiring systems unnecessary, and readily constructs an infrastructure for process integration.

A network aids in process control, resource allocation decisions, daily maintenance and operations, accessibility and monitoring workloads, results, and unwarranted activities. Control is centralized under one network manager. The simplicity of network wiring saves on personnel moves and new equipment installation. Because many resources can be shared, a network is economical and utilitarian. When resources are shared, data processing is independent of location, and machines and information become interchangeable for stability; most fault-tolerant systems rely upon networking technology. Any node station could, if necessary, provide access to information anywhere on the network. This flexibility is part of the attraction of networking technology. Valuable information can be duplicated.

These shared benefits and strategic values are nebulous. They are more difficult to quantify with hard financial evidence than they are to qualify with words and examples. Some of these reasons, like data accuracy and integrity, can be economically determined and become the logical arguments for justifying network costs, while an argument for a network based on accidental discovery and possible innovation is often emotional and instinctual. How does one prove that a worthwhile invention, a future finding, some as yet unknown data discovery, will recoup all the network expenses? How does one justify the value of a telephone system and a "network" of industry contacts, or the value of friendships?

Networks can never be fully justified, nor proven to be a complete solution. Incidental benefits may provide adequate reasons for new peripheral devices and networks in a research and development organization, a think tank, or a university setting. However, budgetary constraints create pressure for careful selection of such projects as a network installation. As a consequence, the cross-fertilizing power is an argument stated as an aside, and carefully skirted thereafter. This benefit is too intangible to justify with economic arguments.

Presenting Networking

The reasons listed in Figure 1.9 are a good starting point for framing a convincing economic argument. The key function of a manager is communications. A network's key function is to promote communications. A presentation coordinating these two—the problem and the solution—is an appropriate strategy to win acceptance of a new (or expanded) network. Networking transforms the way an organization does its job by improving the quality and effectiveness of marginal communications. In those cases where such a proposition may *frighten* upper-level management, the analysis is best replaced by economic approaches.

For example, suggest that it is better to be the "bankruptor" than the "bankruptee." Successful exploitation requires creative management, thus aggressive leadership from the top of the organization. Therefore, the leaders must accept the plan and promote it. Shift the burden of the decision making. As stated in later chapters, consensus rather than the lone-wolf attack is a powerful tool for accomplishing goals. A straightforward economic argument is also applicable.

Talk costs, not technology. Technology is often perceived as a solution in search of a problem. Instead, present clearly the financial expenses to be incurred, the initial investment outlay, reliability, service and cost containment. Demonstrate that networking provides cost-effective efficiency. Present the risks of the operations involved, the risks of failure. Present the vendors, their equipment, why their equipment is the most cost-effective solution. Explain why Ethernet does not tie the networking technology to a specific vendor, or to a volatile industry. Extrapolate what transformations are required, what impact the network will have on the people of the organization.

Talk benefits, not technology. Present the savings to be accrued with the networking technology. Indicate the benefits, whether soft or hard. Explain where the organization will gain short term and long. Make clear the *risk of not maintaining* competitive information and communication technology, as well as the need for a strong posture in the marketplace. Figure 1.10 contrasts the costs and benefits of installing a new technology.

Costs	Benefits
Financial Risk of failure Downtime Human disruption Time Organizational change	Financial Cost savings Flexibility Strategic gains Reliability Efficiency Service Support Control

Figure 1.10 The costs and benefits for networking as provided by Ethernet.

Contrast the costs and the benefits. The standard methodology is to outline a *cost-benefit* relationship. Quantify both costs and benefits within the same framework, usually economic, and make a direct comparison. Ascribing a monetary value in current dollars (all present and future income and expenses relating to a project, a *present value* formulation) is also an effective method to justify a network. However, many benefits are financially intangible. Justify one absolute improvement and explain the additional "free" resources acquired as well. This strengthens the argument because the tenuous benefits are not erroneously subjected to the same stringent analysis as that of the basic design solutions.

Most strategic advantages are soft and intangible until someone bushwhacks the way. The path is murky, uneven, dangerous, anxious for those at the cutting edge. This is why there is little ascertainable difference between strategic initiative and a "hare-brained" idea. It has been said that for a strategy to be effective it must be implemented correctly before the competition even begins to understand what that strategy is and how the technology can be applied.

When the path is clear—if the explorers have been successful—the results may already have been achieved, thus frustrating the hopes of those who follow in safety. Innovation is risky, benefits and opportunities shadowy except to the visionary few. The strategic advantages provided by networks inhabit this same jungle world. The dangers are clearly seen, the simple economic benefits are quantifiable and justifiable, whereas the more intangible aims—securing a market niche, accessing critical information before a competitor, automating production processes, simplifying the purchasing process for a customer, and capturing his or her business—are only available for those willing to risk innovation. It is a floating crap game with rules tempered by experience, changing costs, performance, and technological breakthroughs. Seize the opportunity on your own terms rather than being driven to it by others' successes and pressures.

Chapter 2

Benefits of Networking

This chapter describes Ethernet in overview. It defines the concepts of *networks* and *local area networks* (LANs), then describes the benefits of the networking environment. Common network configurations and transmission protocols are expounded upon and compared to Ethernet configurations and protocols. The final section of this chapter describes the problems with Ethernet.

Definition of a Local Area Network

A *processor* is anything with computing power such as a microcomputer, a mainframe computer, or an intelligent workstation. A *device* is anything that performs processing, input and/or output services, such as a computer, a printer, a terminal, or a plotter.

A *network* exists whenever two or more processors are connected to one another with a cable and with networking software (software that directs the flow of information between processors and that monitors requests for access to devices). A network connects processors that may have been isolated from one another. Each processor or device on a network is called a *node*.

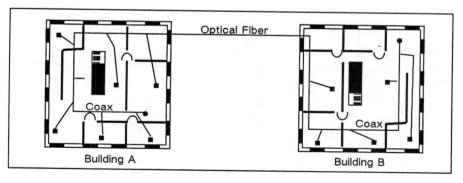

Figure 2.1 A local area network (LAN) services a "local area" such as two buildings on the same block.

A *local area network* (LAN) transmits large amounts of data at high speeds over limited distances. A local area network generally services a single room, a single floor, a building, or a two-building facility, as shown in Figure 2.1. The LAN is generally limited to a compact geographic area, perhaps a 1500-meter circumference.

A mainframe servicing remote terminals provides *centralized* processing while a LAN is *decentralized*. On a LAN, the network processing power is distributed among all the processors and peripheral devices. While a mainframe that serves remote terminals may structurally look like a local area network, the LAN differs because each workstation and processor operates independently of the others and can connect with many devices. Usually, an inexpensive and general-purpose cable provides the network backbone. In fact, the network is only a utility that uses all the devices. See Figure 2.2 for a definition of a LAN.

> - Limited geographic area (0.1 to 1 km)
> - Moderate to high data rate (0.1 to 100 Mbits)
> - Inexpensive medium ($0.60 to $10.00/meter)
> - High interconnectivity and access
> - Decentralized control
> - Interconnectivity between manufacturers
> - Device independence
> - Control independence

Figure 2.2 The definition of a local area network.

A LAN is oriented to benefiting a group with a common cause, common equipment, and similar and shared needs. A local area network should interconnect equipment from different manufacturers, as shown in Figure 2.3. This capability is termed *peer-to-peer exchange.*

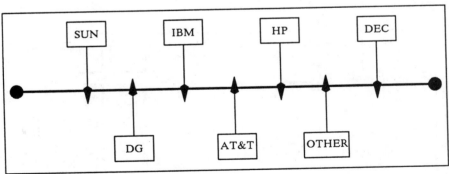

Figure 2.3 LANs provide "peer-to-peer" vendor intercompatibility.

A LAN interconnects equipment with many specific functions, allowing resources to be shared by all network users as shown in Figure 2.4.

Information can be shared across the network and stored to disk. Programs can be stored in a single location and made available to multiple users, thus saving expensive disk space and increasing availability of data and tools.

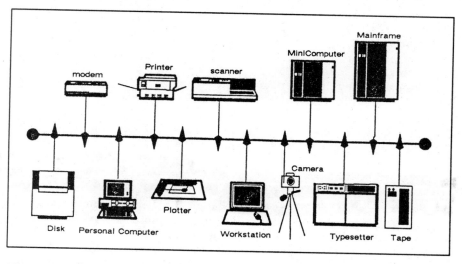

Figure 2.4 A local area network provides many services .

Benefits of Establishing a Network

There are both operational and economic benefits to setting up a network that replaces either distributed processors that can connect only through telecommunications, or a single mainframe. Operational benefits include wider access to devices, faster access to devices, greater independence, more shared information, and reduced transmission errors. Economic benefits include few equipment purchases, more equipment available to each user, and lower cost per device. See Figure 2.5.

- Wider access to devices
- Greater Independence
- Faster access to devices
- Shared Information
- Reduced transmission errors
- Specialized communications
- Fewer purchases
- Extra processing power
- Lower cost per workstation
- Simplified wiring

Figure 2.5 A local area network provides many services.

Operational Benefits

A network provides wider access to peripheral devices because all devices become available to all processors on the network. On a network, a user whose workstation is running off *Processor A* can use a printer on *Processor B*. Printers, plotters, typesetters, CAD/CAM workstations, scanners, video entry systems, and specialized disk and tape storage devices can be shared.

Network access can facilitate remote usage of a peripheral device otherwise accessible only through data transfer by magnetic medium, a slow and irksome process. A network therefore provides faster access to devices.

With a network, distributed processing permits stand-alone microcomputer workstations to function undisturbed by such things as remote failures, peak loads, and limited resources; the processors are not dependent on the availability of one mainframe. The distribution of work load requires at least the same aggregate central resources as any mainframe environment, but with networking the processing occurs at greater speeds, with more flexibility and greater independence. The distribution of peripheral loads also frees the central mainframe for more important jobs.

Many distributed processing sites that are not on a network experience problems in providing data file backup, in sharing information, or in coprocessing. Tasks that were formerly isolated on individual processors can be consolidated to improve operational efficiency. For example, computer-aided design, publishing, and manufacturing processes can be on one network. Programs can be made available to more users with less disk space across a network, and specialized processors are easily accessible. Networks make possible electronic mail for internal communications. Electronic mail is a "free" network service that provides rapid delivery, high success of delivery, message broadcasting, and automatic reply options.

Telecommunications via PBX modems is inherently slow and error-prone unless expensive error-checking and correcting equipment is used, whereas a network has fewer transmission errors. Telecommunications is also a simplex (unidirectional) transmission in that only one workstation can talk at any time to only one other workstation, in one direction. A local area network allows two-way (duplex), simultaneous access to all facilities from all facilities, at transmission speeds thousands of times faster.

Networks with optimized architecture provide high data rates on tuned channels that often interconnect supercomputing processors or scientific data acquisition equipment, offering access to specialized communications.

Economic Benefits

Rather than support each workstation with local data storage and local printing, plotting, typesetting, and tape facilities, a network permits sharing of these resources among multiple processors and users. Therefore, fewer purchases are necessary. In a distributed processing environment that does not use networking, growth means that many basic resources like printers, winchester disks, and modems need to be duplicated whereas networks provide these critical services more economically.

Resources that might not be cost-effective to purchase for a single purpose may become attractive when a network makes them available to multiple network users. Often, extra processing power, which is like an empty airplane seat because it has little value, can be accessed across a network and used.

The economics of LANs are similar to those of any mainframe environment. There is a high fixed cost for initial installation but an increasing economy for additional nodes. An example of this economy is presented in Figure 2.6. While a nodeless network installation costs $10,000 and the first node costs $8000 with printer, modem, and local data storage, the tenth unit costs a marginal $3000 for a total expenditure of $80,000; peripheral devices are shared rather than duplicated for each additional unit and network costs are amortized over a wider base as the concave graph indicates. The effect is a lower cost per workstation than on distributed processing systems.

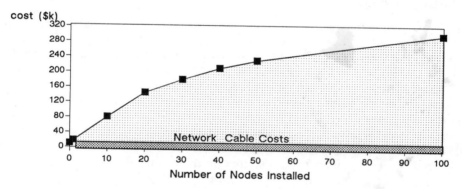

Figure 2.6 Networks provide economies of scale. The shape of the curve emphasizes the decreasing costs for marginal additions. The basic network cable cost is a fixed asset that must be provided independently of the number of nodes.

In summary, networking logically divorces the workstation from both the file structure, the disk storage and the CPU. A novel application of this concept is *networking computing,* which means that underutilized CPUs will broadcast their status and provide automatic parallel computer power. *Network databases* are a specialized application of network computing. IEEE seeks to define a *Network Interface Definition Language* (NIDL) to promote parallel processing and logical process partitioning, although the complexity to date defies solution on even single CPU processors.

Network Topologies

A topology describes the geographic relationship of the network nodes. The three most prevalent topologies include the bus, ring, and star configurations. See Figure 2.7 for representations of these architectures.

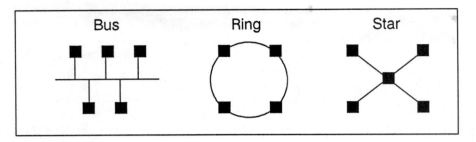

Figure 2.7 Common local area network topologies.

Star Topology

The star network is often the choice where many units are dependent upon a single processor, as in a typical mainframe situation where personal computers require frequent access to a mainframe. In this situation all cable connections are separately wired to a centralized patch panel. Although the mainframe environment is not strictly a "network," most mainframe computing wiring is handled in such a manner and it is operationally complicated. The phrase "spaghetti" describes common results of even carefully installed star networks since each node requires a separate connection. Multiplexing units, concentrators, and cable pairs only reduce wiring requirements without eliminating them, and this topology provides few economies. It is cheap when well-planned, but increasingly expensive for each additional node, particularly for any nodes that exceed planned capacity, as each added unit will require wiring from the node location to the central location. Physical movement of a node can be a very expensive process since rewiring would need to be rerouted to a central patch panel. It is, however, a stable design in that any failed node would affect few if any other nodes, although centralized failure would affect all nodes. It is an old but an enduring design.

Ring Topology

The ring configuration is designed as just that, a circular architecture, with each node directly connected to two other nodes. All network traffic passes through each node in series on the ring until it reaches the intended receiver. This wiring scheme demonstrates few economies over the star design. The ring is easily expanded to insert more nodes, although this process is disruptive since the ring is broken while a new unit is installed. Also, physical movement of a node requires two separate steps: disconnection to remove a node and again to install the node in its new location. Likewise, should any single node fail, the network fails just as the failure of one decorative tree light causes the whole string to fail. It is a fragile design despite the addition of various automatic mechanisms designed to bypass failed cable sections or nonresponsive nodes.

Bus Topology

The bus design is an open architecture, flexible and sturdy. All nodes connect in parallel on a single cable *section*. One or more coupled sections and the nodes on it form a complete stand-alone network *segment*. The bus is the basic building block for Ethernet networks, which generally consists of several bus segments joined together for geographic, administrative, or load requirements. One single segment usually forms a *backbone* and connects all other segments. While this division of the network into separate segments improves traffic flow and increases reliability, it also allows all nodes to reach all other nodes. This inherent flexibility, as shown in Figure 2.8, permits the addition and extension of several segments to the originally small network. *Gateways* are devices that provide connectivity between segments, and *repeaters* boost communication signals to extend the total length of the network to remote locations.

Because the bus topology is a parallel design, new nodes can be installed at any location without disrupting communications, an important concern

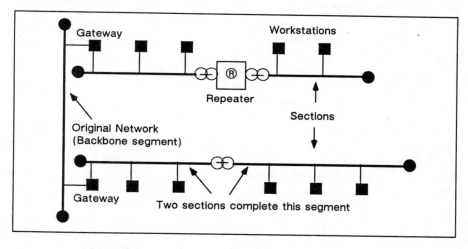

Figure 2.8 The extended bus network topology.

since 50% of all equipment industry-wide is moved each year. The back-bone can also be expanded from the end points with minimal disruption, and new sections can be inserted into the middle of any segment. Unlike the ring topology, a failed node on a bus topology does not affect the transmission among the remaining nodes. The main benefit of a bus design is that all nodes receive a signal in parallel so that failure is localized, whereas the serial nodes in the ring architecture must receive and repeat each signal, and stars must route traffic through a critical central facility.

Available Protocols

The last section described physical topologies. Networks also vary by *transmission protocol,* which is the method used to transmit data. The common networking protocols include RS-232, CSMA (carrier sense multiple access), CSMA/CD (carrier-sense multiple-access with collision detection), token bus, token ring, and optimized token bus. Figure 2.9 shows which protocols can be used on each network topology. Protocols range from simple one-way or two-way transmissions, as on an RS-232 network, to controlled token-passing and polling schemes or probabilistic broadcasting schemes. Ethernet is CSMA/CD, and this protocol will be described in explicit detail. Each protocol has certain benefits and efficiencies as well as limitations. Benefits include simplicity, speed, and compatibility. Efficiencies are reflected in computer processor overhead, transmission timing, and loading factors. Limitations lie in the lack of a class of computers to accept that protocol, the relative difficulty of installing or maintaining a specific protocol, relative speed, and relative cost.

Configuration	Available Protocols			
Bus	CSMA	CSMA/CD	Token	Optimized token
Ring	CSMA	Token	Polling	
Star	CSMA	RS–232	Polling	

Figure 2.9 Available network protocols.

RS-232 is generally run on twisted pair, which is better known as telephone wire. RS-232 often can run on *existing* telephone cabling, and if not, this common wire is simple to install. Modems (sound modulator/demodulator) alter digital voltage changes into an analog sound pattern that is transmitted over twisted pair. RS-232 is often used for mainframe to dumb-terminal communications, because such communication is relatively low load and slow speed. Two-way connections are established between a destination and a source, and this link is inflexible during the transmission session. RS-232 is often bundled into a T-1 network framework. T-1 is a dedicated high-speed digital link that connects distant locations. This *wide area network* (WAN) differs from the LAN because of the lack of distance limitations between nodes. T-1 is served via PBX and common carriers like AT&T. Speeds of communication range from 300 baud up to 19,200 baud. This corresponds to approximately 30 to 1920 characters per second. Generally, a limit of 1200 baud is achieved on voice-grade phone lines due to limitations inherent in this technology. New technology is bringing higher speeds to market, although higher speeds often create disproportionately higher error rates.

Carrier-sense multiple-access protocol runs on *baseband* or *broadband* cable. These cables are physically larger and more usage-specific than telephone cable and were invented to carry CATV signals. Baseband and broadband cable is a special type of electrical cable designed to transmit video and high-speed data signals. Baseband carries a single signal whereas broadband carries multiple signals on the same cable. The CSMA protocol involves a *trans*mitter/*receiver* unit, hence "transceiver," that checks the network for a busy signal (i.e., a carrier tone) before broadcasting a message. A message is broadcast like a radio signal, and all other transmitters/receivers perceive this signal. Only the target transceiver actually accepts and reads the message. Figure 2.10 outlines how CSMA works.

Carrier Sense:	Listen before transmitting
Multiple Access:	Transmit when channel is free
Control Process:	Persistent
	Nonpersistent
	Collision detection
	Collision avoidance
	Equal access (no priorities)
	Algorithm generates delay
Advantages:	Efficient for personal computers
Disadvantages:	Nondeterministic; jams under heavy loads

Figure 2.10 Carrier-sense multiple-access protocols (CSMA).

Carrier-sense multiple-access with collision detection is a refinement of CSMA. The conflict from the interfering signals is termed a *collision*. Collision detection is a euphemistic description of a busy network unable to handle the transmission volume. Collisions occur when two or more units transmit simultaneously, a factor largely of the significant two-way transmission delay over the full network length. Collisions are handled by rebroadcasts. Figure 2.11 outlines how CSMA/CD works.

Carrier Sense:	Listen before transmitting
Multiple Access:	Transmit when channel is free
Collision Process:	Transit delays allow collisions Detect collision and retry Delays a random length of time Algorithm generates delay
Advantages:	Efficient with load less than 40% capacity
Disadvantages:	Non-deterministic, jams under heavy loads

Figure 2.11 Carrier-sense multiple-access with collision detection protocols (CSMA/CD).

Token protocols are more orderly than CSMA/CD protocols. If the analogy of CSMA/CD is the swinging door, token passing is analogous to a revolving door. Rather than each transmitter competing for a window in which to broadcast a message, a token is passed from one workstation to the next. The token conveys the permission to transmit; no workstation can transmit without the token. Figure 2.12 illustrates the token-passing protocol and the mechanics of token permission in operation.

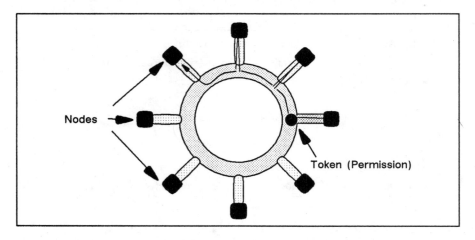

Figure 2.12 Token grants transmit permission to only one node at a time.

While this scheme seems more orderly, it suffers certain inefficiencies. For example, the token can get lost and not be regenerated for a time long by communication protocol standards, or duplicate tokens could be mistakenly generated. Token-passing protocols often limit the maximum time a workstation can actually hold the token, and this scheme assumes a uniform traffic level and penalizes high-volume users. Also, time is lost in the protocol of passing and accepting the token when a workstation may simply pass the token along without a need to communicate. The overhead for token passing becomes a constraint that finger-waving benchmarkers decry when load reaches 40% of rated capacity.

All the protocols have best uses. Sometimes the choice is dictated by the higher initial expense of one protocol and the equipment it requires, a protocol's incompatibility with existing equipment, the cost of retrofitting an existing building for one type of network, the recommendations of an equipment vendor, or the availability from a vendor of a specific protocol. Other times, the software, production, or intercompatibility issues dictate the choices. A protocol is usually chosen in conjunction with many competing considerations. Ethernet has a higher initial cost than RS-232. However, RS-232 cannot provide adequate file transfers, the pixelated screen pagination necessary for most desktop workstations, or graphic support at transmission rates consistent with current technology. These two and several other protocols are compared for speed, costs, and installation flexibility in Figure 2.13.

Protocol	Transmission Rate	Cost/node	Flexibility
RS-232	300–19200	200–600	low
X.25 (star)	300–19200	200–600	low
Ethernet	10 Mbits	1200	high
Token Ring	1–5 Mbits	100	medium
Token Bus	40 Mbits	20000	low

Figure 2.13 Comparisons of various protocols in common usage. Note the additional cost per node not including workstation or amortized network backplane expenses.

Ethernet is often selected because it is flexible, very expandable, and compatible with the equipment of many manufacturers and software vendors. Not only are communications achievable among different vendors, often different machines can talk and share information in a transparent manner, because Ethernet conforms to a generic network design specified by the International Standards Organization communications model, as described in Chapter 3.

The Problems of Ethernet

The problems with Ethernet include the lack of built-in resources for debugging and testing, the likelihood of electrical failure, the inability to track network traffic and predict overloading problems in advance, and the difficulty in expanding network capacity. These are common problems often created in the initial installation or by creeping growth of a network, although they can be resolved and hidden from an organization by good vendor installation teams or good administrative management and a large network budget. Unfortunately, networks do grow, equipment does age and fail, and random events do unfold that can break a network. Repair times range from *minutes* to *months*.

Most of these problems plague the inexperienced manager, while the seasoned network manager can forecast with ease the problems that will arise, and he or she will know how to dispatch them quickly. The experienced network manager will have acquired the necessary tools and hired competent people who understand how to operate these special network tools, interpret findings and apply expedient solutions. The problems of Ethernet are not insurmountable with knowledge and experience; a good book guides the inexperienced along the path to learning.

Most mechanical problems, once understood, are quickly recognized by symptoms. Mechanical problems are also categorized by frequency and likelihood of occurring. A partially failed network, single malfunctioning nodes, high collision rates, all, for example, point to electrical shorts or breaks. Continuous shutdowns of the network suggest failed transmitting gear or improper component installation. High traffic loads and high collision rates suggest improperly installed cabling, a network overloaded with traffic, or faulty software. Cabling connections can be checked to solve such problems, and if the problem is an overburdened network, various options exist to first verify this theory and then reduce load or provide alternative communication routes. Additionally, more channels can be installed to match capacity. Software problems are resolved by system restarts, programming repairs, or replacement of corrupted file systems.

The common network problems masquerade as either hardware or software failures. Without guidelines, it is often impossible to distinguish one from another. Network testing and monitoring provide the means to identify the root causes of Ethernet problems, the understanding of how to isolate or remove the problem, and the experience to repair it. This book addresses these issues and provides a practical approach to Ethernet problem solving.

Part 2

Software and Hardware

This section describes the mechanical processes of Ethernet networking, the hardware, the software, and the installation process. It builds a basis of understanding for the operations and management of an Ethernet network.

Chapter 4 describes the hardware and the mechanical process of Ethernet. The components of an Ethernet network are described and illustrated to help the reader understand the ingenious simplicity of an Ethernet network. Chapter 5 explains the Ethernet process. This includes the transmission methodology and the characteristic features of network-level software. Chapter 6 details the planning procedures for the mechanical components of Ethernet networks, completing what spartan vendor instructions omit. This chapter outlines those issues that an experienced network manager considers before building or expanding an Ethernet network. Chapter 7 explains the installation procedures for the mechanical components of Ethernet networks, completing what spartan vendor instructions omit. This chapter suggests what steps an experienced network manager takes for testing and benchmarking a newly installed network. Chapter 8 explains why bridges, fan-out units, gateways, and repeaters are necessary on a large Ethernet, and how these units are installed. Since organizational growth is likely to outstrip the capacity of an original network, bridges, fan-out units, gateways, and repeaters are presented as solutions to overloaded networks.

Chapter 3

Ethernet Configurations and Variations

This chapter uses the ISO OSI model as a reference to describe the functions and variations of Ethernet. It describes three types of transmission media: baseband cable, broadband coaxial cable, and optical fiber. It shows how variations of Ethernet are used for each type of transmission medium. Ethernet network configurations conclude this presentation.

The ISO OSI Model

Ethernet was designed by Xerox at the famed Palo Alto Research Center (PARC) in the early 1970s to provide communication for research and development computers. While the Ethernet design preceded the development of the open system interconnect (OSI) model by 5 years, nonetheless, it conforms to this layered architecture model of networking.

The OSI model was developed by the International Standards Organization (ISO) as a generic model for data communication. Because modularity of communication functions is a key design criterion in the OSI model, vendors who adhere to the standards and guidelines of this model can supply Ethernet-compatible devices, alternative Ethernet channels, higher performance Ethernet networks, and bridging protocols that interconnect other types of data networks to Ethernet.

The OSI model specifies seven layers of functionality as shown in Figure 3.1. It defines the layers but does not define the protocols that implement the functions at each layer.

Although the transmission medium is not formally, but generally, included in the OSI definition, it can be thought of as "layer 0" of the OSI model. Layer 1 is the physical layer (electrical, mechanical, optical). Layer 2 is the data link layer (flow, standards, connections). Layer 3 is the network layer (routing and switching of the actual transmission). Layer 4 is the transport layer (transmission and transfer of data). Layer 5 is the session layer (administrative control of transmissions and transfers). Layer 6 is the presentation layer (interpretation and data transformation). Layer 7 is the application layer (system computing and user applications).

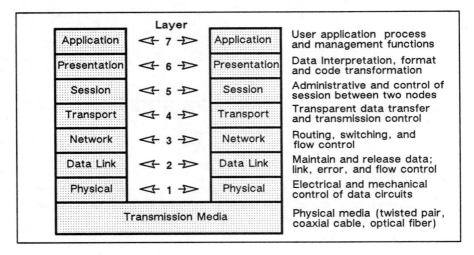

Figure 3.1 The International Standards Organization (ISO) open systems interconnect (OSI) Model.

Implementations of the OSI model provide for a protocol for communication at each layer on two processors (that is, session to session) and an interface for communication between layers on one processor (that is, presentation to session). Physical communication occurs only at layer 1 (the protocol for electrical transmission on the transmission medium, bit by bit). The protocols for the other layers define virtual connections in the software. The following paragraphs describe the functions of each layer.

The transmission media-layer specifies the physical medium used in constructing the network, including size, thickness and other characteristics of the actual medium. The electrical, mechanical, or optical pulses travel along a transmission medium which may be twisted pair telephone line, coaxial cable (which Ethernet currently uses), optical fiber, or microwave. Increasingly, the demand from LAN users for a multiple-channel Ethernet is giving rise to a multichannel broadband Ethernet that runs on broadband cable (cable-TV cable), long-haul microwaves, or optical fiber.

Layer 1, the physical layer, specifies the electrical and mechanical control of the actual data circuits. This function is managed by the Ethernet transceivers and by the Ethernet controllers, and the cabling between them.

Layer 2, the data link layer, is software that manages transmissions and error acknowledgment and recovery. The mechanical devices, like transceivers, are mapped data units to data units, to provide physical error detection and notification, and link activation and deactivation of a logical communication connection.

Layer 3, the network layer, is the borderline between hardware and software. At the network layer, the protocol mechanisms activate the data routing by providing network address resolution, flow control in terms of segmentation and blocking, and in the case of Ethernet, collision handling. The network layer also provides service selection, connection resets, and expedited data transfers. The Internet Protocol (IP), a common Ethernet program on most Ethernet networks, runs at this layer.

Layer 4, the transport layer, controls data transfer and transmission. This software program is called Transaction Control Protocol (TCP), a common Ethernet software on most Ethernet networks.

Layers 5,6, and 7 are generally supplied by vendor-specific software and are not part of Ethernet. Layer 5 recognizes the nodes on the LAN and sets up the tables of source and destination addresses. It also establishes, quite literally, a handshaking for each session between different nodes. Technically, services at layer 5 are called *session connection*, *exception reporting*, *coordination* of send/receive modes, and of course, the actual *data exchange*.

Layer 6, the presentation layer, transfers information from the application software to the network session layer to the operating system. The interface at this layer performs data transformations, data formatting, syntax selection (including *ascii*, *ebcdic*, or other numeric or graphic formats), device selection and control, and finally, data compression or encryption.

ISO	Example Architectures
Media	twisted pair, thinnet, coaxial cable, optical fiber cable
Layer 1	IEEE 802.3, Ethernet, RS-232, RS-449, V.24, V.35
Layer 2	IEEE 802.2, Ethernet, DDCMP, LAP-B, SDLC, HDLC
Layer 3	X.25, IP (as in TCP/IP), XNS, DECnet, vendor specific
Layer 4	TCP (as in TCP/IP), XNS, DECnet, vendor specific
Layer 5	vendor specific
Layer 6	NAPLPS, MAP, vendor specific
Layer 7	X.400, vendor specific

Figure 3.2 Examples of standard protocols in the ISO architecture. RS-232 and RS-449 are twisted pair network standards. DDCMP is Digital Data Communications Message Protocol. LAP-B is Link Access Control-Balanced. SDLC is an acronym for Synchronous Data Link Control whereas HDLC is an acronym for High-Level Data Link Control. TCP is Transaction Control Protocol. IP is Internet Protocol. XNS represents Xerox Network System. DECnet is a TCP/IP implementation from Digital Equipment Corporation. MAP is Manufacturing Automation Protocol.

Layer 7, network application layer, supports identification of communicating partners, establishes the authority to communicate, transfers information, and applies privacy mechanisms and cost allocations. It may be a complex layer. The application layer supports file services, print services, and electronic mail. These "applications" are not to be confused with user applications. The application layer is the network system software that supports user-layer applications, like word or data processing, CAD/CAM,

and image scanning. Figure 3.2 lists specific examples of standard protocols for each layer of the OSI model.

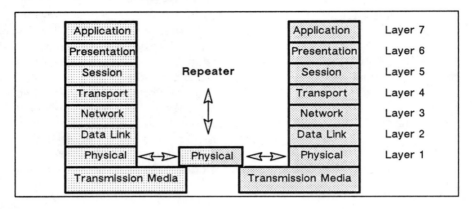

Figure 3.3 The OSI Repeater Model.

The ISO standards also specify how repeaters, bridges and gateways are
established to extend the topology of a network. The simplest of these OSI
definitions is the LAN *repeater* which duplicates the transmission signal
from one network segment onto another network segment. On Ethernet, a
repeater allows a single network segment to exceed the maximum length
limitation of 500 meters. See Figure 3.3 for the ISO repeater model. In this
example, both network segments communicate with the same protocol.
Signals from one network are sent to the other network. *Smart repeaters,*
devices which provide special performance improvements, communicate at
other layers including the data link, network, transport, and session layers
to filter Ethernet transmissions for higher traffic rates.

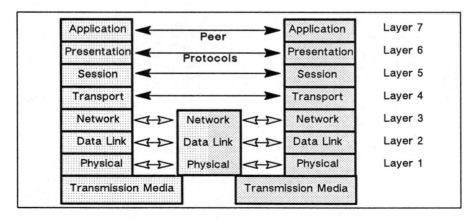

Figure 3.4 The OSI Bridge Model.

The *bridge,* as shown in Figure 3.4, interconnects networks that use different transmission or physical media or different data link protocols. A bridge, for example, might connect an Ethernet baseband with an Ethernet broadband or optical fiber network. A bridge can convert a digital signal into a frequency-modulated electrical signal or a laser signal. Transport, session, presentation, and application layers are not affected by the bridge, so the bridge is totally transparent to the user.

A bridge can connect Ethernet with Thinnet and Cheapernet (transmission medium variants), although there are no electrical conversions required. On Ethernet, a bridge can convert TCP/IP to Domain, X.25, or RS-232.

A *gateway* in the OSI model interconnects networks and equipment with different characteristics. Information, presentation (*ascii* to *ebcdic* for example), source and destination addressing, and physical connections are translated by the gateway. A gateway might, for example, translate a file into a stream to be directed over an RS-232 phone link or translate that same file into an IBM file format and X.25 interconnection. See Figure 3.5 for an example of this translation. The gateway is a strict definition within the context of the OSI model and differs from the common connotation of a "software" repeater, which is a workstation interconnected to two different network segments.

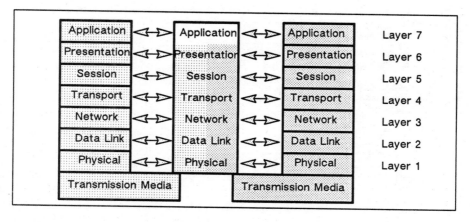

Figure 3.5 The OSI Gateway Model.

The Definition of Ethernet

Ethernet is layers 1 and 2 of the OSI model. Layers 3 through 7 are not part of Ethernet, although Ethernet is often packaged with the TCP/IP protocol; TCP/IP provides network-layer functions. The XNS, DECnet, HPnet and other vendor-supplied protocols also communicate with

Ethernet. TCP/IP was commissioned by the Department of Defense, and standardized by the government, but also is being applied by a rapidly growing list of manufacturers. The great virtue of TCP/IP is its open systems approach to communications.

Ethernet consists only of hardware. Software protocols build upon the basic hardware that is Ethernet. The operating system components at each node that provide the communications functions build upon the Ethernet controller function. This is where Ethernet-related software diverges significantly and incompatibilities, if any, emerge. However, foreign languages are easily transmitted, or even secret code. Ethernet, like a telephone, will handle different network software. Just as with any phone that accesses a network of other phones, it must adhere to certain standards. These standards are the software protocols and processes described in Chapter 5.

Figure 3.6 translates the ISO/OSI model into the comparable IEEE 802 model, of which Ethernet is one example. Ethernet is specified solely by the physical layer, the media access control layers, and the logical link control. The most common application for ISO layers 1 through 5 in an Ethernet environment is version 2.0 and some variation of Transaction Control Program/Internet Protocol (TCP/IP). The network layers are not defined by the IEEE standards, although Ethernet generally runs "standard versions" of the TCP/IP protocols. The distinction to convey is that "Ethernet" is physical, although popularly an Ethernet network includes a network software like TCP/IP.

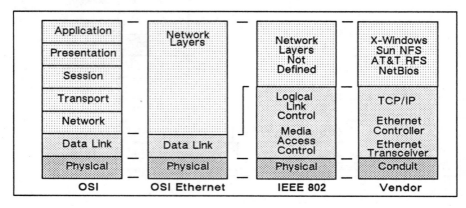

Figure 3.6 Comparison of the OSI model to the IEEE 802 standard.

Ethernet Variations

This section defines the Ethernet hardware, the variations, and the physical differences among them. It also describes mechanical standards for the various transmission media including baseband and broadband coaxial cable, and optical fiber. Since baseband coax cable single-strand,

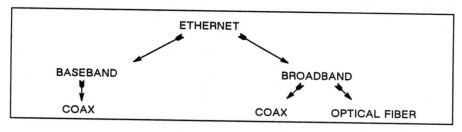

Figure 3.7 The Ethernet media family.

single channel, is the prevalent medium, most of this chapter addresses this variation. *Coaxial* cable consists of a conducting outer metal tube enclosing and insulated from a central metal conducting core. It is called *coaxial* because the core and shield conductors share a *common axis*. *Optical fiber* is a glass tube that carries signals on laser light.

The generally accepted and applied standards for Ethernet networks allow several variations that include both baseband and broadband. The standards also specify various transmission media that include baseband cable (50-ohm *Thicknet* coaxial cable, 75-ohm *Thinnet* and Cheapernet replacement cable), multichannel broadband Ethernet (cable and optical fiber), and various data transmission and encoding schemes. Figure 3.7 presents the Ethernet family tree.

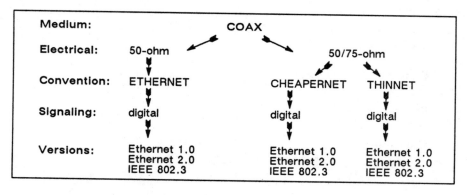

Figure 3.8 The Ethernet baseband family. The Thinnet and Cheapernet coaxial cable itself has an impedance of 75 ohms, although the network is specified to be a 50-ohm network as is standard Ethernet. The higher cable impedance limits Thinnet and Cheapernet to shorter segments.

The Ethernet family includes the predominant baseband coaxial cable network. Major specifications for baseband Ethernet cable describe a single-strand cable with a tinned copper core, surrounded by a foam material that insulates it from the tinned and braided copper shield. Coaxial cable is often used because it provides an electrically balanced signal.

Figure 3.8 shows the typical baseband Ethernet coax configurations. Baseband coax includes standard Ethernet, and Thinnet variations. All use digital signaling techniques and run Ethernet standard versions 1.0, 2.0, or IEEE 802.3.

Broadband Ethernet, both coax and optical fiber, generally is installed to provide longer network segments than otherwise available and to increase channel capacity or channel transmission speed. It is called *broadband* because it provides a wider frequency range than baseband. A broadband coax cable is similar in function and appearance to baseband, although the cable is physically several times larger. Optical fiber cables, which are thinner, lighter and contain no metal, are installed to solve long-haul or security problems, and fiber might be used to interconnect buildings miles distant for electronic mail or file transfers.

Broadband cables adhere to analog communications, although optical fiber broadband transmits digital transmissions as well. The transmission technology is oblivious to the Ethernet version and conveys information to its nodes. As a result, broadband networks often carry voice, video, and data communication signals concurrently on the same networks. Because there are few conventions among vendors, none between coax and fiber, a bridging mechanism is required to transmit data coherently between networks using different transmission media. Ethernet provides the necessary bridging. Figure 3.9 shows the family of typical Ethernet broadband configurations.

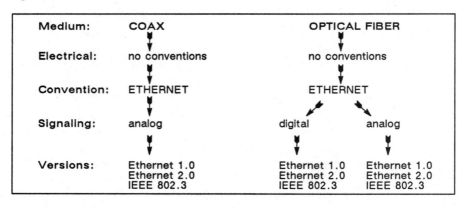

Figure 3.9 The Ethernet broadband family.

Despite the obvious performance improvements and capacity extensions provided by broadband, baseband cable is the most common transmission medium on Ethernet networks. A single coaxial cable transmits a single channel of information. It applies digital rather than analog communication. The main difference between a standard Ethernet network and the Cheapernet and Thinnet variations is the maximum length of cable each

	Ethernet	Cheapernet	Thinnet
Segment length	500	200	200
# Transceivers per segment	100	100	100
Minimum transceiver spacing	2.5 meters	1 meters	1 meters
Maximum number of interconnected segments	3	3	3
Network length	1500	600	600
Propagation speed	.77 c	.66 c	.66 c
Maximum drop cable length	50 meters	--	50 meters

Figure 3.10 The difference between Ethernet baseband variations.

version supports and the minimum distance between nodes. See Figure
3.10 for the characteristics of baseband Ethernet versions.

Ethernet, which runs on 50-ohm cabling, supports a maximum
500-meter segment and nodes spaced no closer than 2.5 meters, whereas
Cheapernet and Thinnet, which run on the thinner 75-ohm cabling, support a maximum 200-meter segment and nodes can be spaced no closer
than 0.5 meters. Both can support a maximum of 100 nodes per segment;
all support Ethernet 1.0, 2.0, or IEEE 802.3 versions. The 50-ohm thicknet coaxial cable is physically thicker and stronger, better shielded, and
more expensive than the 75-ohm Thinnet cable. Consequently, freedom
from signal interference and durability suffer on Thinnet and Cheapernet
networks, slowing the signal propagation speed, thus limiting the segment
length to the 200 meters.

```
• DC to upper frequency limit
• One channel per coaxial cable
• No carrier
• Various encoding schemes (depend on version)

    . Manchester (Ethernet 2.0, IEEE 802.3)
    . Return to zero (Ethernet 1.0)
    . Non-return to zero

• Digital transmission (no modem translations)
```

Figure 3.11 Baseband signaling characteristics.

Because Cheapernet and Thinnet both are terminated with 50-ohm
terminators and are electrically compatible with 50-ohm networks and each
other, they can be interconnected with cable adapters. Cheapernet expects
workstations at each node to have built-in Ethernet controllers and transceivers, devices which are pictured in the next two chapters. Thinnet is
identical to standard Ethernet in all respects, except for the coaxial cable

diameter and the limitations imposed by 75-ohm cable. Figure 3.11 outlines transmission characteristics.

Broadband Ethernet offers multiple-channel intercompatibility with the baseband versions when connected by a bridge. Broadband utilizes a television tuner-like modem that converts each channel to a separate frequency so than many channels can coexist. Different vendors provide from two to eighty channels per broadband cable. This extra capacity bears a price. Broadband modems replace the transceiver and are many times more expensive than the simpler baseband hardware, and signals from different channels often overlap, thus confusing transmissions. This type of confusion is prevalent when different vendors supply the voice, video, and data communications equipment. Broadband Ethernet can run for longer distances than baseband—up to 2 kilometers. Despite the improvements, the selection and commitment of broadband is a far more serious undertaking than baseband because modulation encoding schemes vary by vendor. Figure 3.12 presents broadband transmission techniques.

Broadband cable technology is more mature and, consequently, more durable than optical fiber technology. Optical fiber technology is new and provides greater bandwidth and higher transmission speeds than broadband coaxial cable, but it is an unproven, more expensive, and difficult technology. Fiber cable is difficult to extend, comparatively difficult to splice and repair, severely tests those expecting to add news nodes and rearrange locations of existing nodes, and suffers transmission degradation over time due to exposure. Expansion and contraction, and extremes from heat and cold fracture the cable. Heat and cold and particle radiation discolor the optical qualities and gradually decrease the bandwidth. Managers at several sites with very large installations have discovered this first-hand.

- Uses separate frequency for each channel
- Many channels on one cable
- Carrier tone supplied by modems
- Various modulation encoding schemes

    . AM – Amplitude Modulation
    . FM – Frequency Modulation
    . PM – Phase Modulation
    . PCM – Pulse Code Modulation
    . PSK – Phase Shift Keying
    . FSK – Frequency Shift Keying

- Analog transmissions (requires modems)

Figure 3.12 Broadband signaling characteristics.

Ethernet Compatibility

Ethernet is consistent with the IEEE 802.3 standard for the physical interconnection of nodes on a network. In effect, all Ethernet systems conform to 802.3 specification unless the physical medium is not the standard baseband medium. Despite these apparent similarities among Ethernet family members, considerable incompatibility exists. Ethernet 1.0 is a receive-based collision detection version, whereas both Ethernet 2.0 and IEEE 802.3 apply transmit-based detection that relies upon the collision interference signal. These later refinements are less susceptible to noise and coaxial cable resistance loss. These three versions are incompatible with each other and have a tendency to cause interfacing problems with each other. IEEE specification 802.3 adoption was delayed a year because IBM proposed token ring as an alternative. As a result the IEEE split the 802 committee into separate subcommittees to define a standard for the logical link (802.2), Ethernet (802.3), token bus (802.4), and token ring (802.5). Vendors released an upgraded Ethernet 2.0 before the 802.3 formulation was finalized.

IEEE 802.3 and Ethernet version 2.0 provide a signal heartbeat and do not function concurrently with Ethernet version 1.0 because of this signal and data encoding differences. Note that while TCP/IP is supposed to provide a consistent application-layer function, these definitions leave enough gray area for different vendors to define inconsistent software standards. Vendors see no reason to agree with competitors on application-layer compatibility. However, Ethernet 2.0 and TCP/IP do provide a high degree of intercompatibility because they do conform to the ISO model.

OSI is not generally accepted by industry, nor will it be a de facto standard for some time despite the many vendors claims that OSI architecture and compatibility are priorities for new products. Standardization implies comprehensive testing for conformity to OSI, and this is a monumental undertaking.

Economic and Operational Comparisons

Figure 3.13 shows the composition of a typical baseband cable. Thinnet and Cheapernet cables have similar compositions, although all layers are physically smaller, less durable, and less expensive. The *dialectric,* a foam electrical insulator, and the exterior insulating jacket are manufactured either from polyvinyl chloride (PVC) for standard office applications, or from the more expensive, fire-resistant Fluorinated Ethylene Propylene (FEP) teflon for installation in building plenums and walls.

Baseband Ethernet coax supports a bus topology with a maximum circumference of a kilometer and a half, provides network access to a maximum of 1024 nodes (address space is limited to 10 bits), and provides

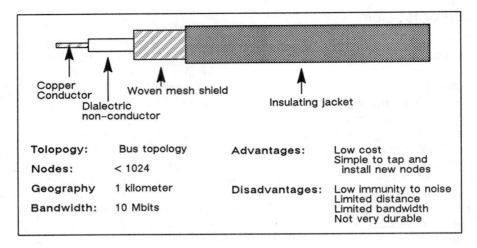

Tolopogy: Bus topology   **Advantages:**   Low cost

Nodes: < 1024   Simple to tap and install new nodes

Geography   1 kilometer   **Disadvantages:**   Low immunity to noise

Bandwidth: 10 Mbits   Limited distance / Limited bandwidth / Not very durable

Figure 3.13 Baseband Ethernet cable.

a bandwidth of 10 megabits. It is low cost, and very to simple to expand. It is, however, sensitive to noise, and physically not very durable. The distance and bandwidth limitations do constrain the network to either a small geographic area with a large number of low traffic users, or to a small number of large, peak-load users, unless planning and specialized hardware are employed to partition networks into manageable subnetworks.

Broadband networks provide more bandwidth, higher speeds and larger geographic network service than baseband networks, but at a high cost. While physical medium and transmission differ from baseband, the Ether-

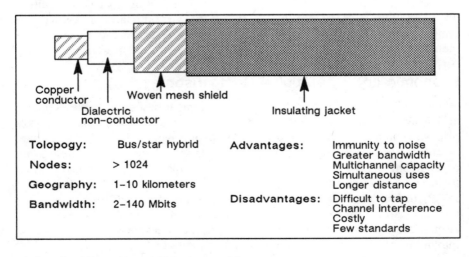

Tolopogy: Bus/star hybrid   **Advantages:**   Immunity to noise

Nodes: > 1024   Greater bandwidth / Multichannel capacity / Simultaneous uses

Geography: 1–10 kilometers   Longer distance

Bandwidth: 2–140 Mbits   **Disadvantages:**   Difficult to tap / Channel interference / Costly / Few standards

Figure 3.14 Broadband Ethernet cable.

net protocols can transmit on baseband, and interconnect via a bridge. The broadband cable is physically larger, stronger, and better shielded than baseband cable thus yielding a network that can be geographically larger and faster, supporting more users. Because of the cable characteristics and transmission methodology, broadband has a better immunity to signal interference, with higher transmission integrity and data security. Broadband can simultaneously carry voice, data, video, or any other digital or analog traffic at different frequencies, and this makes broadband networks very attractive for applications in which a variety of traffic types can utilize the same cable installation. Broadband disadvantages include its initial expense as well as the difficulty and expense in moving or adding nodes to expand the network. Consequently, broadband is a hybrid topology, part bus and part star network, in which modem/multiplexing converters provide from 1 to 64 ports for workstation connections. Figure 3.14 shows the composition of a broadband cable and the advantages and disadvantages of this medium.

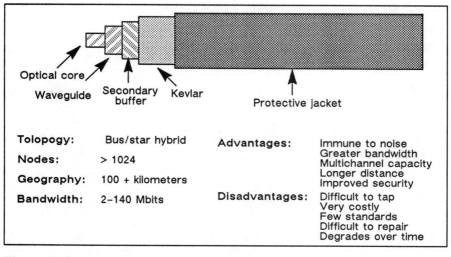

Figure 3.15 Optical fiber cable.

The broadband technology does provide offsetting transmission speed improvements for specialized needs and better noise isolation than baseband for constructing long-haul networks with a wider geographic service area. Note that very specialized hardware is required for long-haul networks, because the speed of light is finite, and Ethernet specifications allow only 96 milliseconds for collision detection. Assuming that fiber optic cable can transmit 30 percent faster than baseband electrical cable, this speed improvement would only allow a 30 percent lengthening of the 500 meter limitation to 650 meters. Smart bridges that connect segments provide a long-haul capability in excess of 10 kilometers.

Optical fiber networks have some of the same transmission characteristics as any broadband cable with these differences: it is more expensive and more difficult to debug, maintain, and expand than electrical network. However, because optical fiber cable is the newest technology, optical networks currently offer better security. Figure 3.15 shows the composition of a fiber cable and its advantages and disadvantages.

The economies of scale for baseband, broadband, and optical fiber networks are significantly different and changing as the technology develops and matures. Baseband provides a moderate-cost LAN. Initial cost is moderately high, although each additional node is inexpensive. It is highly flexible. Broadband increases channel capacity and transmission speeds and provides growth capacity and larger networks. However, the initial cost is higher and it is expensive to add nodes. It is generally an inflexible medium. Broadband fiber networks provide higher speeds and multiple channel capacity, although the greater bandwidth is available at very high initial costs. There are also very high costs for additional nodes, for repairs, and for configuration changes. It is highly inflexible. See Figure 3.16 for the economies of scale for these Ethernet media.

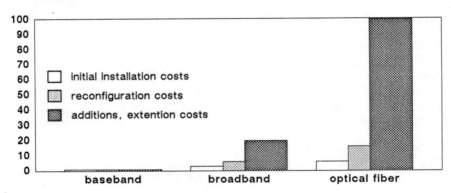

Figure 3.16 The cost comparison between cable and fiber networks. Baseband is standard cost at 1 unit.

Baseband Ethernet is more common than Ethernet broadband or fiber networks, although some users install twisted pair in place of the expensive coax, or even route network sections through existing telephone lines. This economizing is clearly effective, although distance limitations are apt to create severe reliability problems and legal problems as well. Baseband coax networks are a more likely for new Ethernet installations because of cost, availability, cabling options, performance, and compatibility considerations. Therefore, the remaining parts of this book will emphasize baseband coax technology.

Chapter 4

Ethernet Hardware

This chapter describes the hardware commonly employed to construct Ethernet networks, and the physical channel limitations inherent in Ethernet. Ethernet is often selected because the hardware is simple and readily available. Furthermore, hardware is interchangeable among vendors and most installations require compatibility between different manufacturers' workstations. Ethernet is often selected because it can bridge operating systems and ignore inherent differences in data and file structures to promote reliable interconnections. Relative to other network building blocks, the hardware for Ethernet is simple, reliable, and very powerful.

Hardware

The hardware required for Ethernet is minimal. A cable interconnects all nodes. This cable is commonly available, often designated as RG-50, RG-59, or RG-225 coaxial cable. The 50-ohm cable performs better than 75-ohm CATV cable because it has better insulation against insertion capacitance and resistance to low-frequency electromagnetic noise — which means it contains the signal and is not affected by external noises. Thinnet and Cheapernet are 75-ohm cable and suffer these limitations. Rigorous manufacturing specifications ensure a generally accepted conformity among different lots of cable, and different manufacturers. In the analogy used throughout this chapter, the coax is the Ethernet party-line telephone.

As Chapter 2 explained, Ethernet requires a *bus* design and nodes connect independently to a coaxial cable. Cable traverses a facility, and special bridging hardware interconnects stand-alone segments and lengthens network cable. Figure 4.1 shows a typical network configuration with a simplified representation of the Ethernet hardware.

An Ethernet network consists of coaxial cable; connectors, including both section end connectors and coupling "barrel" connectors (male–male), terminating resistors, coaxial taps, and transceiver drop cables. The network has electronic components, limited to transceivers and controllers at each node location. Fan-outs, gateways, repeaters, and other specialty equipment only expand this basic transmission capacity.

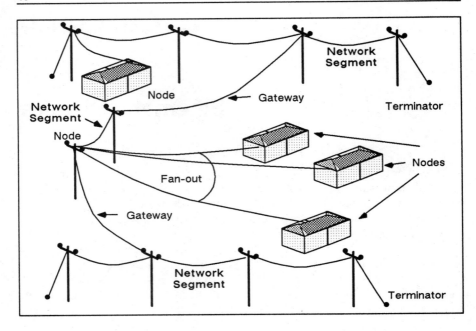

Figure 4.1 Ethernet networks function as a telephone party line.

Conceptually, Ethernet is simple. The coax provides two-way simultaneous connection between communicating parties, which are the *nodes*. The cable is the data communications pathway. A *packet* or Ethernet *frame* is the transmission vehicle. While Ethernet is a one-line country telephone network (only a single transmission can proceed at a time), the transmission protocols, which are rules of privacy or silence, accomplish an orderly transition for deciding who can transmit. Figure 4.2 pictures this analogy.

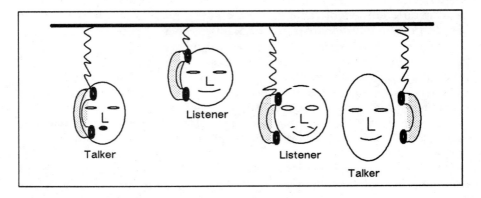

Figure 4.2 The party line telephone analogy.

Each node has transmission and reception hardware, telephone handsets, if you will. This hardware controls access to the cable and monitors traffic. Additionally, each node has hardware that builds the messages to match the required Ethernet frame format. The transmission/reception hardware is called a *transceiver*, for *trans*mitter/re*ceiver,* as explained in the last chapter. This is analogous to the earphone and microphone. The traffic control hardware is called an *Ethernet controller,* analogous to the box and dialing mechanisms of a phone system. The transceiver taps into the coaxial cable and interfaces with the cable for signal transmission and reception just as a telephone cable stretches to the overhead wire from each house. The Ethernet controller connects to the workstation hardware via the computer bus, and interfaces with system software. Often these two transceiver/controller hardware functions are built together as part of the workstation hardware rather than as separate pieces, and this is particularly the case with Cheapernet. This raises reliability and lowers cost.

Transceiver Functionality

Continuing the telephone analogy, transceivers limit access to the telephone to one caller at a time and direct the transition from one transmission direction to another. Figure 4.3 summarizes the functionality of the transceiver. The transceiver listens for a quiet period. When the network coax is not busy with another transmission, the transceiver transmits the data signal. This signal is transmitted at a fraction (approximately 66 to 77 percent) of the speed of light (3×10^6 meters per second), and despite this enormous signal propagation velocity, two or more transmitters may simultaneously observe a quiet period and transmit.

- Receive signal
- Transmit signal
- Broadcast jam signal
- Test for reception
- Test for transmission
- Test for jam (collision)
- Test for heartbeat
- Test for carrier sense
- Transmit preamble
- Transmit delay signal
- Sense collision

Figure 4.3 Transceiver functionality.

The result is a *collision* and, as a result of a collision, the transmitting transceivers will broadcast a "jam" signal when they determine that the electrical signal properties have been "overwritten." Upon receipt of this signal, each station contributing to the collision will wait a random period of time (ranging from 10 to 90 milliseconds) before attempting to transmit again. Each transceiver on a network also awaits a transmission directed to it and forwards that packet to the Ethernet controller.

The collision is detected by the transceiver hardware. Each Ethernet version utilizes a different mechanism for collision detection. Transmission-based detection monitors the DC voltage level of the network. Receive-based detection is dependent upon the DC persistence of the coaxial cable. In all cases, nontransmitting nodes should be able to detect collisions. These differences in collision detection mechanisms explain why some hardware will be incompatible with other hardware and why network incompatibilities exist.

Controller Functionality

The Ethernet controller dials the number and builds the metaphorical phone call that is actually transmitted. This *packet*, or *frame* as it is also termed, must conform to a rigorous format that ensures that party calls are minimal and that the transmitted packet is addressed to a designated node; by analogy the caller dials the number assigned to the person intended to receive the call. The controller also disassembles packets and transfers this information to the receiving workstation's operating system. Figure 4.4 charts the functionality flow provided by the Ethernet controller.

- Convert serial/parallel and parallel/serial
- Transmit and receive buffering
- Frame packets
- Encode and decode broadcast signals
- Recognize addresses
- Detect errors and collisions
- Generate and parse preamble
- Provide carrier sense and deference
- Generate timing for backoff and retransmission
- Filter collision fragments
- Generate and verify frame check sequences
- Filter allignment errors and overruns
- Limit data rate to prevent overruns
- Manage receive and transmit links
- Build/Disassemble frame
- Request retransmission

Figure 4.4 Controller functionality.

Transceiver and Ethernet controller functionality are specified by the OSI model and by the IEEE 802 specification as layers 1 and 2. Some vendor "Ethernets" are only marginally compatible with other vendor equipment and network software. Equipment from several different vendors will access an Ethernet bus and communicate with other equipment from the same vendor and coexist, but will not communicate with these other vendors. Such specification definitional differences or upper-layer software incompatibilities in no way detract from the power of Ethernet, and are often circumvented with special software when complete network access is required.

Gateway Functionality

The Ethernet gateway, as presented by the OSI model in Chapter 3, provides network expansion capabilities for fan-outs, network splicing, and packet repetition. The gateway unit provides multisegment access, signal retransmission, and medium or software presentation conversions among networks with differing protocols. This mechanism is not applied unless a network has grown complex or exceeded the basic topology. By analogy, the gateway is either a long-distance switchboard (in the case of a gateway repeater) or a telephone call into Western Union Telegram Services when it translates format for retransmission to other types of media.

Ethernet Physical Channel Limitations

CSMA/CD protocols place certain limitations on the physical channel. These limitations specify maximum signal propagation times, and as a consequence, maximum cable lengths, since cable lengths and propagation time affect the *slot time* as defined in the data link layer of the OSI model. While the precise electrical specifications are provided in Figure 4.10 at the end of this chapter, the more practical physical configurations are presented below. These commonly stated limits were derived from the actual electrical specifications of the OSI and IEEE 802.3 Ethernet models.

These limitations are determined by the clock rates, the speed of electrical transmissions, and cable lengths, although throughput is limited by collisions and packet overhead. These limitations are explored in greater depth in a later chapter.

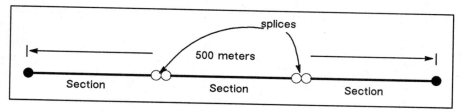

Figure 4.5 Maximum Ethernet segment length. Many sections can be spliced to construct an Ethernet segment. Sections in fact ease the burden of debugging most types of network hardware faults. Note the proper 50-ohm termination required to complete a segment.

The coaxial cable must be terminated in its characteristic impedance at each end. This cable may consist of many spliced *sections*, the smallest unit of cable. One or many sections constitutes a cable *segment*, which is a stand-alone network. A segment may not exceed 500 meters. Figure 4.5 illustrates these limitations.

There may be a maximum of two repeaters in the path between any two stations. Repeaters do not have to be located at the ends of a segment. Repeaters can be used to extend the length of the segment or to extend the one-dimensional bus topology into three-dimensional configurations encompassing different groups, floors, and buildings. Repeaters occupy transceiver positions on each cable and count towards the maximum number of transceivers on a segment (100 units).

The total worst-case roundtrip delay for all coax in the system is 13 microseconds. Therefore, the maximum total coaxial cable length along the longest path between any two transceivers is 1500 meters (this specification does not include terminated sections beyond the two transceivers, and the cable itself actually can be longer). The propagation velocity is assumed to be 77 percent light speed (300,000 meters per second, in a vacuum), in the worst case. Figure 4.6 illustrates these limitations.

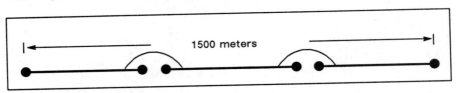

Figure 4.6 Maximum Ethernet path length. No more than two repeaters may be placed between any two connecting nodes.

There may be a maximum of 50 meters of transceiver cable between any station and its node transceiver. This is reduced to 40 meters if a fan-out unit provides multiport access for the station. This reduction is a factor of the propagation delay due to the multiport electronics and its extra wiring. This limitation is exhibited by Figure 4.7. In the worst case, the signal must pass through six transceiver cables, one each at the transmitting and receiving stations and two for each repeater, before that signal reaches both ends of a complete network. The propagation velocity in transceiver drop cables is assumed to be 65 percent light speed, in the worst case.

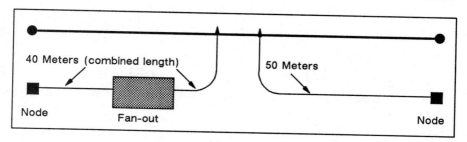

Figure 4.7 Maximum Ethernet transceiver cable lengths.

There may be a maximum of 1000 meters of point-to-point coaxial link anywhere in the system, as illustrated in Figure 4.8. This will typically be used to link separate segments in distant buildings. The propagation velocity is assumed to be 65 percent light speed, in the worst case.

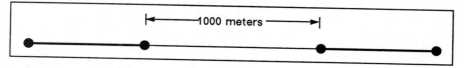

Figure 4.8 Maximum Ethernet point-to-point coaxial link.

Transceivers may be placed no closer than 2.5 meters (0.5 meters on Thinnet), but under no condition can transceivers be spaced further than 1500 meters apart when separated by a repeater. Additionally, each segment may have no more than 100 transceiver units on each coaxial segment, as illustrated by Figure 4.9. Transceivers too close together create transmission interference and an increased risk of collision. This limitation applies to repeaters and specialized devices that may have built-in transceivers. Each node transceiver lowers network resistance and dissipates the transmission signal; a sufficient number of transceivers reduces the network below the specified electrical operational threshold.

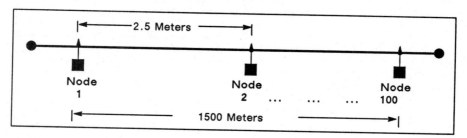

Figure 4.9 Ethernet minimum and maximum node spacing.

	Unit Steady–State Delay	Unit Start-up Delay	# Units Forward Path	# Units Return Path Note 1	Total Delay
Encoder	0.1 μs	0	3	3	0.60 μs
Transceiver cable	5.13 μs/m	0	300 m	300 m	3.08 μs
Transceiver (transmit path)	0.50 μs	0.2 μs	3	3	1.50 μs
Transceiver (receive path)	0.50 μs	0.5 μs	3	0	1.65 μs
Transceiver (collision path)	0	0.5 μs	0	3	1.50 μs
Coaxial Cable	4.33 μs/m	0	1500 m	1500 m	13.00 μs
Point-to-Point Link Cable	5.13 μs/m	0	1000 m	1000 m	10.26 μs
Repeater (repeat path)	0.8 μs	0	2	0	1.60 μs
Repeater (collision path)	0.2 μs	0	0	2	0.40 μs
Decoder	0.1 μs	0.8 μs	2	0	1.80 μs
Carrier Sense	0	0.2 μs	3	0	0.60 μs
Collision Detect	0	0.2 μs	0	3	0.60 μs
Signal Rise Time (to 70% in 500m) Note 2	0	0.1 μs	3	0	0.30 μs
Signal Rise Time (50% to 94% in 500m) Note 3	0	2.7 μs	0	3	8.10 μs
Total Worst Case Round-trip Delay					44.99 μs

Figure 4.10 Worst-case channel propagation delay.

Note 1: the propagation delay has been separated into forward and return delay. In one direction it is carrier sense which is being propagated through the channel, whereas in the return direction it is collision detect which is being propagated. The two signals have different propagation delays as shown in the table above.

Note 2: In the worst case, the propagated signal must reach 70% of its final value to be detected as valid carrier at the end of 500 meters of coaxial cable. The signal rise time must be included in the propagation delay.

Note 3: In the worst case, the propagated collision signal on the return path must reach 94% of its final value to be detected as a collision at the end of 500 meters of cable.

Chapter 5

Ethernet Software and Process

This chapter explains the Ethernet data communications process in terms of the operational mechanics. First, data transmission process and structures are outlined. Second, the transmission/reception procedures are presented. Third, transmission deficiencies are described. Last, layer protocols are described.

Transmission Process

Baseband Ethernet transmits a single digital channel. This transmission is digital because the information is shipped in a cyclic representation, the cornerstone of digital representations. Analog transmission, on the other hand, would convert each digital bit into a voltage representation that parodies the analog value. For example, *0* might require 10 nanoseconds of no voltage, whereas *1* might require 20 nanoseconds of positive voltage. Alternatively, sound could be employed to represent data, whereas gaps might represent lack of data.

Ethernet 2.0 or IEEE 802.3, the most common versions, generate a base voltage level of 0.7 volts which provides a carrier sense signal for all nodes on the network. When transmitting, a transceiver unit lowers the voltage level to -0.7 volts. By modulating this voltage level, the transmitting node propagates a digital signal wave outward in both directions down the coaxial cable. Figure 5.1 demonstrates this *broadcast* process. In this Manchester encoding scheme, the digital signal represents the *0* as a high voltage with a transition to a low voltage, and *1* as a low voltage with a transition to a high voltage.

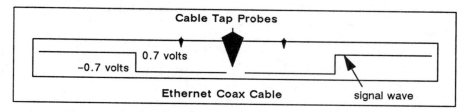

Figure 5.1 Voltage-modulated signal wave broadcast.

The cycle time for each partial broadcast is 50 nanoseconds, thus the time to broadcast each individual bit is 100 nanoseconds; 100 nanoseconds translates into one tenth of a millisecond or into $1/_{10000000}$ seconds, thus yielding the 10,000,000-bit-per-second transmission capacity of Ethernet. Figure 5.2 illustrates the Manchester encoding scheme, and shows how Ethernet achieves these high transmission rates. Note that *data compression*, a method of packing data into a smaller space, and *signal interphasing*, a method of transmitting multiple signals simultaneously, conceivably will increase the effective speed above this raw transmission capacity.

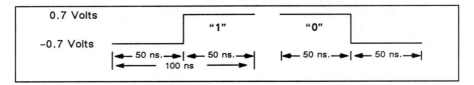

Figure 5.2 The Manchester encoding method.

Packet and Frame Components

Ethernet transmits information in a "packaged" format. This means that individual bits are not transferred from location to location without a preamble or explanation, as they are in a dedicated link between mainframe and terminal or between modem-connected DTEs. The information to be transferred, however small or large, must be packaged, weighed, mailed, and checked upon receipt for proper delivery. This packaged format is called an information *packet* or *frame*. Like any postal letter, this packet or frame contains a destination (the *destination address*), a return address (*source address*), a delivery weight (*length/type* field), the letter contents (actual *data* field), and a registered receipt (*frame check sequence* field) as pictured in Figure 5.3.

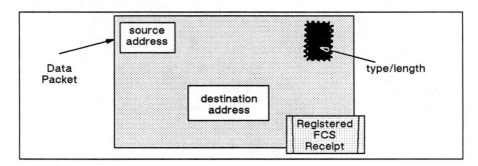

Figure 5.3 The Ethernet mail packet (or frame).

Furthermore, to prevent the letter contents from being shuffled and intermixed, an envelope is supplied (the *transmission preamble*). Since Ethernet is an electronic letter carrier, and letter transits can occur simultaneously, an agreed-upon handshaking between transmitting and receiving nodes prevents letters from crashing into each other and being scrambled (the *delay* time). When the network is not busy, an idle signal is transmitted by all source/destination nodes, which is the 0.7-volt carrier sense. This base voltage is sometimes called the *heartbeat*. The packet is represented by Figure 5.4.

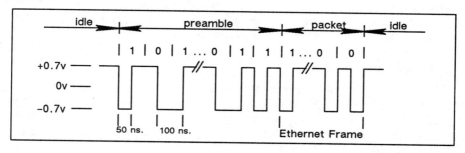

Figure 5.4 The digital Ethernet wave.

This voltage information will be referenced in later chapters, specifically for cable testing and troubleshooting. More specific information is contained in Chapters 11 and 12, and again in Chapters 20, 21, and 22 which detail the troubleshooting techniques required by a network management team. Rather than concentrate on voltage-level representations of data, the frame format is presented pictorially in Figure 5.5. The voltage transmissions are handled by the transmission media and the lower layers of the OSI model: media, physical, and data link layers. Above these layers, data are handled within the structure of the frame format. The frame consists of four components: address, type, data, and error-detection fields.

Frame Element	Byte Location
destination address	1–6
source address	7–12
type or length field	13–14
data field	15–1515
FCS (CRC error check)	last 4 bytes of frame

BYTES

1–6	7–12	13–14	15 1515		last 4 bytes
destination	source	type/length	data field		FCS

Figure 5.5 The Ethernet frame.

The Address Components

The address fields of an information frame consist of source and destination. Every Ethernet-compatible device has a *unique* Ethernet address. The first two bytes of this field represent a unique manufacture code, the next two bytes represent a unique model designation, and the last four bytes represent individual units. This address is permanently encoded on a computer chip somewhere in the CPU or the Ethernet controller of a node unit. The Ethernet transmission software does not directly access this address; upper-layer protocols build symbol tables to reference this address. TCP/IP, for example, uses a 2-byte Internet address. When a packet is transmitted, these logical TCP addresses are resolved to the actual physical source and destination Ethernet addresses.

The Type/Length Field

The type/length field represents the types of data contained within the frame in IEEE 802.3 Ethernet, or the length of the packet in most other (and more common) implementations of Ethernet. When this field represents type rather than length, the specific vendor implementations decide how this field is used.

The Data Field

The data fields contain up to the maximum 1500 bytes of information. The minimum packet size holds 46 bytes. A *byte* may be referred to as an *octet* to confirm that it is an eight-bit byte. Transmission of less than 46 bytes requires a minimum-sized packet, and the unused data space is padded out to this minimum. Transmissions of data streams longer than 1500 bytes, as in a file transfer, a bit-mapped screen display, or document printing, require multiple packets. Since many nodes contend for channel time, a large transmission might not be a contiguous broadcast. The upper levels of Ethernet protocol understand this. In fact, many less powerful computers cannot accept a full 10 megabits per second because these slower machines need time between frames to disassemble and process received data. The upper-layer protocols on a receiving machine accept such block data communications and modify the rate of frame transmissions to prevent overload.

The Frame Check

The Frame Check Sequence, or *FCS,* is an error detection scheme designed to indicate transmission problems. FCS is sometimes referred to as a *Cyclic Redundancy Check*, or *CRC,* or simply as a *checksum,* since the FCS field contains a CRC checksum value. The encoding is defined by the generating polynomial, where x is packet length:

$G(x) = X^{32} + X^{26} + X^{23} + X^{22} + X^{16} + X^{12} + X^{11} + X^{10} + X^8 + X^7 + X^5 + X^4 + X^2 + 1.$

Address fields always contain 6 bytes each for both source and address fields. The type or length is always expressed in 2 bytes. The data field varies in size from 46 to 1500 bytes depending upon need. The FCS field always contains the 4 bytes of the CRC checksum. These fields complete the Ethernet frame.

Packet Preamble and Delay Components

There are two more related frame items. Each transmitted frame is preceded by an 8-byte preamble. This "field" serves to synchronize clocks and base transmission timings on all nodes network-wide. This also serves to forewarn transceivers that a packet may be headed in their direction and that they should check its destination address. The second item, the 9.6-millisecond interpacket delay, provides a delay between packet transmissions. This *slot time* delay allows for the worst-case network propagation delay to provide adequate time for collision detection. Figure 5.6 illustrates the complete Ethernet frame elements including preamble and delay components.

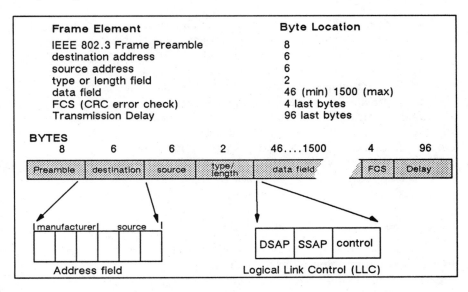

Frame Element	Byte Location
IEEE 802.3 Frame Preamble	8
destination address	6
source address	6
type or length field	2
data field	46 (min) 1500 (max)
FCS (CRC error check)	4 last bytes
Transmission Delay	96 last bytes

Figure 5.6 Packetized Ethernet transmissions. The first 3 or 4 bytes of the data field are reserved for the Logical Link Control table. The DSAP is the Destination Service Address Port, while SSAP is the Source Service Address Port. The Control field contains the packet field control information. The rest of the data field contains the actual information transferred by level 3 of the ISO model.

Ethernet Protocol Control Fields

While the reader might assume that data field is strictly application-oriented data, this is not the case. Data link layers require control information to initiate, maintain, and conclude any conversation. TCP/IP, as do other data link protocols, requires a *logical link control*. This field often contains additional source and destination addresses and status codes. These status codes are called *service address points*. Figure 5.7 maps these service address points. Two addresses define the link level source and destination, and monitor the framing and synchronization of network transmissions.

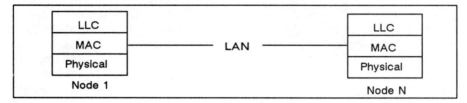

Figure 5.7 Ethernet service address ports of the logical link control field.

Logical Link Fields

The logical link control field specifically provides framing and synchronization, error control and recovery, message acknowledgment, link initialization and disconnection, and addressing. Additionally, this field varies in format depending upon its function. When the data field contains instructional information, this field is called a *supervisory frame*. As stated previously, some receiving stations cannot accept data at the sustained Ethernet rate of 10 megabits per second; one of these supervisory control field functions synchronizes packet transfer rates. When the data field contains acknowledgments and control information, this field is called an *information frame*. Otherwise, when the Ethernet frame contains only user application data, this field is called an *unnumbered frame*. All logical link control fields contain 16 bits.

Usage–Specific LLC Frames

The supervisory frame differs in format from both the information frame and the unnumbered frame. It contains a 4-bit reserved field, a 2-bit supervisory command code, and 2 bits indicating the control field format. Seven bits define the transmitter and receiver sequence numbers, and 1 bit serves both as a poll and final bit. The control field for an unnumbered frame is only 8 bits, and the data field contains an extra byte of application level data. Five modifier bits define the function code. This information is mapped in Figure 5.8.

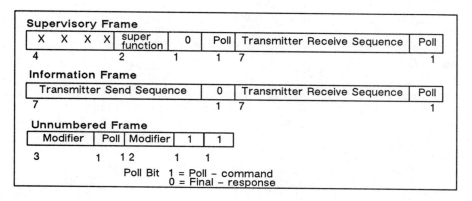

Figure 5.8 The Ethernet control field format.

Depending on the Ethernet implementation chosen, the data link layer may do the initial address recognition. Other connection oriented communications functions may be provided at this level including message acknowledgment, link initialization, and disconnection. The upper layers provide additional link control, to be discussed in the next section.

How Ethernet Transmits

The data and other frame components are built into a special buffer on the Ethernet controller. This buffer is a critical component of the controller. In fact, the Ethernet controller should have several buffers for better performance, one for building packets to be transmitted and at least two buffers for packets received. Often the 10-megabit transmission far outstrips the node processing speed. As an example, most Ethernet personal computers process information at only 1.3 to 3.8 million instructions per second. If the PC processor were exposed to this Ethernet high data transfer rate and not buffered, it would soon be swamped with packets. While the control field of each information packet moderates some of this power, the Ethernet controller handles multitasking operations for the PC. Figure 5.9 represents the importance of the controller buffer.

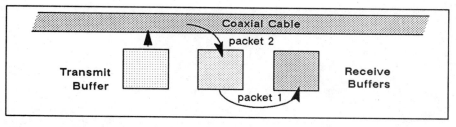

Figure 5.9 Ethernet controllers require packet buffer space.

Once the data are packaged into a frame, the Ethernet controller polls the transceiver for network state. If the network is busy, it waits until the network is free and then transmits the packet. The packet signal propagates in both directions over the coaxial cable. Each transceiver on the network hears the transmission preamble, synchronizes its clock, and awaits the packet. This clock synchronization is important to delineate the beginning and the end of the packet, as illustrated by Figure 5.10; the preamble provides this frame alignment, as shown.

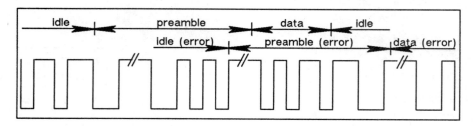

Figure 5.10 Synchronization prevents mistiming transmissions. If the frame were mis-aligned, the FCS checksum would show an alignment error indicated by the lower line. The packet would be discarded, and depending upon the network system software, a request would be made for frame retransmission.

Every transceiver on the network reads the address information. When a packet destination address matches the Ethernet address of a node, the transceiver for that destination node transfers the Ethernet signal into the receive buffers on its Ethernet controller. The signal is not removed from the coaxial cable; it is received in the same way that a radio listens to – but does not "take" — the broadcast. The signal wave continues traveling down the cable until absorbed by the terminators. This process is displayed in Figure 5.11.

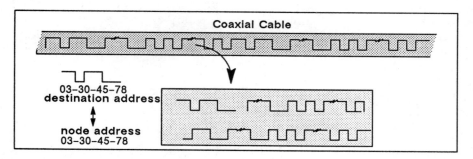

Figure 5.11 Ethernet "receives" a broadcast. All transceiver unit listens to the coax broadcast signal. When the destination address matches the Ethernet address of a receiving node, that transceiver reads the signal, and "copies" the transmission into its own buffer without changing or damaging the signal wave.

The received packet is disassembled by the Ethernet controller into three major components: the data, the data length (or type), and the CRC checksum. The controller verifies that the length of the data message matches the value in the length field, and generates its own CRC to compare against the transmitted CRC value. Any discrepancies are passed to the software protocols. TCP/IP, for example, will request a rebroadcast of the damaged packet. TCP/IP also reports receipt confirmation to the transmitting node via that logical link control field, whereas Ethernet does not. If the transmission has been successful, the data are passed to the software protocols and eventually transferred to the application level for its ultimate use.

Ethernet Deficiencies

Ethernet has a few wrinkles. The contention method of broadcasting allows more than one transceiver to broadcast at the same time. Because of the finite speed of Ethernet, two or more transceivers may simultaneously sense a quiet network. In that interval, each will begin to transmit packets. The signals will collide, corrupting each transmission as in Figure 5.12.

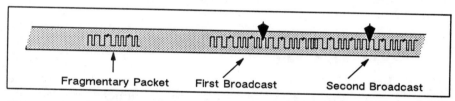

Fragmentary Packet   First Broadcast   Second Broadcast

Figure 5.12 Collisions create fragmentary packets. The first transceiver broadcasts on the open channel. During the time it takes for the signal to propagate to the second transceiver, the second transceiver has also seen an open channel and begun transmission. The first unit recognizes the collision and broadcasts a jam signal, but as a consequence, two fragmentary packets are transmitted in each direction for each broadcast.

Each transmitting transceiver is listening to the network for such a broadcasting overlap, and when sensed, ceases packet transmissions and issues the "jam" signal. This sequence informs all other transmitting units that a collision has been sensed and ensures that the other transmitting units also recognize that same collision. When a collision has been sensed and acknowledged, the Ethernet controllers create a random number (usually provided by the node computer equipment) that is used to delay further retransmission attempts. This random delay serves to restart the *contention* for the network. All nodes thus contend for network access, much as users of party line telephones compete for a free line.

To continue the party line phone analogy of Chapter 4, Ethernet can be likened to a one-line, hand-cranked phone system. When you want to make a phone call, you pick up the line. If it is busy with someone else's call (carrier sense), you hang up. If the line is not busy, you crank the phone and ask for the operator to connect the call (transmit). The call is placed and the phone line is now busy. Only the person receiving the call is supposed to listen. If two or more parties crank for the operator at the same time, there is collision and no one can get the operator. Each caller hangs up ("jams" in Ethernet jargon) and waits a random length of time. The first caller to retry gets the line. The other callers now recognize that the line is busy and wait until they hear that it is free again, as per polite protocol.

Collisions on the Ethernet create fragmentary packets and lower the achievable transmission rate from 10 megabits per second in three ways. First, the collision requires a minimum of 50 bits before that transceiver can recognize this collision. Second, a jam signal is broadcast for a minimum of 32 bits. The channel logic asserts the carrier sense within 2 bits, however. Third, all colliding packets must be retransmitted. Chapter 15 explains this in statistical terms.

No priority is enforced to get the line after a collision, and no originally colliding caller knows if a new preemptive caller entered the system when he or she hung up. This process is random with no assurance of timely service. Ethernet, like the party line, is public, and all transceivers can listen to every call; hence indeed, the "party line" moniker.

Network-Level Software

The last sections of this chapter describe the network-layer software corresponding to OSI layers 3 through 7. For the purposes of this book, the functionality of these layers will be compressed into administrative and content layers. The administrative layer directs the packets and deals with traffic problems independently from packet content; whereas the content layer controls content, decides what should be transmitted, and processes the transmitted information. Figure 5.13 illustrates this layering.

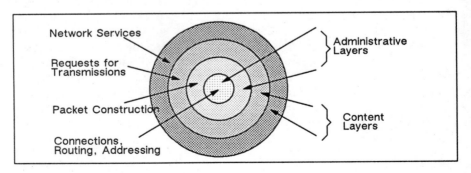

Figure 5.13 Ethernet software layers.

The administrative layer software provides the functionality to know what nodes exist. Some systems map network workstation names into logical *Internet* addresses, which are in turn matched with physical Ethernet addresses. The network software also provides the interface between the Ethernet process and the network software processes. This interface, additionally, maps user data into the packets. In other words, failed transfers are indicated for retry. Ethernet will attempt to transmit sixteen times after a collision, but it has a backup limit of 10 retries. A node is considered "dead" if retransmissions continue to fail. Observe that some network software has blind spots to failed transmission attempts, and this software will continue to load the network in error. Compare the role of this administrative layer to that of the telephone operator. The operator provides connections, distributes telephone numbers and verifies wrong numbers, retries the connection after a "busy" signal, switches connections onto other networks when the main network fails, troubleshoots the mechanical connection, and informs the calling party of network problems. Figure 5.14 demonstrates the operator role in terms of Ethernet.

- Resolve data location into an Internet address
- Resolve Internet address into an Ethernet address
- Accept data set
- Build Ethernet frame:
  - Include addresses (source and destination)
  - Insert data
  - Calculate packet length
  - Calculate checksum
- Send controller frame to Ethernet controller
- Await successful transmission
- Generate reconnections
- Wait until "circuits" not busy
- Inform calling party of network problems

Figure 5.14 The "operator" role.

This network content software can be likened to the language and the grammar, and any cultural standards applied to phone conversations. The role that the calling party assumes is presented in Figure 5.15. Just as the telephone transmits language transparently, the Ethernet administrative software transmits packets without inquiring into packet content. Content depends on the two parties communicating.

The network software builds, accepts, and interprets the packets, and applies the information. The range for Ethernet data application is as large as that of the telephone. Not only can many languages be spoken over a telephone, but each can be encrypted. The language could convey news about the weather, be a sales call, contain a request for help, or provide an explanation or the solution to a problem. In just such a manner, the content and logical composition of Ethernet packets can vary.

- Request a connection
- Initiate a connection
- Await the connection
- Handshake ("say hello")
- Build the data for insertion into data frame
- Pass data to administrative level software
- Await results
- Process responses
- Process errors

Figure 5.15 The "party" role.

The data link layer also provides a special function in the event of a collision. The binary exponential backoff algorithm requires software support for the generation of a random wait time. The 32-bit jam signal initiates this calculation. Some machines implement this in hardware, whereas other machines provide this function in a software module. See Figure 5.16 for an illustration of this feature.

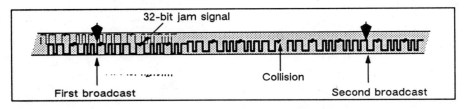

Figure 5.16 A jam signal is broadcast upon collision. The jam signal is a low voltage pulse which overrides all transmission.

Network and Transport Services

Protocols also initiate system and network operations. Just as a phone call to the fire station precipitates a frantic rush to save a burning building, an Ethernet packet can contain information that initiates events. Network software, consequently, will provide such functionality as system boot, network initialization, electronic mail and bulletin boards, transfer file data, simple message routing, file services and print services, and system monitoring. Figure 5.17 shows this upper-layer network functionality.

TCP/IP Protocol

Simple networks build upon TCP/IP protocols (the predominant Ethernet software) to provide intercommunication between nodes for messages, cumbersome file exchange, and terminal services. Such a network configuration would appear to be a mainframe computer serving dependent terminals, although the hardware wiring scheme has been simplified through the application of Ethernet. More complicated networks simplify

- Remote workstation boot
- Network software initialization
- Internode addressing
- Electronic mail
- Computer bulletin boards
- File services
- Print services
- System monitoring
- Network performance monitoring

Figure 5.17 Upper-layer network services.

the file transfer operations, provide electronic mail instead of message capabilities, and add bulletin board operations. Improvements to this include block file transfers, remote workstation operation, system kernel services (that is, the "remote boot"), file interchange capabilities, multiple node access, multiple file sourcing, single sourcing of network-wide software (for example, word processing, databases, and engineering programs), and remote device access and services, like printing.

These user-layer applications are represented by such vendor offerings as DECnet, Aegis, Sun NFS (network file system), HPnet, and other proprietary and nonproprietary network systems. Perhaps more of a manager's time will be devoted to network software problems than hardware issues. As a consequence, manuals describing specific vendor networks need to be reviewed for the specific details of upper-level software. While hardware problems are easily diagnosed (see Chapters 11 through 13), network software problems can be narrowed to specific nodes with software tools and protocol analyzers, as explained in Chapter 14. However, many specific software failures often need to be resolved with vendors' own technical support people, because the additions to the basic TCP/IP are extensive and complicated. Figure 5.18 illustrates the relation between the Ethernet packet, IP, and TCP.

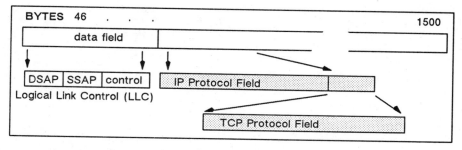

Figure 5.18 TCP/IP mapping from the Ethernet frame data field.

IP Protocol

Internet protocol provides the lowest level of software access and inter-face to the Ethernet environment. This protocol provides the link initializa-tion and termination, node recognition, and packet control operations. The Internet control field, part of the LLC unit, resides within the first few bits of the Ethernet packet data field. Figure 5.19 maps its components.

V	HL	TS	LN	ID	FO	TL	PR	CS	Source	Dest	Option	Data

```
V   = Version                PR      = Protocol
HL  = Header Length          CS      = Header Checksum
TS  = Type Service           Source  = Source Address
LN  = Total Length           Dest    = Destination Address
ID  = Identification         Option  = Option
FO  = Flag and Offset        Data    = Level 4 Data
TL  = Time to Live
```

Figure 5.19 Internet protocol.

TCP Protocol

Transmission Control Protocol is a higher level communication protocol. This protocol sequences data transfers and the actual packet transmissions. It exists within the IP data field. In fact, TCP resides at the OSI layer 4, whereas IP is OSI layer 3. Figure 5.20 illustrates the components of this control field.

SP	DP	SN	AN	OF	W	CS	UP	Option	Data

```
SP  = Source Port            W       = Window
DP  = Destination Port       CS      = Checksum
SN  = Sequence Number        UP      = Urgent Pointer
AN  = Ack Number             Option  = Option
OF  = Offset and Flag        Data    = Level 5 Data
```

Figure 5.20 Transmission control protocol.

Chapter 6

Planning an Ethernet Network

Ethernet installation encompasses both planning and physically connecting the media-level hardware. This chapter describes the planning process and the components that must be included in the plan. The components include: the coaxial cable; cable fittings like end connectors, barrel connectors, and terminators; and the coaxial tap units, transceivers, and transceiver drop cables. The discussion of components addresses cable hangers and cable tie mechanisms, and concern about the physical and dimensional stability of the cable itself. An experienced network manager understands the value of blueprinting the installation, and this chapter describes how and when to blueprint. This presentation serves to augment vendor-supplied technical documentation. Figure 6.1 illustrates Ethernet components described within this chapter.

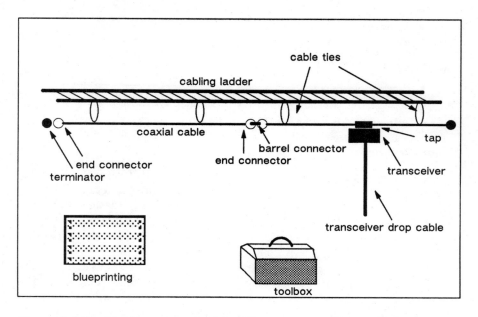

Figure 6.1 Typical items required in Ethernet network installation.

Designing and Planning a Network

The first step in planning any installation is to analyze the user requirements and understand the network technology. The network plan should
address both current and future needs by allowing for expansion at a later
date. If at all possible, it is wise to begin with a small network and expand
over time. A small network will simplify the learning process and minimize
the complexity of problem solving.

Designing and planning the network configuration builds the foundation
for long-term success of that network because improper estimation of
network loads and user needs at this stage will lead to poor network
management by overloading the staff with problems; poor network
performance and sloppy control of network staff are the key issues that
form the basis for the operational evaluation of the network administrator,
but they depend upon the foundation of network design. While operation
and implementation issues addressed in Chapter 9 ultimately make or
break a manager, design and planning concerns addressed in this chapter
ultimately define the complexity of daily network implementation and
operation. These basic items are expanded in Figure 6.2.

- Network design configurations
- Network user needs
- Physical plant limitations
- Power protection
- Network installation
- Compatibility
- ANSI and IEEE standards
- Cable connector integrity
- Network profiling
- Network blueprinting

Figure 6.2 Practical network design concerns.

Design Criteria

The design of a network is a complex problem, with far-reaching ramifications. Insufficient capacity, incorrect media, and inadequate loading
characteristics frequently cause performance lags. These design shortcom-
ings are avoided by understanding organizational needs and network
performance issues *before* configuring the network. Break the analysis into
small pieces. Understand who will use the network, what load each user
will place upon the network, what access to devices each user requires, and
how growth or organizational change might strain resources. See how
competitors or other LAN customers are applying networking technology
and what loads are transported by these networks. Compare this to your
organization's needs. Lease versus purchase decisions hinge upon financial

concerns and are not addressed here although the reader might consider lease or rent as a viable alternative to the outright purchase of a system. Additionally, turnkey systems and professional installation save time, money, and personnel without the need to hire people normally associated with a network. Also consider the availability of spare parts and outside expertise to solve internal network problems. Figure 6.3 shows these network design and maintenance questions.

- Who will use the network?
- What load will each user place upon the network?
- What access to devices should each user have?
- What individual growth is anticipated?
- What centralized resources are needed?
- What load can the network sustain?
- What peak loads are sustainable?
- What spare parts are needed?
- What outside expertise is available?
- What *other* networks must interface with Ethernet?
- How will a network conform to physical plant limitations?

Figure 6.3 Network design and maintenance questions.

Construct the network from small, separable building blocks. Cable connectors and RF switches are just some of several mechanisms to segment the network. Complementing these devices, gateways, repeaters and subnetworks divide the size and complexity of the network into comprehensible units. Such segmentation adds reliability, design simplicity, and may, in extreme cases, provide the only means to trace Ethernet problems to their source.

When designing a network, insist that all classes of components come from the same manufacturer. Slight interpretative differences in ISO or Ethernet specifications could mean parts are not compatible. This issue is expanded on in a following section. When it is not feasible to select uniformity, segregate the parts that differ. If node equipment includes personal computers and engineering workstations, place these units on separate segments of cable. Problems from one class may create problems for another class, masking the source of the problem. Thus, segmentation is an appropriate design criterion.

Last, do not overstate the capacity of single Ethernet channel, or of the Ethernet system as a whole. Capacity saturates at about 55 percent of theoretical rated capacity (see Chapter 15). Select versions compatible with existing equipment and install a capacity sufficient to match forecasted needs. Be certain that a vendor has provided the necessary references to verify not only his version of Ethernet but also his postsale support. Ethernet is at its best for occasional file transfers, paging, distributed databases, and communication. It may not be appropriate for massive file backups or data transfers, single keystroke terminal support, or single-channel support of 100 engineering workstations. Understand the limitations of the medium and the organizational needs. Where one medium is insufficient, research the benefits of another. Understand how expansion can be effected to support user and traffic growth, and technological change.

Design to Meet User Needs

When designing a network, it is important to envision the purpose of the network, the type of traffic it will accommodate, the distances between areas that need to be serviced, and the total load to be placed upon the network. Realize that Ethernet specifications may inhibit or hinder your design; consider distance limitations and node counts, as well as repeater placements. Figure 6.4 outlines issues to consider when designing a network, some of which are considered in this chapter. Because Ethernet is a collision detection medium, it will handle a maximum of 10 megabits of transmission under the best of conditions, minus traffic collisions, minus the results of all suboptimal hardware and software, minus a random error rate. Effective usage may yield 5 to 10% of the rated capacity.

```
• Network purpose
• Traffic volume
• Peak traffic volume
• Traffic composition
• Network size and configuration
• Network user community size
• User work load
• Network cost
• Network functionality
• Security
• Reliability
• Suitability
```

Figure 6.4 Network design issues.

Consider the very suitability of Ethernet. A bus configuration network with a token passing scheme may be better suited than CSMA/CD. For example, network with periodic peak loads, direct connections, and localized computer processing may be advantageous. Ethernet may be precisely the proper medium, in cases like project design and programming, if multiple channels are installed. For other situations a broadband version of Ethernet is a viable option. Some vendors carry 3-megabits, 5-megabits, and 10-megabits multiple-channel Ethernet. As many as a hundred separate channels might be carried by a single broadband coaxial cable. Although the television-type channel selection transceivers are expensive, perhaps twenty times as expensive as a baseband transceiver, the effective cost is somewhat lessened, because the broadband transceivers often provide eight ports, reasonable if all eight ports need to talk on the same selected channel.

All factors add to the cost of Ethernet; these should be established prior to the actual installation process. The cable itself is an expensive proposition at several dollars per foot installed, possibly more if local building codes specify special fire-proofed cable. The transceivers and other related Ethernet hardware are also a cost. While Ethernet hardware is also an expense to consider, installation and maintenance are other cost factors. Large Ethernet configurations are difficult to maintain, therefore costly. The interaction of large networks, disparate hardware, and disparate loading are prime considerations in defining costs, because problems increase rapidly as a network grows in complexity and load.

For lower-volume serial lines, cheaper and lower-capacity networks are options worth consideration. This encompasses T-1, RS-232, Starlan, direct serial connection, or repeated parallel lines, as well as twisted-pair Ethernet or proprietary PC networks. Note that Ethernet volumes can become sizable and require the organizational resources of a dozen full-time staff. RS-232 networks are a very mature technology, both in terms of the hardware and management techniques. An IBM computer network may support 40 users each on 100 separate channels. This means a single network will support 4000 terminals. That is, by the numbers, a very large management problem, because there would be at least 4000 users, maybe as many as 12,000 with channel multiplexing and multiple users sharing each terminal. Each user requires a login, accounts, and file storage space. Often, each account must be billed, and this creates a need for an accounting organization.

An Ethernet network can be as complex, although not in the same terms. Ethernet is far more difficult to manage because it is relatively newer, has a shorter track record, and has not demanded the vendor support applied to the more developed serial line technologies. Not only is

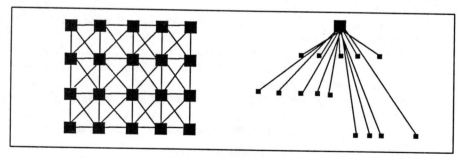

Figure 6.5 Ethernet is an interconnected network. Ethernet on the left supports complete global access. The mainframe network on the right provides link to link access for the dumb terminals to the mainframe. A user at one such "node" seeking access to another "node" must connect through the mainframe and the power is more limiting than in Ethernet.

the hardware still developing, management and tools are less developed than in the mainframe environment. Additionally, Ethernet supports a traffic load at least equivalent to an RS-232 network. At 9600 baud (about 900 bytes or characters per second), 4000 users on an RS-232 network account for a maximum of 3,640,000 bytes per second which is similar in volume to a *single* Ethernet channel. While the physical and administrative demand is numerically greater, the frame in an RS-232 environment is also transmitted from the mainframe to the terminal. Characters are returned only to the mainframe. An Ethernet environment is a true interconnected network, not a tree of decreasing importance. The topology is very different and loads distribute differently as illustrated in Figure 6.5.

Physical Plant Limitations

Sharing computer resources and exchanging electronic mail through a built-in computer network is not reserved for the preplanned, well-funded startup ventures in newly built industrial parks. Older buildings, unplanned sprawling complexes, and high rise buildings can have networks too. No building, no matter how old or how busy, will prohibit the installation of the type of equipment your organization wants. While it is possible that the layout of the building may constrain the wiring efficiency, neither the building design nor the lack of space will limit the kind of network that you can install. If your building is of an older design, examine the premises more carefully because there may be additional cost for installing network coax cable because the ceiling is inaccessible. Plenums may be small or nonexistent. Existing pathways between floors or buildings may be unsuitable for cable. In such cases, new conduits or cable trays may provide part of the answer. PVC cable produces a toxic gas when it burns, and is often banned from return air plenums, the space above the hung grid ceiling. Teflon cable, although more expensive than PVC, exceeds most building codes without any restrictions.

Twisted-pair, the cable most often existing in old buildings, may provide a ready means to network a system via Starlan, for example. If growth, large numbers of far-linked machines in different directions, or video imaging are required, it may be uneconomical to reroute, add, or maintain twisted-pair. Coax has some distinct advantages. Ethernet coaxial cable provides a linear bus architecture with an appropriate flexibility. When a contractor has to drill holes through walls, ceilings, and beams, in order to route cable through narrow plenums, it makes more sense to pull a single coaxial cable through a facility from floor to floor than multiple sets of twisted-pairs.

Locations of computer rooms may be suboptimal but possible in a host of locations. Select the location with the best cable access, the most environmentally stable conditions, and one that will provide security to meet design requirements. Computer facilities are best if locked and if the temperature remains constant. Overheating and low humidity, which increases static, cause component failures. Climate control equipment generally solves these problems. However, these concerns are best addressed during the planning stages rather than as retrofitted necessities.

Finally, consider how best to schedule installation. If cabling conduits and coaxial cable are installed as part of new construction, the work is just one more item for the building contractors. Cabling an existing facility may require working around physical limitations and the office hours. If your organization cannot be closed during the network installation, the contractor may have to coexist with employees and customers. Additionally, scrap, dirt and constant traffic may create a need for frequent cleanings.

Power Protection

Most network managers are aware of the danger of lightning striking outside wiring and sending a jolt down the line to damage anything unfortunate enough to be plugged into the outlet. Most managers are also aware of power surges and spikes that can cause premature failure of computer chips and magnetic media. Some have experienced the slow degradation that occurs during a power brownout when voltage levels decay. Everyone knows the effects of a power blackout. The problem for the network manager is what can be done about these disabling situations.

Figure 6.6 lists the typical problems that can create network havoc. Also, radio frequency interference (RFI) and electromagnetic interference (EMI) can travel through the power lines with disastrous results to sensitive computer equipment. The damage from such events is not limited just to damaged computer equipment, data loss or corruption, and downtime. There are also lost opportunity costs, aggravation from frequent crashes, and additionally, the certainty that other damage will be spawned. A crash can destabilize a chemical reaction, a long clinical test, damage patient records and lose critical allergy information, or ruin a part in a computer-controlled manufacturing process.

It is important to weigh the importance of uninterrupted service and the cost of downtime. Frequent downtime affecting order entry, order processing, or accounts payable may be of little consequence, but it may represent the germinal stages of a bad customer relations problem. The cost of the computer equipment is apt to exceed significantly the cost of protection, although the purchasing decision rests on the risk that the organization is willing to assume.

There are solutions to these problems. Specifically, filters screen out electrical noise from the incoming power, while suppressors level out the wave crests of power surges. Isolation equipment provides capacitance to level out the wave troughs of low power. Voltage regulators filter the electrical power so that the voltage is stable. Standby battery supplies and

- Power surges
- Power spikes
- Power sags
- Brownout
- Blackout
- Lightning strikes

Figure 6.6 Electrical problems that threaten networks.

uninterruptible systems provide the same emergency power function, although the uninterruptible power system usually provides electricity automatically, if its sensing apparatus detects power problems. Figure 6.7 lists commonly available electrical computer protection devices.

- RFI/EMI filters
- Surge suppressors
- Isolation transformers
- Voltage regulators
- Hot standby battery backups
- Uninterruptible power systems

Figure 6.7 Power protection devices.

Compatibility

Ethernet provides some measure of compatibility. Not only does it offer a certain mechanical consistency, but many vendors sell products to interface disparate "Ethernet" components. Compatibility is often used as a *selling point*. However, this doesn't always mean that Ethernet-compatible equipment will *transmit* to other Ethernet-compatible equipment; different equipment on the same network can blindly share the coax with each other. There is a potential for interfacing problems. While the physical media and the transmission standards may be the same or similar, electrical and hardware differences may make the three Ethernet versions listed in Figure 6.8 functionally incompatible.

Ethernet is defined as a medium and an electrical configuration. Other so-called Ethernet networks transmit on nonspec cable. These broadband networks, which transmit on many simultaneous channels, apply a different technology to either coaxial or optical cable, and even to microwave transmissions. These versions may be "Ethernet compatible," but not Ethernet comparable. This means that these versions will interface to a standard network through a specified mechanism; it does not mean that these alternative networks are physically, electrically, or procedurally compatible with standard Ethernet. An ISO bridging or gateway mechanism, sometimes called a *linkage* product, connects totally separate networks for intranetwork communications.

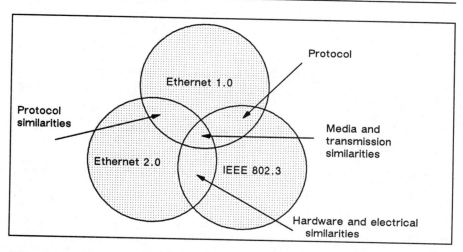

Figure 6.8 Ethernet version compatibility. The three major Ethernet versions all share the media and transmission standards. All additionally share most of the packet fields, but differ in packet signal generation, collision recognition, and sometimes, the actual broadcast protocol.

In order for any third-party vendor products to function correctly with the existing network, all transmission and reception hardware must synchronize timing. Subtle differences will become more apparent as the network grows in size and loading factors; these differences should be understood and the ramifications explored prior to actual purchase or installation. Likewise, secondary sourcing of so-called commodity items may breed incompatibilities later when a network is upgraded. Be aware that prime vendors may substantially alter their equipment or software over time for any number of reasons including bug fixes, better performance, a new sales strategy, or an attempt to undermine other vendors, and as a consequence, third-party solutions may no longer be ideal. In any event, get verified customer references from both happy and unhappy customers. Assess carefully compatibility and the eventual upgrade and customer support policies. The vendor must support not only his own product, but also other network items that will interface with the vendor's equipment.

Compatibility must be supported on the first three ISO layers for machines to share the same physical transmission highway. Compatibility must be supported on layers 3 and 4 for differing hardware to even acknowledge another protocol. Layers 5 and 6 must be identical for machines to interconnect. Layer 7 is only the application layer, and compatibility at this level is necessary only insofar as different machines need to share code, mail, and other user-level application software.

A network ideally requires hardware and software components that match a single specification. Where components deviate from a single design criterion, isolate those unique components with subnetworks, Radio

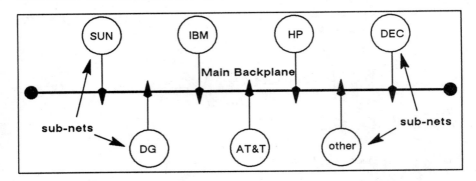

Figure 6.9 Isolate different equipment on separate networks.

frequency switches, or gateways. For example, Ethernet, Thinnet, and Cheapernet standards vary. Ethernet has three distinct variations, Ethernet 1.0 and 2.0, and IEEE 802.3, all of which are electrically incompatible.

Also, since Ethernet is a physical specification for a communication network, this network design only specifies the media and the electrical transmission standards; it does not define file transfer, screen refresh, network equipment boot parameters, mail systems, or other upper-layer protocols. These processes are supplied by XNS, DECnet, or TCP/IP, and other such ISO layer 3 definitions; differences in the programmer's implementation of TCP/IP cause one major incompatibility. Figure 6.9 outlines possible Ethernet discrepancies.

Different vendors supply their own interpretations of Ethernet and especially TCP/IP. While Ethernet should be robust enough to provide access to all these devices, in practice, slight differences are indeed likely to create transmission problems. Such incompatibilities are more prone on saturated networks. Different networks should isolate different types of equipment. Gateway and bridging mechanisms could interface these networks as in Figure 6.10, if this is an organization requirement.

- Physical channel dissimilarities
- Transmission media dissimilarities
- Transmission preamble and delay incompatibilities
- Electrical signal differences
- Electrical timing differences
- Controller buffering limitations
- Packet incompatibilities
- Logical Link Control field differences
- SQE nonsupport
- Transmission Protocol varieties
- Error handling discrepancies
- Acknowledgment differences

Figure 6.10 Possible Ethernet incompatibilities.

Not only are there three Ethernet versions, but each equipment and component vendor can redesign the functionality to minimize costs or maximize features. Small details, such as controller buffer parameters or how upper-layer software device drivers will access physical devices, can make difficult-to-trace problems. Furthermore, vendor-supplied components can vary in small ways. While these minor deviations may not disrupt communications, incompatibilities may mean machines from different vendors can share a network without the ability to talk to each other.

Network Limitations

The Ethernet specifications outline the requirements for a functioning network. Most of these specifications present maximum configurations for the following: length of coax segments; cable size; cable conductivity; number of transceivers; length of transceiver cables; types of transceivers; numbers of protocols running concurrently on the network. As previously mentioned, Ethernet fails when it is statistically overloaded. Therefore, these specifications are more suggestion than an absolute figure. It is wise to plan a network with enough capacity for growth and not assume that the specifications can be stretched to accommodate that growth. Therefore, Figure 6.11 reiterates the Ethernet configuration parameters.

Ethernet Network Components

Because planning requires an understanding of the Ethernet components, this chapter continues with a discussion of the options available for basic network components. Figure 6.12 outlines items of importance when

Parameter	Ethernet	Thinnnet/Cheapernet
Data rate	10 Mbits/sec	10 Mbits/sec
Maximum segment length	500 meters	200 meters
Maximum network span	2500 meters	1000 meters
Maximum nodes/segment	100	30
Maximum nodes/network	1024	1024
Minimum node spacing	2.5 meters	0.5 meters
Maximum node spacing	1000 meters	1000 meters
Maximum number:		
Repeated segments	3	3
Interconnected segments	3	3
Lan cable:		
Type	RG-50/RG-58	RG-6, RG-6a, RG-225
Connectors	N-type	BNC
Impedance	50 ohms	50 ohms
Transceiver cable:		
Connectors	15 pin/D-plug	BNC
Maximum length	50 meters	50 meters or not used

Figure 6.11 Ethernet network parameters.

- Ethernet cable
- Network cable sectioning
- Section end connectors
- Ethernet terminators
- Media access units
  - Taps
  - Transceivers
- Transceiver drop cables
- Jack screw replacement of slide latches
- Ethernet cable routing
  - Avoiding water, high-voltage, and temperature extremes
  - Cable trays and cable supports
  - Logical routes
- Selecting components
- Blueprinting

Figure 6.12 The items that must be considered when planning a network.

planning a network. Components required for even the simplest installation include: cable, connectors, terminators, cable ties, taps, transceivers (MAUs), transceiver drop cables (AUIs).

Ethernet Cable

The crucial item in any Ethernet is the cable. Figure 6.13 shows baseband cable. Figure 6.13 (a) shows PVC 50-ohm coax, Figure 6.13 (b) shows teflon 50-ohm coax, Figure 6.13 (c) shows Thinnet, and Figure 6.13 (d) illustrates Starlan twisted-pair and the common telco connector. It is called *telco* because it was designed and is now used for most telephone connections. Figure 6.13 (e) illustrates the undercarpet ribbon; note that like Starlan, it is not a coaxial cable.

Cheapernet is a variant of Thinnet and uses the same cable, and both the PVC and teflon variations have essentially the same diameter and require essentially the same fittings. Installation for each varies only insofar as the connectors fit different diameter cable and in that building codes vary. However, if at all possible, use cable from the same manufacturer, and from the same lot, because extruder differences cause minor signal reflection at connection points.

Network Cable Sectioning

A network does not require a single continuous length of coax cable. The network will work adequately if it is sectioned into convenient lengths. There will be almost no detectable degradation if all the connections are properly installed. End connectors sandwich each coax section, and two or more sections are interconnected with barrel connectors to complete the full Ethernet coaxial segment. Many network managers might assume that

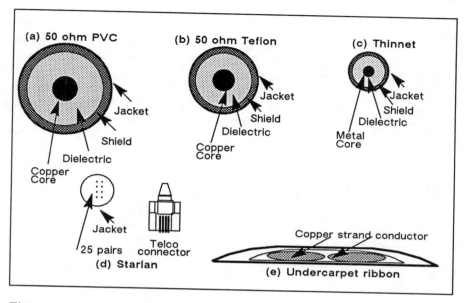

Figure 6.13 Cross sections of baseband coaxial cable. Undercarpet Ethernet ribbon is a specialty application with unknown performance and compatibility. Note the dual conductor design.

such construction of a network is in poor form. However, installation of shorter sections will not only prove easier, but installation costs will probably be less, installation time will be faster, and verification of the new network will proceed smoothly. Also, installation of shorter sections of coax is less traumatic to the copper core.

In fact, such segmentation demonstrates good planning. Ethernet often experiences transmission problems. Problems become more prevalent on longer and busier networks. Longer networks often span rooms, run vertically through ceilings and walls, traverse floors and even buildings. It is unlikely that you will be able to locate a segment of coax cable long enough to meet such needs. Since distributors sell cable in 500-meter spools, "short" tails become useless and expensive under this philosophy. Certainly, you can buy 500-meter lengths of cable. There is no practical benefit to doing so. It is awkward to string a bulky, inflexible cable through tight bends, and pull that entire 500-meter (1645 feet) length through the ceiling. The weight of the cable makes such practice difficult, and the friction along its length makes it virtually impossible. It is likely that the weight of the unsupported cable will break the core conductor.

Another important reason for segmenting the network is that certain test instruments such as a time domain reflectometer (see Chapter 12), don't work well if the network segments are not sectioned in cable lengths of under 500 feet. This tool sends a radar-like signal down the network cable and illustrates blockages or breaks. This signal dissipates over distance, thereby providing less accurate information.

Ideally, a manager would section lengths of runs, and conveniently section these in corners. The IEEE standards suggest that Ethernet 50-ohm coaxial cable is best in sections of 23.4 meters (76.8 feet) or multiples of that measurement to minimize *internal signal reflection*. This reflection is often referred to as cable *impedance*. Segmentation provides a means to partition the network into several functioning segments when transmission trouble occurs, which helps to isolate the problem. The length of 23.4 meters and unit multiples are the magic measurements as shown in Figure 6.14. This length is derived from integral multiples of $1/2$ the wavelength of the Ethernet signal. Some other multiples also work because of the signal harmonics of multiples, but for all practical purposes 23.4 meters is a convenient length and an easy number to remember. Under no condition should a network segment exceed 500 meters without special relay or repeater equipment.

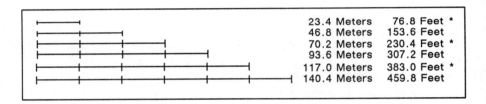

23.4 Meters	76.8 Feet *
46.8 Meters	153.6 Feet
70.2 Meters	230.4 Feet *
93.6 Meters	307.2 Feet
117.0 Meters	383.0 Feet *
140.4 Meters	459.8 Feet

Figure 6.14 Recommended network coax section lengths. The section length of 23.4 meters minimizes internal reflections without significantly altering the cable impedance. Odd unit multiples of this length work best.

Connectors

Ethernet has standardized parts that simplify and improve the reliability of the network, and ease problem solving. These parts include N-type or BNC end connectors; barrel connectors, sometimes called *couplers*; and terminator plugs. For instance, rather than soldering a resister onto the network (which could function), use one of several commonly available parts that screw or crimp onto the cable ends.

N-type connectors and terminators vary in size to fit both PVC (Polyvinyl Chloride) or teflon (Fluorinated Ethylene Propylene) 50-ohm while BNC fit Thinnet (75-ohm) coax cables. Just a reminder: while the cables and connectors are referred to as 75 ohm, the terminator is 50 ohms. Figure 6.15 contrasts the differences between the BNC and N-type cable connectors. The BNC pin connectors are simpler and more positive, although the N-type connector has a larger surface area for electrical contacts. N-Type is the most common Ethernet connector series.

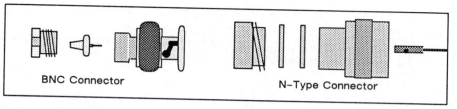

Figure 6.15 BNC and N-type connectors exploded.

Figure 6.16 illustrates some of the standard connectors. A pair of male end connectors and the female-female barrel connector is the standard unit for connecting two sections of coax cable together. The male end connector and the female terminator must be included on each end of the network. The panel mount connector is unusual, often used when the coax cable is routed through a phone closet

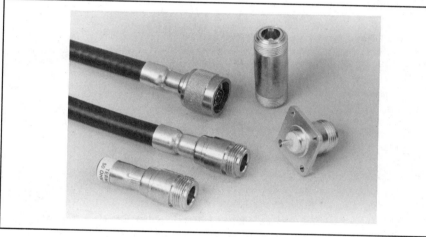

AMP, Incorporated

Figure 6.16 Standard Ethernet Connectors. Pictured items are clockwise: a male end connector (not common), barrel connector, a panel mount connector, a standard 50-ohm terminator, and a female end connector.

Network Terminators

The Ethernet network requires proper "termination." This means that a 50-ohm resistor must be applied to each end of the network. These resistors absorb the spent broadcast packets and prevent them from bouncing back down the network coax. When the Ethernet signals reach these end points, the signals have passed every transceiver on the network and have been read by at least one unit. A nonterminated segment does not provide network service because the impedance is improperly supplied. On such an improperly constructed segment, the Ethernet signal bounces from these endpoints as a partial signal with sufficient energy to jam most transceivers with continuous carrier sense. Figure 6.17 illustrates the function of a terminating resistor.

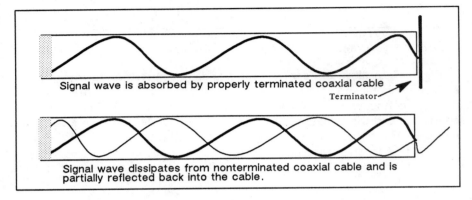

Figure 6.17 Baseband Ethernet requires proper termination.

Note that in an improperly terminated segment the signal is propagated from the transmitting node in *two* directions. If the signal echoes, it will jam the network because it will falsely appear to any transmitting transceiver that more than one transceiver is transmitting.

Media Access Units: Taps and Transceivers

Once coaxial cable is installed, a computer device requires a means to access the cable. Baseband cables require a *transceiver* to provide network signal access and a *tap* to electrically connect the transceiver into the cable. The transceiver and tap together are logically called a *Media Access Unit*, or MAU. The formal term is presented only for cross reference to other literature; it is not as descriptive as "transceiver." Cheapernet requires no special equipment other than a pair of BNC connectors held together by a barrel connector. A "tee" connector and two separate segments of cable provide workstation interconnection.

Taps

The tap provides electrical access to the copper conductor and grounds the braided cable shield. It comes in three basic versions. There is one inline version that is invasive because it requires two separate end connectors (either N-type or BNC) and is installed *inline* between cut sections of coaxial cable rather than surrounding the cable like many other taps. The two other types of clamp are non-invasive in that the coax cables need no

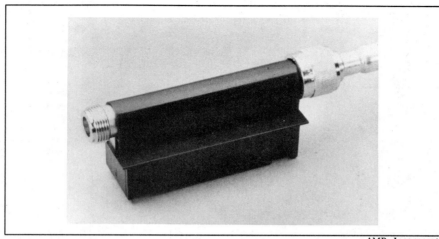

AMP, Incorporated

Figure 6.18 Standard inline tap. Notice that this type of tap requires the installation of a pair of end connectors.

segmentation. They are preferable. They clamp onto the cable with a nut and bolt assembly, and usually can be installed without disrupting network transmissions. Figure 6.18 illustrates one such tap unit.

Another type of unit drives both core and shield probes into contact from the force of installation; these TCL taps are antiquated and have a high failure rate. The most frequently used clamp unit requires a drill bit to ream an access hole for a threaded probe, like the AMP taps. Figure 6.19 illustrates these variations.

The Japanese are introducing a new type of unit that pivots freely on the cable and has a smaller electronics package; Fujikura has a unit with a built-in transceiver cable which means one less potential failure point. It is certain the technology will continue to evolve.

The TCL tap has a retained nut and bolt assembly and strong metal probes. The effort of tightening the clamp around the coaxial cable forces the probes to penetrate the shield and core. The core probe is offset and insulated to prevent shorts between core and shield. The transceiver unit screws into female threads for electrical connections. In many managers' experience, this unit has a low success rate for proper installation, and over time fails because the probes do not maintain good contact with the coax core and shield. A good installation requires repeated disassembly and reassembly. This tap often fails with teflon coaxial cable because teflon is thinner than the PVC cable for which this tap was originally designed. Not only will a faulty tap fail, it is likely to break the network for all network users by shorting the copper core and disrupting the transmission signals.

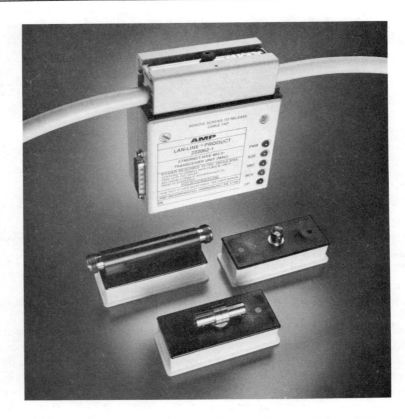

AMP, Incorporated

Figure 6.19 This shows the interchangeability of AMP tap units.

Transceivers

A transceiver is a small box with a computer circuit card inside. The transceiver bolts to the tap unit and electrically accesses the tap probes. The transceiver also connects to a node workstation (or a fan-out unit) through a cable. This cable provides signal, power, and ground to the transceiver electronics. Various styles of taps and transceivers are pictured in Figure 6.20.

The AMP tap has been favored by managers, and is the de facto industry standard. Although different types of transceivers can be mixed on the same network, it is generally advisable to simplify the network design with a *single* diameter of cable and *one* type of tap and transceiver. Note, however, that the transceiver unit is the same in the photograph while the tap unit varies. This modularity is very desirable because it minimizes the need for spare parts and simplifies the replacement and repair of units should they fail.

As Chapter 3 stated, there is a difference between 1.0, 2.0 and IEEE 802.3 standards. It matters because transceivers have internal differences with regard to the electronics. While most transceivers support all three standards, it is important to select units with the same standard.

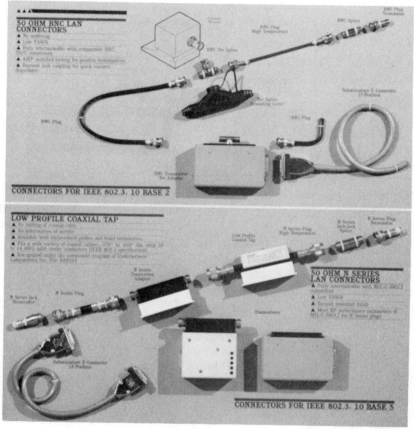

AMP, Incorporated

Figure 6.20 This photograph shows MAU device variations.

Transceiver Drop Cables

A transceiver "drop" cable connects the transceiver with the workstation. This drop cable is officially called the "Attachment Unit Interface" or AUI. This cable cannot exceed 50 meters in length (164.5 feet), or signal dissipation is extreme and propagation timing limitations are violated. Price differences and characteristics of PVC and teflon AUI cable are similar to those of PVC and teflon coaxial cable. Figure 6.21 illustrates the cable connectors and the transceiver connection. The transceiver end is female and the workstation is male.

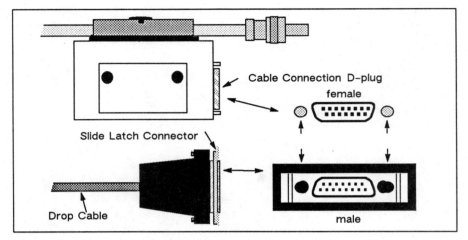

Figure 6.21 Transceiver drop cables and connectors.

The IEEE 802.3 transceiver cable contains eight pairs of wires that power the transceiver and the network coax, and provide transmit, receive, and carrier sensing. Pair 1 and 4 provides the collision shield. Pair 2 and 9 provides collision detection. Pair 3 and 10 provides a transmit signal. Pair 4 and 11 provides a receive shield. Pair 5 and 12 provides the receive signal. Pair 13 and 14 provides power to the transceiver, and 15 completes the wiring with the network coaxial ground. Wire 16 is unused. See Figure 6.22 for this pin-out. Note, too, Ethernet requires that only the AUI cables (transceiver drop cables) be grounded at a single point. To insure proper and reliable communications, this specification should be adhered to with zealousness. This means that the shield braid-to-shell ground is an important part of the AUI cable. Networks installed with multiple grounds frequently work—until growth upsets this balance. Stability problems can easily creep into a network.

There are differences between IEEE 802.3, Ethernet 1.0 and Ethernet 2.0 AUI cables. These differences are in the number of pairs actually used and in how the shields are interconnected, although for most practical applications AUI cables are interchangeable. This premise fails when a network has reached the maximum size specifications or when other design violations exist; mismatched cables amplify these violations.

In actual practice, pins 2, 3, 4, 5, 6, and 9, 10, 12, 13 are wired together pin to pin. Pin 1 is ground, and the cable braid must complete a ground connection between each plug connector shell. Note that the transceiver end is female and the wall or equipment end is male.

Pin Number	Function (PL1–PL8)	Function (SK1)
1	collision shield	collision shield
2	collision+	collision+
3	transmit+	transmit+
4	receive shield	receive shield
5	receive+	receive+
6	see note 1	transceiver power–
7	unconnected	unconnected
8	see note 1	see note 2
9	collision–	collision–
10	transmit–	transmit–
11	transmit shield	transmit shield
12	receive–	receive–
13	unconnected	transceiver power+
14	see note 1	transceiver power shield
shell	protective ground	protective ground

Figure 6.22 AUI connector pin assignments.

Note 1: on PL1–PL8, pins 1, 4, 8, 11 and 14 are internally connected with a capacitor to pin 6. Shells are isolated from all cables and provide a protective ground. The shell is connected to the peripheral devices.

Note 2: on SK1, pins 1, 4, 8, 11 and 14 are internally connected to pin 6.

Jack Screws and Slide Latch Replacement

The original Xerox standard specifies 15-pin D-connectors with slide latch and locking posts at each end of the drop cable. These were illustrated in Figure 6.21. The slide latch is 25 gauge untreated aluminum which is not noted for its strength. As a consequence, any pressure applied to this assembly can bend the slide latch and partially free the D-connectors. This electrically poor connection yields a failed workstation at best, or at worst a network flooded with partial or corrupted transmissions and a continually chattering transceiver. Jack screws and female lock nuts solve this problem. See Figure 6.23 for an isometric representation of the connector components. The cost of these parts is the same as the slide latch and lock posts, and it would be a disaster to overlook this slight nonstandard modification. Retrofitting jack screws and female lock nuts is well worth the added expense in saved network downtime. The jack screw/lock nut combination also yields a more intuitively secure arrangement, and one easier in use.

Cable Routing

The next planning step is to define the route that the cable will take through the building. This route should provide ready accessibility to all workstations to minimize drop cable lengths. This route should also provide

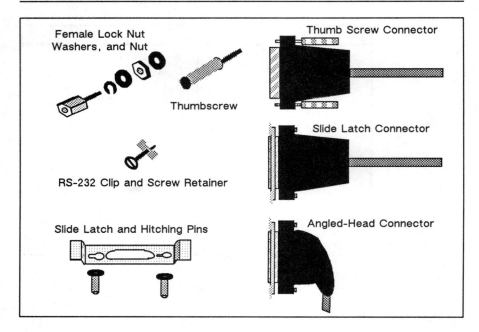

Figure 6.23 Transceiver drop cable connectors.

adequate expansion capability. Specifically, a route that minimizes cable for the current installation may be insufficient for any expansion. The cable should also be easily accessible in case of malfunction. For example, a path that follows a corridor is superior to a diagonal route over cubicles.

Avoid Water, High-Voltage, and Temperature Extremes

Coax is inert. It doesn't require too much concern. However, it is prudent to keep it away from water sources since these can short the electrical transmissions if water seeps along the cable and into a connector or tap, and from high-voltage electrical sources which can interfere with and disrupt the signal.

Electrical or magnetic fields may conflict with the Ethernet transmission and introduce high error counts visible only from the software level. High frequency radio sources disrupt communications. High-frequency lighting—vapor lighting—lab or medical apparatus that transmits—can disrupt network traffic. If possible, route main cables away from such sources.

Continual expansion and contraction from a heat source such as the air conditioning ductwork near the cabling plenum will cause microfractures in the coax core. These invisible fractures alter the electrical properties of a network. The fractures will slow the speed of transmission, increase electrical impedance causing high collision rates, or completely disrupt communications. Slowing the transmission speed is not necessarily a problem unless the network is generally heavily accessed, in which case even a ten percent transmission speed degradation can be fatal. Transmissions less than 96 microseconds apart or not 66 and 77 percent light speed disrupts the interpacket spacing. This would allow packets to ram into each other.

Determine Routing Options

Coax cable can be installed in walls, ceilings, or laid along the floor. Cheapernet requires that two individual strands connect to each workstation. This is accomplished through a "Tee" connector at the back of the workstation, or on the main coax with drop cables. Thinnet is fragile— more so than the 50-ohm cable. Thinnet should be sectioned, perhaps more frequently than the larger cable, if the transceiverless Cheapernet variation is the network of choice; the cable will need many connections, one for each node.

Standard practice suggests that cable be installed in cable trays or cable ladders. A cable tray is a metal gutterlike platform for holding cables. A cable ladder is a metal open-rung ladder for securing cables and wiring. Both items are best installed at the time a building is initially built since false ceilings and ductwork usually preclude retrofitting ladders or trays. J-hooks provide adequate support for retrofitted cable. J-hooks bolt to a stud shot into steel or concrete support beams. See Figure 6.24 for samples of hooks, ladders, trays, and the plastic cable tie.

Cable routing depends in great part on the building design, the available financial resources, and networking goals. Coax can be routed through underfloor ducts, cellular floors with trench headers, or beneath raised plenum floors as found in the standard computer room. The cable tie is an important item to ensure that cable, once installed, stays where intended.

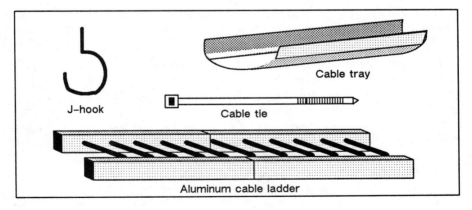

Figure 6.24 Hook, cable tie, cable tray and ladder provide coax support.

Other options include conduit systems in modular office furniture (so long as bend radii are not exceeded), surface raceways, or installation within a ceiling plenum. PVC cabling has a minimum bend radius of 10 inches—a circle diameter of 20 inches, while teflon cabling requires double that. Newer technology may allow high velocity transmission on existing telephone wiring as in Starlan and new telco Ethernet 10MB applications. The routing should address the need for growth and change, equipment relocation, and expansion of basic network services. A good design is patterned on the voice networks which have confronted and solved most of the same issues now effecting data networks.

Opt for Straight Runs

In general, it is better planning to avoid distance-minimizing cable routing. Stair step patterns, wave or sawtooth zig-zag are brilliant ideas whose time *has passed* as shown in Figure 6.25. Such routing patterns create a problem with tracing cable malfunctions and more at operational time; simple, straight runs are better.

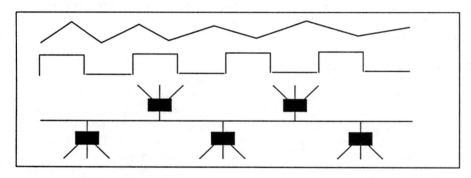

Figure 6.25 Avoid zig-zag cable runs as shown in the top two examples. Repeaters and multitap units provide high-density service without increasing cable needs as illustrated in the bottom example.

Often the "drop" cable will fall from the transceiver inside a wall into a wall plate. The cable can be segmented at a wall plate, although this shortens maximum length slightly due to signal impedance. A separate cable will connect from the wall plate to the computer device. Shorter cables can be used like extension cords and plugged together for longer lengths up to approximately the maximum specified length. Drop cables are available in PVC or teflon depending upon the building codes.

While cable could be threaded over pipes, ductwork, lighting, and electrical lines, and physically tied to any of these items for support, it is best practice to install the coaxial cables in straight runs supported by hooks, ladders, or trays.

Component	Quantity
section	length of coax cable 2 end connectors
two connected sections	barrel connector
segment	two terminators
node	tap transceiver transceiver cable
tap unit	two shield probes core probe

Figure 6.26 Component quantities required for the basic network.

Select Specific Components

Once the route the cable will take is defined, it is appropriate to select the type and quantity of the components. Use the discussion of components presented earlier in the chapter as a guide. Refer to Figure 6.26 for the component quantities required for building a network. Additionally, this chart lists some simple rules for component selection.

Blueprint the Planned Network

A cable installation should be precisely blueprinted. Cable placement is one of the most critical items. Location of a coax can be lost in the false ceiling plenum, thus making shorts and breaks difficult to find and fix.

Sales and Services Trading Company

Figure 6.27 Network photographic blueprinting.

There are several methods for blueprinting. Important items to document are changes in cable direction, end points, and places where the cable is coupled. This is important in order to locate the places where failures are likely to occur and where a time domain reflectometer might connect to the network coax cable. Figure 6.27 shows a ceiling snapshot.

Another method for above-ceiling installations is to photograph the ceiling with the tiles removed and cabling exposed. Installations that have CAD/CAM systems can computerize illustration; computerization improves the access to copies and allows for the construction of overlays. For example, one level might show only the main coax cable, while other layers may show subnets, paths of drop cables, and location of transceivers, bridges, or repeaters. See Figure 6.28 for a sample of blueprinting.

Pictures of the internal coax cable dynamics can be compared against views when malfunctions are disrupting network communications. Discrepancies between the photographs and the current view are apt to indicate the source of these malfunctions. At a minimum, the cable length should be measured. It would be folly to underestimate the network length and at a later time discover that network cable expansion has extended the network length beyond maximum length specifications. The network is certain to fail at some point, and information about where cables are located and transceivers are installed, while expensive to generate initially, will be more expensive to gather later when there are problems.

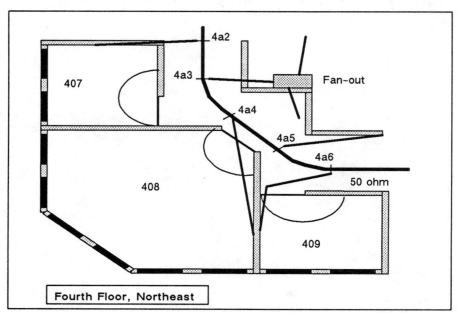

Figure 6.28 Architect's blueprint illustrates coax cabling, transceiver and transceiver drop cable routing.

Chapter 7

Installing an Ethernet Network

With a blueprint of your network design and a list of the required components, you are ready to begin installation. This chapter describes the steps you must take and the tools you will need to put a network together.

Planning for Installation

Installation requires a good plan. Network blueprints should be detailed enough to represent all the network hardware components required for a complete installation. If the vendor does not supply this or provide complete network parts and installation services, it is vital to coordinate the arrival of *all* the network components. The network will not work without transceivers, without transceiver cables, or any number of other components, not the least of which is functioning network software. The installation can certainly be staged, since many installation procedures can be completed concurrently. Just about any missing part can, no matter what its simplicity or general insignificance, become a critically needed component. Therefore, plan your installation timetable with an eye to the steps in network installation and coordinate delivery of components to ensure a smooth process. Figure 7.1 illustrates the major critical steps and a logical progression for network installation. Each step encompasses several individual stages not included in the figure. Coax, for example, requires cutting to length; applying end connectors, couplings and terminators; and installing the actual cable in its final location.

Installation is a mechanically simple process but a challenging experience if the technology is new to the organization. Sufficient skills may not have been developed to adequately identify, and repair network problems.

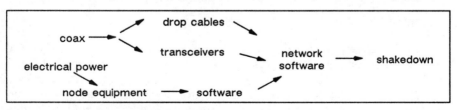

Figure 7.1 Critical paths for network installation.

Therefore, consider the benefits in hiring the vendor or an experienced contractor to string coax and tap this cabling. Gather as much outside experience and expertise as possible to augment the internal network administrative team. The installation procedure requires a shakedown period. Premature acceptance of a new installation is unwise, and making or disseminating promises of network availability before most of the problems have been resolved will devalue the perception of the network administration team. Budget sufficient time for overruns, problems, and missing components.

Be certain to negotiate preconditions for any final acceptance with the vendors. An installation may provide marginally acceptable operations, but fail to perform the level of service desired. To forestall any future problems, define clearly what your expectations are. This is critical for successful vendor relations.

Preparing for the Physical Installation

Installation of a new network goes smoothly if you gather the preliminary blueprints, and all the equipment and components before beginning, and if you proceed in the order listed in Figure 7.2.

Steps	Equipment
1) Inspect cable (visually)	Cable
2) Test cable	Cable, test equipment
3) String cable and label	Cable, tool kit, blueprint, tape
4) Secure cable	Cable ties
5) Install connectors and terminators	Tool kit, connectors, insulation
6) Test connectors and terminators	Test equipment
7) Install taps and transceivers	Taps, probes, tool kit, ladder
8) Test taps and transceivers	Test equipment
9) Install and test other components such as fan-outs and gateways	Tool kit, test equipment, ladder
10) Secure network components	Cable ties
11) Update blueprint	Preliminary blueprint

Figure 7.2 Steps and equipment required for installation.

Installation Tool Kit

Installation requires a sizable tool kit. The contents are enumerated here solely to provoke some ideas. This kit should contain screwdrivers; pliers (including needle-nosed); diagonal cutters; a cable cutter; a wire stripper; a bright flashlight, preferably rechargeable; rosin-core silver solder; a soldering iron; desoldering equipment; a crimping tool; a coring tool; a shorting plug (a connector with a wire soldered to short the core conductor); and various spare parts like connectors, tees, taps and probe tips, junction boxes and wall plates. Include specialty tools for undercarpet cable, or corers for vendor-specific or antiquated taps and connectors.

Less obvious tools include ladders, a stud finder, walkie-talkies, and a radio. In a clever application of a standard carpenter's tool, the electric stud finder also locates active cables. A portable AM/FM radio serves not only to relax hard-working installers, but also provides cheap testing of any audible EMI sources that might disrupt network communications. Given the location of most cabling a ladder or scaffold is suggested; a special multijoint ladder that acts like a scaffold fills both needs. A floor tile lifter for extracting raised floor panels may be another choice. Walkie-talkies or similar mobile communication devices provide a simple way to keep the installation or repair team in touch. A multitester and various other test equipment are suggested; Chapters 10 through 14 describe these network-specific tools in more detail.

Installing Cable

Before installing any new, repaired, or added coaxial cable, the cable should be inspected for visual defects. The cable segment should have no obvious physical defects like cuts, tears, or bulges in the outer jacket. Electrically, the copper core and the braided shield should conduct electricity without discontinuities. The copper core and the braided shield should be electrically isolated and not short out to each other. Techniques for cable testing with a multitester and time domain reflectometer are presented in Chapters 11 and 12. To install cable you will need the tool kit; the preliminary blueprint; the cable; cable ties; and colored electrical tap for labeling the cable. An unlikely tool to bring is an AM/FM radio to check for any radio or electrical interference on the cable route.

Begin installation by extending the cable along the route mapped out in the blueprint. Any deviation made from this planned path should be noted on the blueprint. Deviations might be needed to avoid a ceiling light, an air conditioner, or a steel beam.

There are several details that the installer must not overlook. Avoid cable jacket abrasion, excessively bending the coaxial cable, and installing the coaxial cable with too extreme a radius (the minimum approximates a 10-inch radius for PVC, and 18-inch for teflon, both Thin and Thicknet). Generally, prudent concern and attention to these details will yield a successful Ethernet installation.

An AM/FM pocket radio, a simple and cheap tool, can locate radio interference. Each Ethernet is usually shielded enough so that cross-interference will not create a problem. Note, however, that high traffic situations may actually generate enough traffic that bundled cable may experience inductance problems. The internal cable shielding is required to meet FCC requirements to prevent electromagnetic interference from nearby devices; the shielding also degrades performance due to capacitance effects. Therefore, space the cable and do not bundle many strands of coaxial cable into a compact bunch. Buildings with radio transmitters on the roof or nearby may necessitate special cable insulation. Heat change and extremes of temperature cause a more nefarious problem because contraction and expansion in the coax cable, if sufficient, will break the core. The network, as a consequence, will exhibit degraded performance.

Labeling Segments

As you string the cable, label it with some identifying marks. Color-coded electrical tape at fifteen foot intervals helps sort out the spaghetti. Fluorescent marking tapes provide exceptionally effective identification above false ceilings when you are perched on a ladder nine or more feet high; visibility is often impaired by ductwork, supports, and wiring.

Securing the Cable

Once the cable is properly routed and installed in the cable trays, ladders, J-hooks, or draped over the suspended ceiling supports, the cable should be tied with plastic ties. This ensures that the cable will not get damaged. The cable tie as illustrated in Figure 7.3 is also useful to secure other components that attach to the network coax.

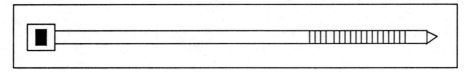

Figure 7.3 The cable tie provides important coax cable support.

Installing the Connectors and Terminators

To install connectors and terminators, you must have already installed the cable (or at least measured and tested the cable). Sometimes, it is expedient to cut the coax cable and install connectors on a bench before stringing the cable. You will need the blueprint and tool kit to complete this step. The tools required to install the end connectors include cutters, a wire stripper, a soldering iron, and crimping tools. Upon disassembly for installation, you will find that these connectors have a hub contact, a coupler body, several washers, and a retaining nut (or ring). Terminators and couplers are items that don't disassemble.

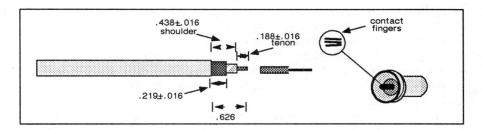

Figure 7.4 Cable end tenons have a recommended critical length.

Care should be exercised that the shoulder, the area where the braided shield is exposed, and the cable tenon, the area where the coaxial core is exposed, are the proper length for all cable types. Otherwise, the hub contact pin will protrude from the connector shell and on the first insertion and the pin will permanently spread the fingers in the barrel connector or terminator plug and possibly ruin the part. Figure 7.4 illustrates this problem, which is most pronounced for N-type fittings that have a three- or four-pronged hub designed to align and retain the male pin from the end connector. Figure 7.5 shows how N-type fittings connect to the cable ends.

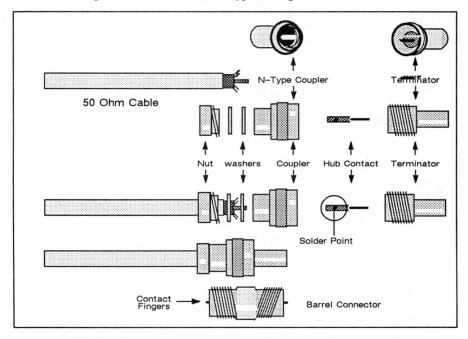

Figure 7.5 Installation of the common N-type connectors. Crimp-on connectors are a variation of the lock-on or screw-on variety with fewer parts. All work equally well when correctly installed, although the lock-on or screw-on variety can be disconnected and restored without wasting parts.

Some outer casings simply screw onto the outer jacket (as is the case for most teflon fittings since teflon is that much more durable), whereas other fittings assemble inside the outer casing and require internal crimping or have an expansion plug that screws into the connector's outer casing. The tools required for installing screw-on connectors are cable cutters, a knife or wire stripper to trim the cable to length, and a soldering iron to attach the hub contact. Crimp-on connectors additionally require the appropriate crimping tools. Figure 7.6 shows how BNC connectors and terminators connect to the cable ends. Different manufacturers supply these same fittings, and they vary slightly in installation. Some end connectors require soldering a center pin to the copper core, others crimp to the core.

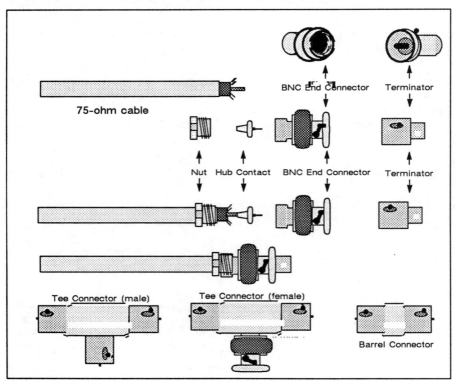

Figure 7.6 Installation of the BNC connectors, common for Thinnet and other proprietary vendor networks.

Grounding the Network

At all steps during installation of both cable and connectors, be aware that all metallic outer casings, terminators and fittings that connect to the shield should be insulated with a nonconducting sleeve—a potential source

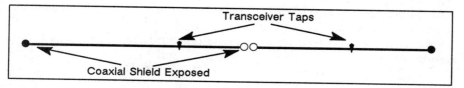

Figure 7.7 Ethernet specifications prohibit random grounding. All exposed conductive fittings should be insulated with a rubber boot or wound with insulating electrical tape to prevent a random ground.

of ground-induced noise to the coaxial shield. Transceiver casings, if metal, should be isolated from any possible accidental grounding. Figure 7.7 shows these critical points. Installation of rubber sleeves prevents random grounding. The transceiver taps and transceiver drop cables provide the necessary ground.

All connectors and terminators should be protected by a rubber sleeve to insure that the coaxial cable itself doesn't accidentally ground to cable trays, cable hangers, ductwork, and any metal object within the cable ducts or ceiling plenum. One simple and inexpensive solution is to purchase a rubber coating dip (often sold at hardware stores) and brush or dip end connectors and terminators. Figure 7.8 shows a typical rubber boot.

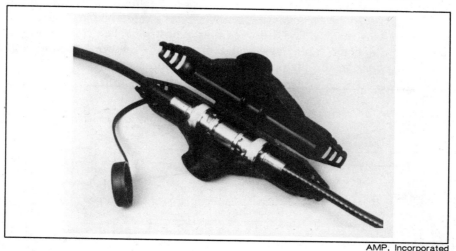

AMP, Incorporated

Figure 7.8 Typical rubber insulating boot for a Thinnet .

Testing the Connectors and Terminators

A quick check with a multitester as explained in Chapter 11 will verify that the end connectors are not shorting and have a sufficiently good contact with the cable to actually carry the electrical signal, and that the terminators are not defective. As with any installation, a check that the terminators and end connectors are properly installed is good policy. Verification with a multitester and a time domain reflectometer should be standard practice as outlined in Chapters 11 and 12.

Installing the Taps and Transceivers

To install taps and transceivers you must already have installed the cable, connectors and terminators. Proceeding in another order prevents proper verification of the coax cable, and testing the connectors and terminators. Also, it will be impossible to test the proper installation of the taps and transceivers unless the terminators are in place because the coax will not support the correct level of electrical testing. You will need your network blueprint. Tools include a tap drill, an allen wrench, a screwdriver or two, and a pair of pliers. Additionally, you will need the taps and transceivers. It is good foresight to have spare probes, in case of breakage.

Installing the Tap

An exploded diagram of the tap, the access mechanism, and the transceiver electronics box are shown for the reader's reference in Figure 7.9. Notice the two shallow shield probes that almost look like staples. These penetrate the coax cable jacket and provide the network ground and electrically contain the high-powered transmission signal.

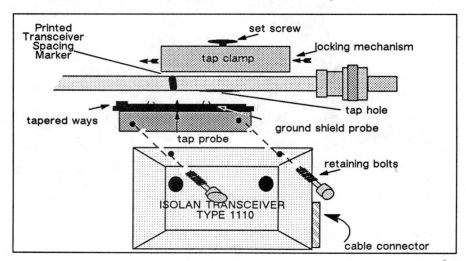

Figure 7.9 The AMP tap mechanism. Notice the spacing mark printed on the coax cable. Taps should be installed as close to that mark as possible.

The AMP tap installation sequence is simple. The tap assembly with the shield probes in their sockets is bolted onto the coax cable on one of the black, printed spacing marks. There are two facts to note. First, these spacing marks provide the correct 2.5 meter transceiver spacing required by the Ethernet specifications. These marks also provide correct signal harmonics; it is insufficient to assume that any 2.5 meter spacing (or greater) is the requirement. Second, note that the process of securing the tap body to the cable drives the shield probes through the outer casing of the cable and into the shield.

This tap is noninvasive because the coax doesn't get severed when it is installed. It is compatible with many different transceiver units. Hold the plastic probe-holding assembly against the cable while sliding the aluminum retaining collar along tapered ways to secure the tap. A set screw tightens the tap securely. Figure 7.10 is a schematic drawing of the AMP tap.

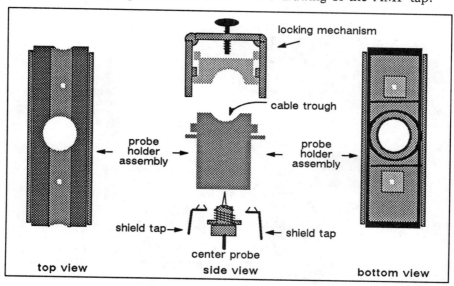

Figure 7.10 The AMP tap in cross section.

Some taps may require that two cable section end connectors are installed for each tap. The tools and process for this are identical to the process for installing end connectors on the ends of the cable sections. The screw-in type requires cutting the coax cable and soldering or crimping end connectors onto the severed ends. The tap subassemblies are then threaded together; there is a female thread for the transceiver unit's electrical connections. Not only is this difficult and time-consuming, it also breaks the network during the installation period; most network managers prefer the clamp-type connectors, either TCL or AMP. Also, there is no guarantee that when the network is reconnected that it will work.

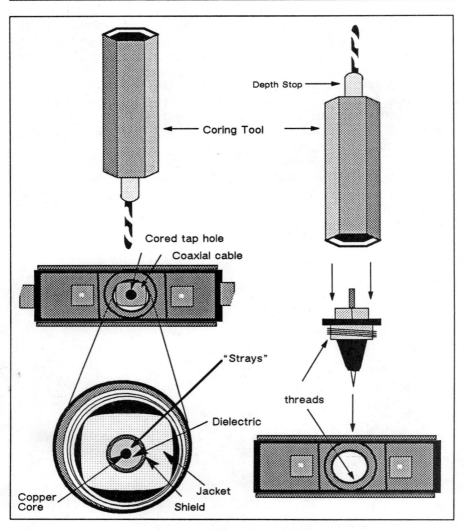

Figure 7.11 Tap center probe installation process. The coring tool is inserted into the plastic tap body that has been bolted to the cable. The built-in bushing guide aligns and centers the drill bit. Core the central tap probe hole and visually inspect the hole for unwanted, stray shield strands. The opposite end of the coring tool will tighten the center tap probe into the threaded retainer.

Coring the Tap

A coring tool fits into the center probe threads of a tap that has been bolted to the coax cable. A drill molded into the handle of the coring tool precisely matches the drilling depth necessary to pierce the braided shield and trim all stray wires from the entry point as shown in Figure 7.11.

This coring tool creates a hole with a diameter several times larger than the probe to prevent shorts. Remember again that PVC and teflon vary in size and that the coring tools are not interchangeable; a PVC coring tool aggressively used will sever the teflon copper core and break the network, and a teflon coring tool will not drill deep enough. Some coring tool vendors also suggest that the drill bits dull after twenty uses and when dull will tear the shield. These vendors suggest periodic replacement of the coring tool. Perhaps the bits can be sharpened instead on a bit grinder.

When a core hole has been drilled, the center probe is then inserted into the threaded hole in the tap assembly. The reverse end of the coring tool tightens the tap probe into the probe holder. The completed component is now securely fastened to the coaxial cable, and the three probes, one core probe and two shield probes, should be electrically connected to the network. At this stage, the transceiver electronics may be connected and secured with the two retaining bolts. Often when a set of pre-existing tap holes is available, the transceiver can be installed without disassembly from the tap unit. On a functioning network, however, it is better to remove the electronics from the tap shell and install this unit first to allow intermediate testing because the tap may not have been installed correctly.

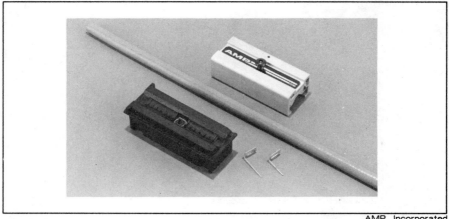

AMP, Incorporated

Figure 7.12 The tap unit disassembled.

Assembling the Tap

The next three Figures show the sequence of installing a tap. Figure 7.12 shows the AMP tap disassembled. The parts include the tap holder with core probe installed, two shield probes, and the tap clamp. Figure 7.13 shows how the clamp slides over the probe assembly to secure it. Figure 7.14 illustrates the final step of tightening the bolt.

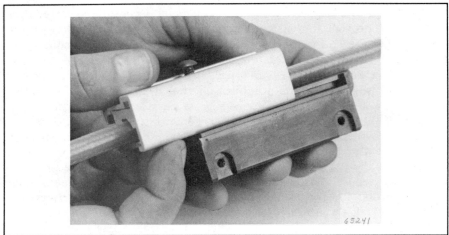

AMP, Incorporated

Figure 7.13 Slide the tap clamp over the probe assembly.

AMP, Incorporated

Figure 7.14 The cap screw holds the clamp in place and drives the shield probes into the coax shield.

Transceiver Configuration

As explained in Chapter 3 and in Chapter 6, Ethernet 1.0 detects collisions by a receive-based DC persistence; Ethernet 2.0 and IEEE 802.3 detect collisions by voltage level. When the network is configured for version 1.0 or 2.0, the output is DC coupled, that is, the idle voltage is nonzero; whereas, when the network is configured to operate with version

802.3, the SQE test is performed. When in this mode, the output is AC-coupled, and the idle voltage is −0.7 volts. This discrepancy creates a timing problem if different hardware is installed on the same network, or if the transceivers are not configured to a single standard. Switch settings within the transceiver determine the configuration.

The SQE heartbeat adds a measure of difference. When the network is conFigured to run Ethernet version 1.0 or version 2.0, each transceiver does not check the SQE; whereas, this test is performed after every transmission by an 802.3 or Ethernet 2.0 transceiver. SQE checks whether the collision detection circuitry in the transceiver is functional. It is worthwhile at this stage to confirm uniformity in transceiver configuration.

Installing the Transceiver

Once the tap assembly and center probe have been installed and tested, the transceiver box can be fitted into the tap. Figure 7.15 shows the coaxial probe contacts that fit into an edge connector within the transceiver body.

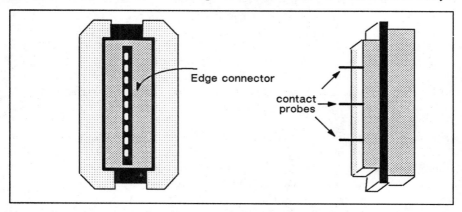

Figure 7.15 Tap contact probes and transceiver edge connector. Bent contact probes are likely to cause tap failure. If care is not used when inserting the tap mechanism into the transceiver body, the three contacts can be mangled and misaligned.

Care must be exercised when connecting these two components that the slim probe wires are not bent or broken, otherwise the transceiver would fail to operate; it is also possible to short the network and halt its operation. In the event that the probe contacts are bent or broken, replace the contacts. The final step is to secure the transceiver to the tap with the retaining bolts.

The transceivers with the built-in booby lights make installation a snap. The vendors sell these units by suggesting that these lights are useful all the time. Frankly, the lights are only useful at installation, or when there is a suspected installation problem—but they are very useful at those times. If the green light (for signal) lights up, the tap probes are making sufficient contact with the network coax. If the light fails to appear, the contacts are incomplete. Likewise, if the red light (for collision detect) remains perpetually lit, odds are that the tap's center probe is shorting the shield to the core. Unless the network is halted purposely, the collision detect light should occasionally appear. The traffic indicator should only appear when the workstation attached to the tap and transceiver actually transmits or receives a signal.

Checkpoint Testing

After the transceivers have been installed, test the installation. It's a good checkpoint in the installation process because the network is now functionally complete. The tools required and how to use them are explained in Chapters 10 through 14.

If the network is broken, disassemble it and restart the process. While AMP taps are superior to the inline invasive types, they are not fail-safe. One of the most common reasons for network failure is either careless installation of an end connector or shoddy installation of a tap. Installation of a tap is a mechanically simple procedure, but is a common cause of problems that break the network.

Assuming the network is still functioning and there is no indication of an electrical short, measure resistance between the shield probes and the core probe. If the multitester is checking the ohms, there should be approximately 25-ohm resistance; on a completed network two terminators are installed and the 50-ohm resistances "add" to 25 ohms. Note too, that each transceiver alters coaxial resistance as well. This reading should not fluctuate if pressure, twisting, and hard knocks are applied to the tap assembly. A center probe that intermittently connects with the core creates a problem called "transceiver chatter." It is also good practice to pinpoint transceiver locations on the master network blueprint in the event of future network problems attributable to that transceiver.

Installing the Transceiver Drop Cable

The transceiver and the Ethernet controller hardware, which is often a separate card, plug into either end of the drop cable. The transceiver provides power and ground to the coaxial cable, transmits and receives data, and listens for network traffic and collisions. The transceiver receives its power, in turn, from the Ethernet controller through the drop cable. The Ethernet controller is the software/hardware interface between the network and the computer device.

The opposite end of the transceiver drop cable connects to the Ethernet controller. Because this unit is a function of the node software and workstation, details of installation are best found in vendor-specific literature.

Replacing the Slide Latch

The slide latch arrangement of the standard Ethernet cable is insufficient as detailed in Chapter 6. It neither assures positive contact between the pins and sockets, nor does it take strain well. The solution is to replace the slide latch assembly with female lock screws on the back of workstations and replace the wall plate and a cable with screw connections. These connectors are changed frequently and often fail to make secure contact with the pins. A standard RS-232 threaded connector kit contains two internally threaded female screws, washers, lock nuts, and hex nuts to fit. The parts kit replaces the slide latch assembly on the workstation. Two kits are required for each workstation. To complete the modification, a cable with threaded screws secures the cable between the workstation and wall plate. Screws can be either standard slotted machine screws with 10/32 thread or standard knurled head RS-232 screws, sometimes called *jack screws*. The cable can then be attached to the wall and back of the workstation with screws, or a new cable with knurled head screws can replace the standard cable.

Note that this change does not conform to the ANSI, IEEE 802.3, or Xerox Ethernet standards. It is, however, very worthwhile. IBM, for example, has ignored such standards and is marketing a modified version of Ethernet that is incompatible with existing Ethernet standards on the electrical and mechanical levels. It is a very secure connection mechanism.

Ethernet Addressing

Although the Ethernet address is part of the vendor-specific workstations, it is reasonable to check the physical addresses at this point in the network installation process. The Ethernet address is usually contained within a Programmable Read-Only Memory chip (PROM), although it is sometimes contained within the switch settings of several banks of DIP switches. In the latter case, make certain that there are no duplicate addresses, a situation which could immobilize the network. Most times, the PROM will contain a unique address to prevent such lockups. This computer chip is located either on the main board of the computer or on the Ethernet controller.

The ID PROM or DIP switch is an important unit in network operations, since it uniquely indicates the address of each and every piece of network equipment. Ethernet addresses can be changed as the location of equipment changes, or the PROM can be physically removed during repairs or replacement of components. If the network as an entity is operational when repairs are effected, changing the PROM is a better policy because other node equipment will not recognize the software address change until crucial node address tables are reinitialized. Also, changing an Ethernet address may require extensive software changes to reflect the new address.

- Cable
- Connectors
- Transceiver and Controller Installation
- Transceiver and Controller Electronics
- Node Equipment
- File Servers
- Network Software
- User Network Access
- Peak Load Operations

Figure 7.16 Shakedown network components.

If PROM chips are routinely exchanged, it is good practice to have some spare PROMs. Pins on these chips can be bent, rendering them useless, and network equipment equally useless for lack of a small component.

Shake Down New Installations

New installations, retrofits, additions, and any changes to the network all require a shakedown period. It is foolhardy and unprofessional to assume that any new installation will, from the start, work as promised. This is particularly the case for extensions and retrofits with new, upgraded or untried components. There are always surprises, like a loose connection, vibration from an elevator shaft, overheating, marginal components, vendor incompatibilities, lot incompatibilities, and overloading. Premature assurances sap credibility. Certainly, basic testing of those items listed in Figure 7.16 is, at a minimum, appropriate.

A shakedown period should be initiated when additions, major network configuration changes, and physical relocations are effected. This requires that additional material and time resources be allocated. Figure half a day for each node of a network for new installations, and an hour for each node when a network is segmented, rerouted, or extended. Figure 7.17 represents a core network that has ballooned to support new groups.

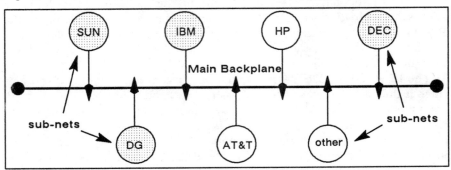

Figure 7.17 Shakedown additions, changes and retrofits. This gradual network growth provides for focused testing of network additions.

Securing the Components

Once the transceivers and the transceiver cables are properly installed in the cable trays, ladders, and J-hooks, or fitted to the suspended ceiling supports, all connecting cables should be tied with plastic ties. This ensures that these connecting cables will not get damaged, or that connections will not be unplugged accidentally. The cable tie as illustrated previously in Figure 7.3 is useful to attach to the network coax as shown in Figure 7.18 and Figure 7.19.

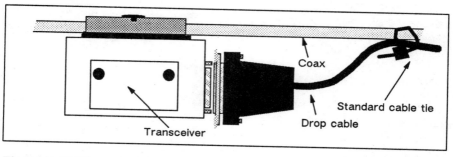

Figure 7.18 The cable tie provides important transceiver cable support, and relieves the stress on the D-plug connection.

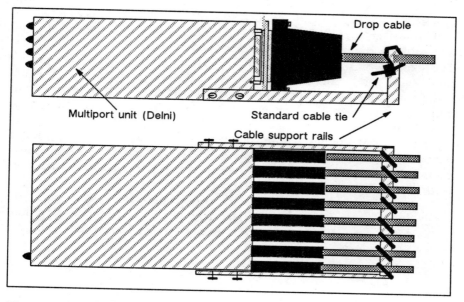

Figure 7.19 The cable tie prevents accidental disconnection from a fan-out unit. This also relieves connector strain. Note the addition of a cable support to the case of the fan-out unit. This can be bought from some vendors, or made from sheet metal in any tool shop.

Installation Blueprinting: Confirming the Design

Once the cable is measured and tested, and connectors installed, it is good policy to benchmark the cable. The time domain reflectometer and an instant film camera or oscilloscope recorder provide extraordinary blueprinting, and a benchmark against which to compare at later times when network problems occur. While the cable is accessible, it can be purposely shorted at the connectors for benchmark photography. An instant camera also can blueprint physical wiring.

Deviation from specifications or original plans should be indicated to update the blueprints. Any subsequent changes should also be added to the network blueprint to maintain an accurate view of the network

Common Installation Failures

Slip-shod work will complicate the installation and subsequent network management problems. Cable jacket abrasion can cause excessive impedance. Over-bending or installing cable with an excessively tight radius will often fracture and break the center conductor.

A crimp-on connector may not make a good contact, whereas the screw-on variety may have been applied without due care to the critical tenon and shoulder lengths. A barrel connector may not be threaded into the receiving sockets tightly enough for sufficient electrical contact.

Transceivers and taps, and their cables, fail in a limited number of ways. The cable or the transceiver electronics can be bad, or can fail over time. The likeliest reason for error is poor installation. Either the tap probes don't make good contact with the coax, or the tap probes make too much contact with the coax cable and short the network. The probe leads that fit into the transceiver could be bent and improperly positioned within the edge guide.

The last point of installation failure is the D-plug connectors. Half a connection is worse than a completely severed connection because the transceiver will transmit a continuous collision detect signal onto the network and jam the network completely.

In this chapter, installation procedures for cable, transceivers, taps, and drop cables have been examined. The next chapter and section delve into devices that expand Ethernet service from a minimal linear configuration to a multidimensional topology.

Chapter 8

Expanding an Ethernet Network

The Ethernet specifications limit a single network segment to 500 meters and 100 nodes, and nodes must be spaced a minimum of 2.5 meters apart on 50-ohm networks and 0.5 meters on 75-ohm networks. This is a very restrictive limitation for some organizations. These bus limitations are circumvented by special devices, such as the fan-out box, the bridge, the gateway, and the repeater. Using these devices, an extensive network can be constructed with a complex, nonlinear geometry to serve high concentrations of users, longer distances, and the global maximum of 1024 Ethernet nodes. The *fan-out* box provides multiple ports from a single transceiver. The *bridge* interconnects different networks into Ethernet. The *gateway* interconnects separate segments of one Ethernet network. The *repeater* boosts signals onto other segments of Ethernet. Another device called a *signal indicator* visually indicates network load and frequency of collisions. It provides, conceptually, the same function as status lights on a computer panel.

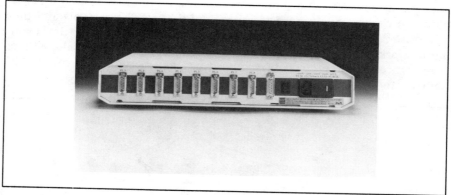

BICC, Incorporated

Figure 8.1 Typical fan-out unit.

The Fan-Out Unit

The fan-out unit is sometimes called a *multitap*, a *multiport*, or a *delni* unit. It is a high-tech version of the three-way plug. Figure 8.1 illustrates one such unit. Common versions provide eight connections from a single transceiver. Some vendors claim that these units can be cascaded two or more units deep to yield 64 ports from a single tap. Also these units provide network services without the need for any coaxial cable.

Thus Figure 8.2 shows a simple fan-out installation that is a minimum network configuration. Such a network requires no coax cable, transceivers, connectors, or terminators. Figure 8.3 presents cascaded fan-out units for expanded network services not requiring extended node locations.

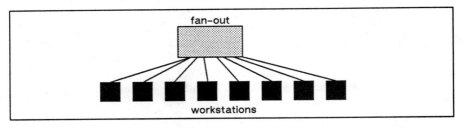

Figure 8.2 A minimum network configuration provided by a fan-out unit and no coax. Some fan-out units require a D-plug terminator to isolate a stand-alone network. Such a plug installs into the plug where a transceiver drop cable would otherwise reside.

A fan-out unit saves coax costs, both initial material and installation costs, and simplifies maintenance. This design is easily transportable, for example, to support trade show presentations, therefore providing an alternative to cables, taps, transceivers, and all the installation tools and time otherwise needed. The fan-out also creates a local subnetwork, thus averting network contention, since the hardware unit filters potential collisions before it reaches the coax; very busy nodes can be linked to the coaxial network through a fan-out unit for a clear performance gain.

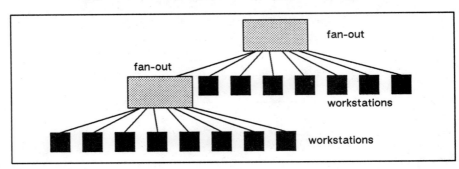

Figure 8.3 Cascaded network configuration with fan-out units.

The Fan-Out for High-Density Service

The easiest solution to high-concentration nodes is the fan-out. This multiport tap provides more than single-station access from each transceiver. This unit overcomes two explicit Ethernet limitations: minimum tap spacing and maximum node count per segment. The single multitap will, for example, provide eight taps for a tightly clustered office, easing the pressure on threading cable a long distance to meet the clustered need. If the transceivers were centered about a single target office, the longest drop cable would be at least 7.5 meters; it would probably be longer to account for ceiling drops, play, and excess. If the transceivers were not centered about the single target office because the adjacent office also requires high-density service, it is not inconceivable that the drop cable would exceed 40 meters. Shorter cables are not only less costly, they are easier to manage, to install, and to qualify; the shorter cable lowers packet travel times for improved network efficiency. The economics of a fan-out unit compare favorably with those of an extending wiring program because each fan-out unit eliminates seven transceivers, shortens cable requirements, and potentially allows very short runs of coaxial cable.

A drop cable could power the multitap within the single area. If a multitap were installed for each node, the maximum 100-node-per-segment limitation, although still in force, now provides 800 stations per segment. In point of fact, unless the computer devices on each of the 800 nodes were low-volume users, a network so designed would saturate. However, this example shows how high density areas can be serviced easily as well as how to increase the effective network node access count with fan-out units. Economies of scale are usually achieved with fan-out units, since they reduce the need for transceiver electronics.

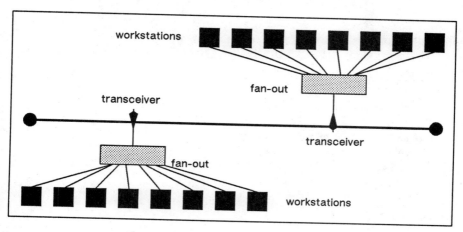

Figure 8.4 Fan-out unit providing high-density service.

Figure 8.4 illustrates two fan-out boxes providing high density services for a densely populated area, thereby circumventing the transceiver spacing minimums. For high-density areas where transceivers and lengthy drop cables could be installed to reach all workstations, this configuration is a cost effective and operationally effective alternative because it partially eliminates the need for transceivers, reduces the number of suspect connections, and shaves cable expenses.

Network Repeaters

A repeater unit boosts the transmission signal from one segment and continues the signal onto another segment. A common unit is represented by Figure 8.5. Ethernet is limited to a maximum segment length of 500 meters (or 200 meters, depending upon the cabling variation), and the repeater can augment this length. Many repeaters can be used on a network, although it is important that no node be separated from any other node by more than two repeaters. There are three variations on repeaters, the simple repeater, the smart repeater, and the half repeater.

Cabletron Systems, Incorporated

Figure 8.5 A typical network repeater.

The simple repeater just relays the signal onto another segment as shown in Figure 8.6. This configuration is apt to more than double the collision rate, since signals from two networks are repeated on both networks. Delay time is increased, a major cause of collisions.

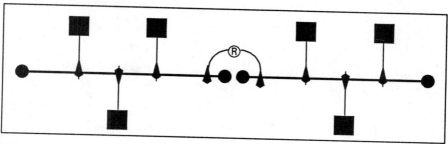

Figure 8.6 Segments linked with a repeater. Note that the repeater unit connects with transceivers and transceiver drop cables. The transceivers take a node location on each segment and subtract from the maximum network configurations.

The smart repeater, or "learning repeater," filters packets by destination. If a packet were destined for another segment, the repeater captures and transmits the packet when that other network is free. Other packets are ignored. This smart repeater reduces the probability for collisions since a fraction of packets are filtered and not retransmitted. Figure 8.7 illustrates these two principles.

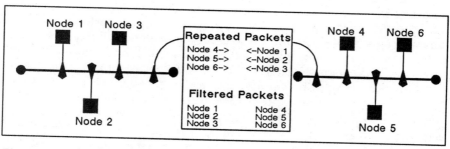

Figure 8.7 Segments linked with a smart repeater. Only packets sourced from nodes 4, 5, or 6 destined for nodes 1, 2, or 3 are repeated across this gateway. Likewise, only packets sourced from nodes 1, 2, or 3 destined for nodes 4, 5, or 6 are repeated. Internetwork traffic thereby is reduced.

Half repeaters transmit signals from one building to another. A half repeater might utilize an Ethernet baseband or broadband coax, fiber optics, PBX network, infrared or microwave, or satellite transmission medium. The half repeater is often a long-haul link between distant networks. Specialized hardware filters, times, and synchronizes transmission and reception in order to eliminate collisions. A half repeater, as illustrated in Figure 8.8, is effectively a network gateway for two distinct networks.

Microwave Interface units often include a store and forward buffer to decouple the microwave transmission from the two networks being coupled. The buffer must prevent packets from colliding, or both coupled networks could exhibit a constant state of collision and saturation. Extra software is required to belatedly indicate transmission completion.

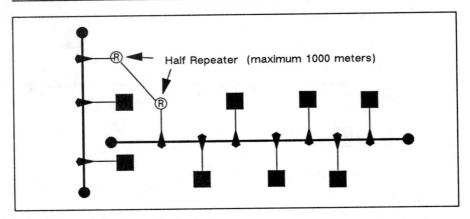

Figure 8.8 Half repeater connects segments.

Network Gateways

Specialized *gateways* interface between different Ethernet protocols and translate the transmission before retransmitting, as per the ISO definition. The gateway also has a software connotation, which is not to be confused with the ISO hardware definition. A software gateway performs the same function as a repeater, although it usually provides a routing mechanism that transmits only those packets clearly destined for that segment in the same way as a smart repeater. It relays traffic to the proper destination.

A gateway has two or more controllers to connect separate networks. The most usual form of a gateway is a workstation or computer processor with two Ethernet controllers, each controller connected into a node on separate networks. The gateway unit supports only one Ethernet address, but two Internet addresses. Most computer workstations support multiple controllers but require specialized software to function as a gateway. See Figure 8.9. Network gateways and foresighted network planning can localize groups and functional units on different networks for significant performance gains.

This subnetting isolates problems to each segment and allows loads, demand, and storage requirements on file servers and print servers to be controlled by the people who use those services, averting the possibility of developing a politically tense situation. Subnetting isolates a group to a subnet while lowering overall network traffic. Chapter 17 provides more detail on improving performance with gateways.

This is a manageable approach to controlling resources by group and division, as well as by individual subnets throughout the company. As an example, a backplane network would provide interconnection to all local subnetworks and supply network-wide access to expensive and low usage specialized peripheral devices such as typesetters, image scanners, video

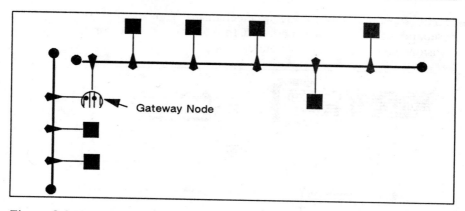

Figure 8.9 Node serving as gateway to two network segments.

entry cameras, pen plotters, co-processors, and tape storage or disk storage devices. Subnets would concentrate each group onto a single Ethernet, so that excessive demand for services could be controlled, analyzed, and prevented from interfering with processing and traffic on other segments.

Network Bridges

The bridge connects different types of networks together and promotes interconnectivity between multivendor networks. Bridges are specialized hardware that translate transmissions from one type of network into a protocol required by another. A bridge could also be a computer device that is compatible with two communication networks, interfacing with both. Figure 8.10 shows a node that bridges two networks.

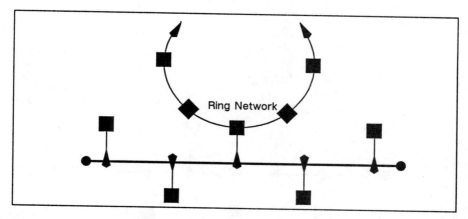

Figure 8.10 An Ethernet bridges to a Token ring network node. This "gateway" is a bridge because the workstation converts data from one protocol into a different one.

The most common bridging mechanism is a modem that converts baseband signals into a broadband format for long-haul or multichannel transmission. Figure 8.11 illustrates this bridging technology.

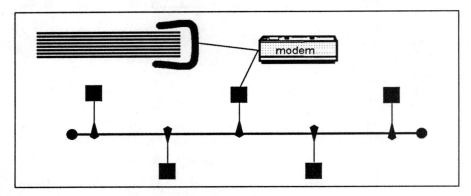

Figure 8.11 Modems bridge Ethernet to long-haul nodes.

Bridges Support Growth

As larger organizations integrate microcomputer technology and microcomputer networks like Ethernet, the importance of the microcomputer grows. Users find the microcomputer less restrictive than mainframes, and more available. It often has software that is unavailable on mainframes. Uploading and downloading of information between mainframe and microcomputer is a growing requirement, and bridges establish a common link, common transmission formats, and increasingly, common data formats. The mainframe to microcomputer bridge is explained by Figure 8.12.

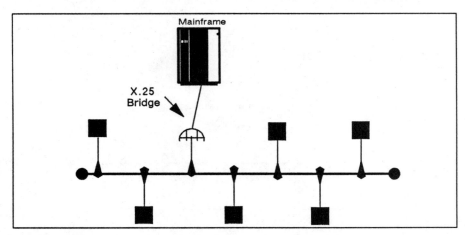

Figure 8.12 A bridge from a mainframe to Ethernet.

Note that while a mainframe can be a node on Ethernet, mainframe protocols differ from the Ethernet protocol, and a bridge is required to translate and interface these protocols. Figure 8.13 shows a large network.

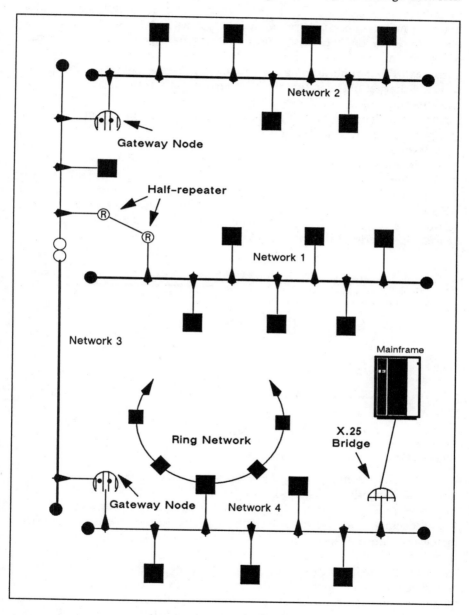

Figure 8.13 An expanded network topology.

The Radio Frequency Switch

Radio Frequency (RF) switches automate isolation and reconfiguration of a large Ethernet network. The switch unit disconnects one section and reconnects another section. The RF switch could disconnect sections after hours to maintain security requirements, to switch networks onto a backplane for data backup, disconnect sections or segments with suspected problems, or break the network into sections for testing or debugging purposes. The switch automates a manual process. These sections could service Ethernet between buildings, Ethernet sections in inaccessible areas, Cheapernet and Thinnet segments, public segments, or "secured" segments. This dynamic reconfiguration is valuable for production environments or for critical applications.

A frequently used technique to isolate faulty hardware requires progressive isolation of suspected segments into smaller and smaller sections, until the problem is contained and located. Such an approach usually requires the physical disconnection of sections. Figure 8.14 demonstrates how an RF switch would disconnect and terminate two sections individually, and of the time required for manual isolation. This manual method, the *binary search*, is described in Chapter 11.

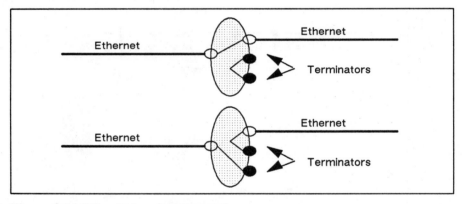

Figure 8.14 RF switches isolate sections.

Figure 8.15 demonstrates how a Thinnet segment could be isolated from the main network. Because RF switches are remote devices, such a mechanized search can be instantly performed from an operator's console.

While taps and transceivers make a basic Ethernet possible, bridges, gateways, and repeaters make larger networks possible. These devices level loads over segments, create specialized backplane segments for data file backup, system-wise monitoring, priority transmissions, and faster response for priority users, among other uses. A fully configured Ethernet can support a maximum of 1024 users, separated by a maximum of two half repeaters and any number of repeaters provided that no node tries to com-

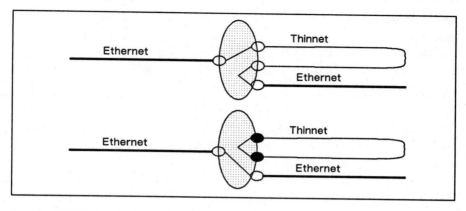

Figure 8.15 RF switches isolate a Thinnet segment.

municate with any other node that is separated by more than two repeaters. Any number of bridges can interconnect into an Ethernet to provide access to mainframe services, PBX services, or long-haul transmissions.

Signal Indicators

If a network does not support fan-out units, repeaters, or transceivers with built-in indicator lights, a signal indicator provides simple feedback on network status. LEDs on a signal indicator light up when a packet passes, during the SQE heartbeat signal, or whenever there is a packet collision. Some network information, like traffic load and approximate collision count, is available by monitoring the indicator lights. The signal indicator is a simple and basic tool, useful and desirable, although now superseded by many other devices. When other devices and tools are seen as too expensive, a signal indicator may provide good information/cost benefits.

Multipurpose Devices

There are some multipurpose devices that can economically expand Ethernet. The Information System Network (ISN) from AT&T is one such unit that provides local area connectivity for asynchronous and synchronous networks, terminals, and peripherals. Specifically, this device provides access to a modem pool, printer support, terminal concentration, host computer concentration, synchronous protocol conversion, Starlan, and Ethernet access. The ISN establishes a uniform plan for multiple networks. This unit is unusual in that repairs and reconfigurations can be performed while the unit remains in operation. Ungerman-Bass and Lattisnet (Synoptics) both produce devices that integrate disparate Ethernet networks into a central wiring closet, and then provide twisted-pair service from a star configuration. These products provide a focal point for controlling a network and asynchronous and synchronous networking services.

Extended Ethernet Network Configurations

Figure 8.16 shows the simple bus structure. Figure 8.17 expands this design with the inclusion of fan-out units to provide star-like clusters which concentrate traffic within each of those clusters. Figure 8.18 contrasts those simple networks with a network expanded by repeaters.

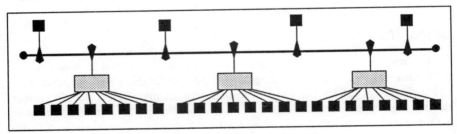

Figure 8.16 The simple bus structure.

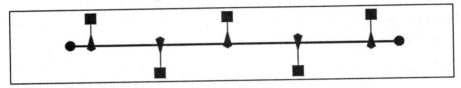

Figure 8.17 A simple bus structure expanded with fan-out units.

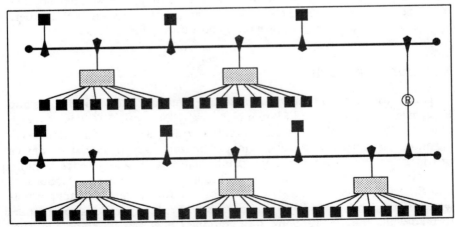

Figure 8.18 The bus structure with repeaters.

Figure 8.19 presents a configuration that might provide service to an entire building, with a backplane coaxial segment serving as the connecting link between all subnets. This last illustration suggests the communications power inherent within the Ethernet network.

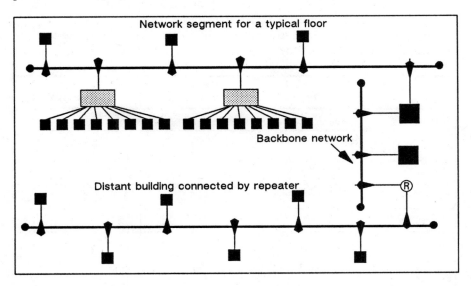

Figure 8.19 A multidimensional network services an extended complex.

These cabling plans describe a single channel coaxial network. For channel growth, many coaxial cables can be strung side by side to provide additional channel capability, and this often yields a simple and cost-effective alternative to multichannel broadband networks. Figure 8.20 only suggests the capabilities of installing multiple networks in order to provide multiple channels, which carry multiple subnets on separate signal bands.

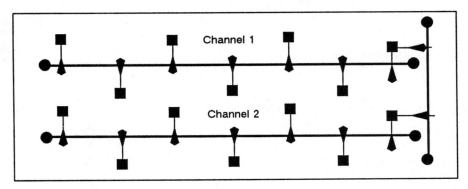

Figure 8.20 Multiple channels are provided by parallel cables.

Multiple channels provide an easily implemented method of expansion for overloaded networks. A segregated network also isolates the affects and interruptions inherent on a network. Furthermore, subnetworks ease accountability, while providing a measure of increased data security. Few alternatives exist to subnets; the most readily available is, of course, broadband cabling. Optical fiber provides the most security.

The chart in Figure 8.21 summarizes the differences among the alternative devices, and suggests their uses.

Expansion Device	Simple Networks	Complex Networks	Capacity Expansion
Bridge	Connection to other equipment	Interconnection to other networks	Connection to broadband
Fan-out	Eliminates Coax	Service high density nodes	Filter heavy volumes and lower inter-collision rates
Gateway	Keep it simple and small	Interconnection to other networks	Decrease network loads onto parallel networks
Repeater	Not appropriate	Major cause of complexity	Length/distance (unless a smart repeater)
RF switch	Not appropriate	Simplifies tracing location of failures	Segregate loads and break network
Multiple Cabling	Keep it simple and small	Load and problem isolation	Increase channel traffic capacity
Multichannel Broadband	Not appropriate	Major cause of complexity	Increase channel traffic capacity and interface to other networks

Figure 8.21 Comparison between network expansion devices.

Now that the details for Ethernet process, installation, and network expansion methodologies have been explained, the next chapters apply this information to practical day-to-day management.

Part 3

Practical Aspects of Managing Ethernet

This section presents rules-of-thumb and suggestions for successfully applying Ethernet. The formal IEEE and ISO specifications do little to explain the hows and whys of success and failure with Ethernet. Therefore, this part presents the design, planning, implementation, operational, and strategic issues. Emphasis is placed upon the practical issues that are often overlooked.

Chapter 9

Managing an Ethernet Network

In most situations, Ethernet has been selected because it was the networking medium most readily available from an equipment vendor. In other situations, Ethernet has been selected for its long-standing acceptance, its growing site installation, or its compatibility.

Rules of Thumb

Ethernet is not necessarily a simple conglomeration of parts, nor is it easily upgraded or maintained; it is often a critical and necessary organizational requirement. However, some simple steps and foresight can ease the burden of those who maintain that network. Building on an understanding how Ethernet works and how it is physically assembled, as presented in Chapters 1 through 8, this chapter addresses the practical and realistic expectations of an experienced network manager in the design and installation stages. Figure 9.1 outlines the organizational and implementational items detailed in this chapter.

Sisyphus would have made the ultimate network manager. The job is never ending, and each improvement—when finally accomplished—begs additional upgrades, changes, and fixes, uncovers oversights, and encourages new user requests. Moreover, as is the case for any service organization, major work and excellent improvements yield no recognition.

All LANs require a great deal of babying. An irascible LAN requires extraordinary craft. Good work habits, good network documentation, and good technicians can keep any network functioning. With sufficient funds and an astute eye for applying those resources, a network will provide growth capability and reliability to yield significant advantages for the organization.

Network Administration

Network administration is a supportive activity just like data processing. As a consequence, network management is very much a vendor in a vendor/buyer relationship, the buyer in this case being the network user community. The audience is captive; the network may be the only game in

- Network administration
- Resource allocation
- Financial planning
- Evaluating resource allocation decisions
- Setting priorities
- Assessing budgetary allocations
- Security
- Environmental problems
- Failures and repairs
- Downtime
- Crashes
- Planning for catastrophe
- Staging upgrades
- Upgrade policies
- Locating potential failure points
- Pilot projects
- Long lead times
- Replacement parts
- Ethernet monitoring
- Backup
- Coordinating network disruptions
- Moving equipment
- Tape backup and storage
- Squeaky wheel versus problem resolution
- Short-term versus long-term planning

Figure 9.1 Implementation and operational issues.

town, like any monopolistic utility, because alternatives are difficult to implement when substitutes don't exist in the *short term*. Network management is a subservient role, and the players must be responsive in a timely manner to the network user community and to network problems. The manager must determine the acceptable level of services required to meet the community needs, the level of resources available to fulfill them, and the effort required to sustain them. Until these parameters are defined— often through consensus of many quarters—network administration will be a hodge-podge geared to crisis-level maintenance, instead of a controlled, foresighted team.

Because a network intertwines hardware, software, and procedural and labor components, resources must be available to assess and repair each of these layers. Not only does a network include these layers, but the network interacts with almost every layer within the organization. Figure 9.2 illustrates the matrix organization often confronted by network managers. Frequently, the network manager and the support team are the most visible persons (other than mail room clerks or front desk guards) within an organization. With this visibility comes responsibility. It is not a secret organization. It does not directly bring revenue to the company; in fact, it is a *cost center,* which is a euphemistic way to say that network administration is a large and difficult-to-manage overhead expense. Also, the network is a support function that rarely creates a discernible value to the organization. Like a telephone switchboard, the network provides a basic support service that defies easy quantification.

	Network Mgt.	Dpmts.	Junior	Senior
Network Mgt.	✔	✔	✔	✔
Departments	✔			✔
Junior Personnel	✔	✔		✔
Senior Level	✔			

Figure 9.2 Matrix management.

The network, like a telephone switchboard, is only noticeable when it doesn't function correctly. When it works well, users assume that they have a right to its resources; when it fails, then and only then, do users take notice of (bungling) efforts of the network administration team. The job is a service-related task: fix and repair, replace and maintain. Planning and implementation for the future are not perceived to be as critical as the immediate functionality; the team must maintain the fragile service. This breeds a reaction to crisis mentality and an emotional bent to avoid any change that could upset the fragile equilibrium. This breeds management conservatism.

Understand the Needs of the Network User

A flattened, decentralized organization fits well with a network strategy because the network provides service to a wide range of people. Some will have computer experience, whereas others will not. Also, users will have expectations brought from other experiences and organizations, or will generate expectations from analogous situations. One example is the data processing department. The services of a network are somewhat similar to those of the DP department, and users may expect the same respect, response, or results. Understand the user community, respond to those needs, and if necessary, educate that community to the benefits, processes, and limitations of the newer networking technology. Nail down specifications for users and your vendors. Communicate policies to all affected by the network. This will build credibility and respect, and alleviate some of the inherent work overload.

Resource Allocation

Because network management is a service organization catering almost exclusively to internal needs, it is a money hole. As suggested above, the network is a cost center, unless the network is large enough to service many departments within a sizable organization. In this case, it may be feasible to assess each department for the cost of network services rendered. Such a ploy generates an *income* for the network administration team, and thus a clearly defined *market*. Increases in service to a particular department can generate valid requests for a larger allocation.

Many Fortune 1000 firms encourage profit center orientation for computer centers, in order to control and contain the rampant growth of a support group. In past years, computer service organizations have sought continuous improvement to the basic installation, adding to cost with new equipment and people. Benefits from such growth never coincide with the addition of equipment and people; increases in network resources are generally infrequently subdivisible by incremental units. This accentuates the cost to the organization of any new resources.

The "black art" of data processing management, the difficulty in attracting qualified people, and the leverage held by such experts provided enough intimidation in the past to increase DP budgets at rates inconsistent with company growth. Eventually, this problem was resolved by assigning administrative responsibility for budget issues to the DP manager, VP, or director, and basing the performance evaluation of such a manager on budget and profit issues. As a consequence, mainframe software and services usually support user accounts and charges, and a fee-charging policy can be directly implemented. Because networks are geographically distributed and network services tend to be more nebulous and intangible, there is no directly applicable fee structure. However, there are clear, concise, and fair methods for assessing network uses and assigning user or departmental costs.

Financial Planning

Three major factors affect the implementation and usage of an Ethernet network; reliability, organizational growth, and technological change. These three items determine the level of service achieved and the success of the network administration group. The solution used by many companies for any network constraint is the addition of more resources. Unfortunately, unlimited DP budgets no longer exist, and networks are usually derived from a different mentality than mainframe services. Networks are new resources to most organizations and despite the many similarities neither appear as glamorous nor are held in as high esteem as the DP groups were in the '50s, '60s, or '70s . Personal computers often supplemented overloaded DP departments. Distributed data processing and improved user-layer software have achieved a higher user sophistication, greater user expectations, and less reliance on a DP department. Also, distributed processing power allows the addition of less costly computers incrementally rather than a single, indivisible mainframe to cope with trickle growth; this better coordinates needs with resources. As the new networking technology unfolds, communication networks complement the desktop "toys." Also, the financial power is applied to the desktop toys instead of the connection among them. This mentality persists. As a result, network budgets are modest and more tightly controlled than DP budgets are.

Good network management requires self-imposed financial controls. External controls devalue the esteem of network administration. Therefore, a planning mechanism is necessary to address the existing network and to acquire additional resources to match organizational growth and technological change. Financial planning can be ad hoc in an environment in which there is a cost-plus mentality, or zero-based budgeting. Either method is better than none. Zero-based is better than ad hoc.

Ad hoc planning devalues the decision-making process, because needs are addressed sporadically and without clear controls. Each newly identified need becomes a battle for budget. Zero-based budgeting schemes are difficult to implement, since they require more management time. All hardware, software, and labor costs are addressed up front, and organizational change becomes a detailed, preplanned financial issue. Growth in head count becomes a known quantity, and technological advancement is no longer an unknown quantity with nebulous ramifications, but rather a clearly stated and clearly controlled financial cost. Figure 9.3 contrasts the advantages and pitfalls of each financial tracking method.

	Ad hoc	Zero-based
Advantages	specific goal orientation easy fast accurate	nonspecific concise informative prestigious
Disadvantages	devalues management creates surprises	inaccurate (assumptive) time consuming

Figure 9.3 Network budgeting choices.

Evaluating Resource Allocation

Financial planning encompasses the entire network. Very often, resources are allocated to many individuals and groups within the framework of the network. When the network is a "free" resource, like telephone, secretarial services, desk space, or other utilities, the network is devalued. After all, it is free. Financial planning provides that first step for understanding the resources applied to intercommunication. A budgetary methodology builds that first stage for inventorying network uses. The second step is to gain an understanding of user needs. A network supplies easily discernible services some of which are listed in Figure 9.4.

- Communication
- Electronic mail
- File service
- Print service
- Centralized coordination
- Centralized maintenance
- Automation

Figure 9.4 Network services.

Understanding the consumption and depletion of these resources completes the picture of network management. Additional resources certainly will be procured to alleviate network overloads. What types of resources, to which sets of problems these resources will be targeted, and how much will be allocated are, in part, within the purview of the network manager.

Setting Priorities

Resource allocation decisions hinge upon the size of the network budget and user demands for services. Unilateral decisions are inappropriate, since the user community mirrors a vendor/buyer relationship. Ignoring the needs of the user is tantamount to a service failure. Applying technical skills without responding to the full measure of user questions, requests, and complaints is certain to breed resentment and distrust. Only two-way dialogue can simplify the resource allocation process.

Users must feel that their issues are recognized and understood. Silent and unpublicized repairs (as though accomplished by the proverbial "elves") may solve network problems per se, but create a public relations nightmare. Therefore, all users must be able to voice their concerns and pet interests and see how this information adjusts the priorities of the network administration group.

The network manager may technically and politically understand the problems facing him or her, but these problems must be clearly presented to the user community as well. The prioritized list of network administration goals and charters must logically match the perception of the identified and acknowledged network problems so that the community "buys into" any plan.

This inclusion in the problem identification and resolution process and in task prioritization will yield a better perception of the network group and a more satisfied community. The priorities should be delineated clearly to avoid possible misunderstanding.

Assessing Budgetary Allocations

If it is preferable to establish a profit center mentality, network costs can be allocated in several ways. All methods require determining a cost basis for equipment, software, labor, and repairs. Additionally, a basis should be established for a matching service level. Figure 9.5 lists some common network costs that form a cost basis.

- Overhead
- Equipment costs
- Depreciation
- Labor
- Maintenance
- Media
- Consumables
- Training

Figure 9.5 Network costs.

Fixed costs include overhead such as floor space, heat, power, and management salaries. This includes semi-variable, fixed-cost items, like the initial cable, transceivers, and node equipment. Consumable materials include file space, paper and other media, and replacement and repair parts. Labor includes a portion of overhead, all network administration labor, and consultants. It also includes the fair cost of training sessions, shows, and documentation purchased. A cost basis should reconcile growth or shrinkage, since new users within a department require additional resources, place additional loads, and often request new types of services never before provided.

The service level is the yardstick for prorating the network costs listed. Fee application schemes for allocating costs of the services are difficult because network service is the pie that all users and groups share. The costs for providing network services are black and white, whereas the value of the services rendered is not as clear. It is usually unreasonable to charge for each individual event because the accounting system will grow large and cumbersome, and will itself affect the level of network service. Complex schemes will win no friends, either.

Therefore, the cost charge-out system should be simple. Some possibilities include assigning costs by head count. This is immediately simple, but may underrepresent the demands some groups place upon network load or network administration services. Another method might apply node counts as an appropriate measure. Either file space or paper output could form a prorated basis. Another basis could be built from the network traffic level. In fact, Chapter 14 includes an example in which Ethernet packets are counted and used as a measure by which to assign costs. Figure 9.6 represents these and other possibilities.

- Head count
- Node count
- File space usage
- Login time
- CPU time
- Prorated traffic level
- Service requests
- Individually negotiated
- Replacement part costs

Figure 9.6 Basis for prorating network costs.

Carefully weigh which measure is to be used as the fee basis since each user will adjust network usage so as to minimize statistics in that area. Users will optimize their usage and play against the system. This can, however, be applied to advantage. If it is important to minimize the growth or utilization of certain resources, the fee basis can be changed to encourage conservation. If a network is too busy and it is important to decrease load until upgrades are installed, arbitrary increases in the fee basis will compel users to conserve. Frequency of reassessing the fee basis is also an important consideration, since users will shift usage during the measurement period. Secret measurements that cannot be validated will infuriate everyone. The system must be open and honest, in addition to being simple. It will be necessary to defend the internal pricing strategy.

Licensing and Warranty Issues

Many organizations assume that the purchase of a software product guarantees the right to use that product in any manner, including multisite installation. This is rarely the intent of the software vendor. Personal computer software is particularly vulnerable to this type of pirating; a single master copy gets installed on all the computers. Most organizations today, however, are too mature for this behavior.

Because networks are often installed as an organization grows, there is usually an installed base of existing tools and products. Software is often sold under a precondition that it is to be used on a single machine. It may not be supported within the context of a distributed network or multiuser environment, not because of legal issues, but rather from technical limitations and complexities in the networking environment. Therefore, it is important to consider whether a software package your organization depends upon is guaranteed to work within a networked environment, will be supported within that environment, or even, whether the product can be legally licensed for your use within a networked environment.

Security

Security is a factor that needs to be built into the initial network design. Security encompasses many aspects, including limits to physical equipment, such as access to the coaxial cable and network communication hardware, and software access to machines, file storage media, and information replicating devices like tape drives, floppy disks, and cartridge tape units.

As a rule of thumb where security is desirable, the physical network as a whole should be as inaccessible as possible. Additionally, as many software keys as possible should be applied to the network. The role of network administrator is a conservative role, and such conservative security measures are best instituted. Therefore, all media backup devices should be locked up to prevent theft of information on portable media. Network servers that provide global services should also be removed from public access in order to curtail marginally qualified network users from trying to fix server problems. Access to power service, fuses, circuit breakers, and any other network transformers should be secured. Building managers regularly lock access to such building power panels; it is a safe and reasonable procedure. Figure 9.7 illustrates these simple and wise steps. Details and rationale for these policies are examined in Chapter 17.

- Limit access to physical network coax
- Limit access to physical equipment
- Limit access to physical network servers
- Limit access to physical backup media devices
- Limit network access to servers and nodes
- Limit access with password protection

Figure 9.7 Rule of thumb security steps.

Environmental Problems

Ethernet is mostly an inert medium, although certain environmental factors will disrupt communication and network data processing. As stated in Chapter 6, electrical or magnetic interference in proximity to the coax can adversely affect network impedance or color packets with random noise. Additionally, many coax cables side by side *may* cause mutual interference despite each cable's internal shielding; this is not a proven assumption for minimum networks, but verified by independent sources for long parallel runs of cable.

Acute vibration causes Ethernet failure at stress points by shaking free cable connections, and jostling transceivers and their transceiver cables. Heavy traffic or construction inside or outside the facility can cause oscillation of insecure coax or transceiver cables, thus straining nearby electrical contacts. Users may unconsciously force a workstation against a wall to create more desktop space and place pressure on slide latch connectors or the coax. Also, extremes of temperature can distort magnetic disk alignment, thus rendering a disk useless. High temperatures can overheat computer chips and cause premature node equipment failure. Likewise, temperature extremes can crack coaxial cable or damage transceiver electronics. Low humidity will cause static electricity to build up, static being a likely candidate as the cause for chip failure (particularly PROM chips) and a contributing factor to momentary power surges.

Figure 9.8 illustrates these environmental concerns. Solutions include installing climate control, securely installing cable to building structures or installing cable conduits, and selecting a site carefully. Also, many facilities install monitoring devices that track deviations from acceptable operating conditions. It is reasonable to track temperature, humidity, smoke levels, security and facility access, system failures, and network failures.

> - Excessive temperature
> - Excessive temperature fluctuations
> - Excessive humidity
> - Vibration
> - Static electricity
> - Fire, smoke, water
> - Security

Figure 9.8 Environmental concerns.

ANSI Standards

American National Standards Institute (ANSI) generates a list of acceptable standards for computer languages, character sets, connection compatibility, and many other aspects of the computer industry. Adherence to a standard in network design may ease maintenance, spare parts, and upgrade problems. Non-ANSI components should be viewed with a healthy skepticism, but not necessarily ignored. However, some standards exist only because they were accepted as de facto before better or more rational solutions existed. One example of a standard that is best circumvented is the Ethernet slide latch, a key failure point because it often fails to maintain good electrical contacts between mail and female connectors.

Mechanical Integrity of Cable Connections

Rules of thumb encompass those soft issues that a practiced manager discusses with peers over lunch. These include hard-learned solutions, as evidenced by this next item. As presented in Chapter 3, the hardware is specified by rigorous IEEE 802.3 descriptions. However, some mechanical features of that specification should be improved. Specifically, the cable, from recently manufactured and not recycled stock, should be installed far from electrical signals and tied to a firm support or installed within a cable tray. Also, the transceiver and cable connectors should be firmed up with cable ties as per Chapter 6.

This last retrofit is simple, inexpensive, and a cure for many network problems. The slide latches, bane of many organizations until replaced with more durable screw connectors or BNC/Thinnet connections, are one item should be avoided. The payback may be immediate. In fact, it is usually less vexing to replace these latches before they fail. When a connection fails, it can be a tedious process to locate the offending latch from among many possible nodes. This alteration is non-ANSI.

This chapter presented static rules of thumb, simple administrative record-keeping systems, and suggestions for envisioning and revising the Ethernet network. The next chapter highlights the realities of network administration and application.

Maintenance and Repairs

All networks require maintenance and repairs. *Maintenance* is defined as repairs performed before a problem exists; they are often preventative measures. *Repairs* are affected when the network fails. While maintenance often saves repairs, some maintenance causes problems which will require unexpected repairs. Understand the consequences of maintenance and understand that it can have far-reaching consequences, including network downtime. Mechanical and software components require repair work. Parts fail, software malfunctions, power surges or failures corrupt both hardware and software. Likewise, network configurations change in subtle ways, requiring hardware and software work-arounds, DIP switch resets, and component changes. Failures in these components create downtime.

Downtime

Problems are endemic even on the best of networks. At the first symptom of trouble, clear the network of users and determine the problem. Determine if the problem is localized or system-wide.

Network downtime is part of the "excitement" of managing any network. Ethernet is no exception. There are many reasons for a network to fail; some of these have been explicitly stated in prior chapters while other reasons will follow in concise detail. Network problems can, in part, be avoided with good initial design, compatible equipment, installation according to specification, and appropriate vendor postsale support. Additionally, network segmentation and planned preventative maintenance may forestall such events from incapacitating the entire network. Preplanned downtime for upgrades and maintenance is preferable to system crashes. Users do not like surprises or the drama that accompanies a forced network halt. Connections, filters, software, device drivers, and the devices themselves can be checked for functionality on a periodic basis. While the unplanned crashes are unpredictable, a stated policy for resolving the crisis and answering user questions can lessen the severity of the crash's impact as well as build confidence in the network team.

Crash Policy

Crashes are inevitable. Hardware and software will malfunction, and many known or totally new problems will incapacitate network sections, segments, or the entire network installation. Since these cannot be prevented with complete success, it is best is to have a crash policy. The network management team must know what to do to solve the problem, and they must also know what to say. Users who depend on the network for completing their jobs might prefer to leave for the day if the problem will not be resolved in a reasonable amount of time. Groups may seek to hold meetings during this dead spot of activity.

While Ethernet network crashes are certain, far-reaching ramifications can be diverted with clear and concise explanations and open answers. The user community has few alternatives to the network administration group and while the network team may feel pressured and overworked, they should also realize that the user community depends on them. The network team should answer the questions in Figure 9.9 for each user.

> - How long will service be unavailable?
> - Why am I affected?
> - Who else is affected?
> - Will I be able to work?
> - When will service be restored?
> - What causes the downtime?
> - What solutions exist?
> - Will the solution be stable?
> - Will the problems reoccur?
> - What can users do to help?
> - What should a user expect?
> - What alternatives exist to complete my work?

Figure 9.9 Typical user questions during downtime.

Planning for Catastrophe

The network manager is responsible for the security and continuing operation of the network. When the network crashes or when node equipment that is under network administration management malfunctions, the manager is pressed to restore service with rapidity. Minor software or hardware fixes are the grist for daily operations, but network disaster could make or break careers, the livelihoods of many people, and the very continuation of the organization. Catastrophe could be the result of a natural disaster, arson, accident, or sabotage. While any one of these is a rare event, the disruption from such an event is too massive to ignore.

Information backups, alternative emergency sites, redundant sites, and spare parts are the basics for restoring service after a disaster. Additionally, skilled and prepared people, a plan of action, an understanding of the critical needs, and a staged implementation are necessary components for network restoration. Figure 9.10 outlines these factors.

- Information backups
- Alternative emergency sites
- Redundant sites
- Spare parts
- Strike team
- Plan of action for recovery
- Understanding of critical services
- Staged implementation plan

Figure 9.10 Data recovery components.

Most organizations prefer for business reasons not to make public disclosures of disasters or interruptions of operations. Likewise, recovery plans are kept secret. Whatever the recovery plan, the procedures should be pretested to ensure the completeness of the plan and to uncover any existing weaknesses, as well as those operations most critical to the business. Some commercial corporations provide "hot sites" and staff and support services for a fee. While this may be advisable for some organizations, others may prefer to plan their own disaster recovery procedures. At a minimum, keep an up-to-date list of the phone numbers of key personnel for users to contact in cases of network emergencies. This is a no-cost solution to many problems, and it generates good will as well.

Staging Upgrades

Planned downtime can include fixes and improvements to the network. Although these are often noncritical, they may be far from trivial to network operations. Because such changes are usually tested and verified prior to their application, these changes can be applied off-hours or concurrent with the repair of an unplanned crash. Notification to the users of planned changes is good public relations because it forewarns users of possible negative side-effects, as well as service improvements. It also serves to remind users of the events that happen behind the scenes, to their benefit. Common courtesy and savvy management dictate that you give users as much lead time as possible before implementing changes.

Upgrade Policies

The time for staging upgrades must be carefully orchestrated and the user community must be made to understand and accept the inherent risks beforehand. Additionally, there should be an upgrade policy coordinated with all vendors. Fixes, improvements, and changes in technology should be applied where optimally beneficial, although technological changes at times may obsolete network components. Vendors should stand by their sales, and they should be willing to support all network equipment. There should be a policy on handling minor upgrades that would unnecessarily outdate components.

Also, it may be that secondary sourcing of so-called commodity items may breed incompatibilities later when a network is upgraded. Be aware that prime vendors may alter their equipment or software, and third-party solutions may no longer be ideal.

Locate Failure Points

The last three chapters expressed a need for network blueprinting. Possible network failure points should be located. While the maintenance logs suggested later in this chapter document what has gone wrong in the past, it is also appropriate to consider what might go wrong in the future. This preparation might encompass listing failures theorized but not actually experienced. For example, it has been suggested that a certain model of fan-out unit *might* lock up and stop providing service. When a failure occurs that defies the usual solutions and is not listed in the troubleshooting section of this book pertinent to your network, peer table talk and theorized solutions are invaluable.

The normally reoccurring trouble spots might also be added to such a list. If the user community has access to such information, it can lend its diagnostic skills when failures do occur. Often, users will have more information readily available than any member of the network administration team and can narrow the possible problem set, thus saving time. Users also have more of a personal reason to see solved a specific network problem.

Pilot Projects

It is anathema to test on unwilling and unknowing users. Few users want to be guinea pigs, and certainly no one should ever be an unknowing test subject. Major network changes, cabling rerouting, or upgrades are best pretested and not indiscriminantly applied with only a vendor's guarantees. As a consequence, it is is often difficult to test changes. Pilot projects are an appropriate solution. They certainly lower the risk of failure and localize the test to an observable network subset.

Pilot projects remove the effect of changes from the daily operational or manufacturing environment of the larger network. Isolated tests concentrate problems to a select and willing group and lessen the risk all will face when such changes are later applied to the complete network. Try changes to spare machines. Build a small network and test on that. Find a willing user who wants to feel that he or she is in the thick of things and likes to talk about what he or she does and what the network team is doing. Locate a subnet that provides less critical services. Select a time when a segment is unused, perhaps after hours. Weekends or after hours may be the best time to effect global changes so that, should unforeseen side affects surface, all changes can be reversed without affecting the user base. Figure 9.11 illustrates when it is best to implement changes with test pilots.

- Network extensions
- Gateway installations
- Network bridging
- Repeater installation
- Subnetworking
- New types of node equipment
- New network configurations
- Cable variant installations

Figure 9.11 Pilot projects.

Long Lead Times

Most projects on the network have long lead times. Either the parts are difficult to obtain, senior-level management is slow to understand and respond, or manpower is in short supply to complete the work load. Projects with long lead times are best launched immediately so that crises and constraints will not deteriorate network performance. Such projects might include installation of parallel networks, gateways, faster machines, and optical fiber. The continued employment of network management may not only be at risk; a competitive advantage might be at stake as well.

Replacement Parts

In the normal course of network operations, components will fail. There are two policies for restoring service. The first is to swap parts from other working equipment to restore service. The second is to have an inventory of spare parts. Either method is reasonable, although in actual operation, some combination of the two will actually be applied sooner or later. Most managers prefer to maintain a parts inventory because repairs are simpler, do not affect functioning network users, and do not require duplicate efforts, that is, repairing the defective components as well as later repairing the unit that was the source of the problem. When a network uses old, antiquated, or unusual equipment, a spare-parts policy is recommended, because parts can be very difficult to obtain. If the equipment is more common and parts are nonetheless difficult to obtain from the manufacturer, a spare-parts inventory is critical.

Most upper-management teams seek to trim expenses. Replacement parts are nonfunctioning items, usually expensive in the quantities sought, and therefore rarely stocked. Convincing upper management that a spare-parts policy is absolutely necessary requires a mathematical analysis. Compare the costs of inventory against the costs of downtime, both partial and complete. Determine through *consensus* how often this might occur. Figure 9.12 presents the mathematics for such an analysis.

Audit the replacement-part inventory as the network evolves and new equipment is purchased and as other equipment is sold or antiquated. A spare-parts inventory must reflect the current network, and not the network as it was months past. Turn over the inventory with regularity, and replace all parts in the inventory that are defective. Bad inventory not only will fail to solve a network failure, it seriously degrades network management's credibility.

+ hourly network costs	Network failure rate
+ hourly network user costs	(by consensus by
+ loss of goodwill	past history of failures)
+ loss of network access	

= **Total hourly network costs**

$\div$ Spare inventory valuation lifespan and turnover rates

= **Depeciated cost of spares**

$$\frac{\text{Total hourly network costs}}{\text{Spare inventory valuation}} * \text{Network failure rate} \leq \text{Depeciated cost of spares} =$$

Figure 9.12 Spare-parts inventory justification. The inventory should cover the expected loss of network downtime in the event that spare parts are unavailable. The spare-parts inventory does not need to equal the suggested inventory valuation if the organization is willing to accept some risk of downtime. Note also that an inventory does not guarantee that the necessary part is always in stock.

Ethernet Monitoring

Network monitoring is good policy. The network management should know how the network is performing and should see problems before users are aware of them. While this is often impossible, traffic monitoring and performance analysis yield information about the state of the network that will aid in design, planning, implementation, and control over network operations. User complaints can be answered with an informed response such as that the network is overloaded, that certain nodes have failed, or that a network server has malfunctioned. Answers like those breed trust, respect, and a happy user community. Ethernet monitoring is possible with node software or special network monitoring equipment. This equipment is the subject of Chapters 10 through 14.

Maintain a Network Profile

Every organization requires a good inventory system. This holds true for network management as well. Not only must spare-parts inventories be maintained so that component failures do not hamper network access, but network node component inventories should be maintained. These high-profile items are partially outlined in Figure 9.13.

- Spare parts
- Network equipment
- Node equipment
- Node variations
- Software variations

Figure 9.13 Maintain a network profile.

A network manager finds a complete hardware and software profile invaluable. Network failures can often be traced to incompatible equipment, mismatched revisions, outdated standards, or any number of other configuration differences. Furthermore, when a component is suspect and there are no replacement units, swapping such a part with a comparable item from another node is an efficacious method of verification.

It is worthwhile to track network equipment and node locations. Include in the node profile such information as part revision codes, versions, date of installation and repairs, plus any maintenance information. Additionally, it is sound procedure to track software versions, installation dates, and dates when patches of test code were applied, since "tests" that work become permanent. Furthermore, certain networks allow nodal interlinking with ease, and this accessibility should be tracked at least for performance evaluation, if not for security reasons. Some of these items are documented with blueprints and notebooks as the next sections discuss.

Blueprint the Network

A complete network profile includes a schematic rendition of the network, with cable, electronics, node equipment, repeaters, and any other device which might need to be located at a later time. Several styles of physical blueprinting were presented in Chapter 7 and repeated elsewhere, and Figure 9.14 lists common network items that are best charted.

- Location of coaxial cables
- Connection points of coaxial cables
- Location of transceivers
- Path of transceiver drop cables
- Location of node equipment
- Location of fan-outs, gateways and repeaters
- 2.5 (or 0.5) meter locations on coaxial cables
- Lengths of all sections and segments
- Cable stress points and repair points
- All completed physical plant alterations

Figure 9.14 Common items to blueprint.

Keep Notebooks of Work Requests and Changes

An organized network manager keeps a network notebook. Not only will the organized manager track all the coaxial cables, network communication hardware, and node hardware, he logs many other aspects of the physical network. These include address cable changes, transceiver and tap fixes, work currently in progress, a wish list of major or minor network improvements, and both a problem log and problem resolution log. This is represented in Figure 9.15.

- Work completed on coaxial cables
- Work completed on taps and transceivers
- Work in progress
- Wish list
- Problem log
- Problem resolution log
- Network traffic level log
- Network collision rate log
- Symptom -> Solution workbook
- Version -> Compatibility workbook

Figure 9.15 Network administration notebook.

Databases and MIS

Often all these lists can be maintained across the network on a database for rapid access from any node. The database also coordinates information and simplifies the data-entry and data-tracking requirements, and concise reports can be generated to provide otherwise unavailable insight into local or global causes of network problems. Figure 9.16 shows the interrelationship among several tracked components and suggests the power inherent in database tracking.

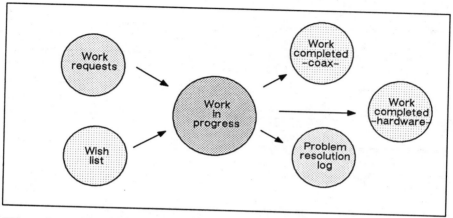

Figure 9.16 Database interrelationships between work logs.

Management Information Systems (MIS) yield flexibility to deal with change and uncertainty through information technology. They foster creative thinking and innovation, because information can improve both performance of the organization and the manager's ability to solve operational problems. "What if?" becomes easily tested when the data have been collected over time. Tools and the experience to use them are also already in place. MIS can also reduce the need from other problem-solving activities, because the information raises new issues not considered previously. It also requires additional resources not necessarily available. However, the basic MIS technologies can be bootstrapped with networking technology to provide new opportunities otherwise not available within the narrow context of the network team. Figure 9.17 lists these possibilities.

The next several illustrations represent database output or typed pages a network manager might maintain. Changes to the network coax (Figure 9.18) and node-site transceiver drop cables (Figure 9.19) are logged on

- Define the implications of network technology
- Construct relevant business scenarios
- Evaluate alternative network architectures
- Select a technical direction
- Establish a review process
- Uncover otherwise unknown relationships

Figure 9.17 MIS and networking benefits.

separate files or pages. Work in progress (Figure 9.20) provides a managerially inspired progress check on the status of all user- or management-initiated requests. A wish-list (Figure 9.21) compiles those nonessential repairs or changes that should be completed. A problem log (Figure 9.22) tracks all network failures and the problem resolution log (Figure 9.23) reflects the work actually completed.

#	Date	Location	Change/Repair	Tested
34	10/14/86	100 feet(al)	Repl. abraded sect.	okay

Figure 9.18 Work completion: coaxial cables.

#	Date	Location	Change/Repair	Tested
35	10/14/86	31´ from lab/3	chattering TCL	marginal

Figure 9.19 Work completetion: taps and transceivers.

#	Date	Location	Change/Repair	Status
35	10/14/86	31´ from lab/3	chattering TCL	no parts
36	10/14/86	node #31	file space full	
37	10/14/86	node #67	bad node/aiu	

Figure 9.20 Work in Progress.

#	Date	Location	Change/Repair	Due Date
38	10/14/86	node #31	reformat disk	10/17
39	10/14/86	node #67	install fan-out	10/26
40	10/14/86		gateway and segment engineering group	???

Figure 9.21 Wish list.

#	Date	Location	Change/Repair	user
35	10/14/86	31´ from lab/3	chattering TCL	JSL
36	10/14/86	node #31	file space full	CJP
37	10/14/86	node #67	bad node/aiu	DRF

Figure 9.22 Problem log.

#	Date reported	completed	User	Notes
34	10/14/86	10/14/86	AMcD	Bad cable caused by faulty initial install.

Figure 9.23 Problem resolution log.

Recurrent problems and users that seem prone to destroy equipment or software may regularly appear within the database reports. A database pays off by providing comparisons among network traffic statistics not otherwise noted. Correlations between collisions, volume, peak volumes, particular equipment manifestation, and cross-linked malfunctions are more easily recognized. Figure 9.24 maps this relationship.

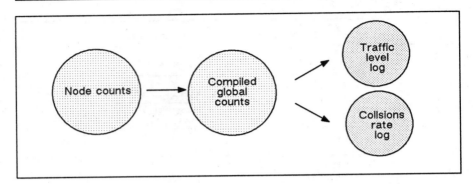

Figure 9.24 Databases provide insight into network traffic problems.

Figures 9.25 and 9.26 illustrate two important traffic reports that can be generated on an online database. Other pertinent statistical information and formulae to generate such information are presented in Chapter 15.

Date	Node	Packet Count	Percent	Notes
10/14/86	1	525,678	.11	
10/14/86	2	34,580	.005	
10/14/86	. . .			
10/14/86	Total	4,457,820	1.0	busy day

Figure 9.25 Network traffic log.

Date	Node	Count	Percent	Notes
10/14/86	1	52,568	.10	Chatter???
10/14/86	2	0	.00	
10/14/86	. . .			
10/14/86	Total	4456	0.001	no problems

Figure 9.26 Network collision log.

Backup

Backup of information, services, hardware, labor, and sometimes even backup processing is an important function of network management. No network is fail-safe; malfunctions and invasions happen. In order to protect the organization, a backup policy is suggested. Chapter 18 details backups and redundancy issues at length.

Tape Backup and Tape Storage

A good portion of any network is resident in unique files that define the relationship of nodes on the network, the operations of the network itself, and, quite possibly, scripts that have been programmed to automate many arcane processes that have become complicated over time. This information usually has value to the organization. Network backup is, therefore, a crucial procedure to ensure network integrity and security. Chapter 18 details network backup, including data, equipment, and software, as critical operational concerns.

Coordinating Network Disruptions

Network disruptions happen mostly by surprise, although some are planned. Those few times when downtime is actually planned, it is a good policy to inform the user community. It is a common courtesy. Users do not like surprises. If the user work schedule is disrupted by the network management team when advance notification was possible, users have every right to shout their displeasure. Also, the power the user community wields in part affects the courtesy that the network administration group shows. If the user community has control over operations common to many DP departments, almost no courtesy will be shown. Whatever policy is applied, remember to be consistent. Users will assume that each change is a permanent improvement. A downtime schedule should include the actual period of downtime, warnings beforehand, and notification if the duration of downtime will exceed the initial schedule. Courtesy wins respect. Consistency breeds trust.

Once a schedule is determined, it is most efficient to fix everything during that downtime. Backups, equipment repairs, reconfigurations, network tests, additions, and the like are best performed during this same time frame. The only caveat is that repairs or changes with a high likelihood of failure or a possibility of a surprising complication should be explained to the user community. Users like to be informed.

Moving Equipment

Physical equipment moves can be planned events and, like scheduled downtime, should be coordinated with the user community for minimal disruptive effect. Few other events can erode valuable network management credibility more than bungled prearranged events. Problems are apt to occur and simple transitions are rare.

Inform those affected in the user community how much time is required for the actual change, what can go wrong, and what will happen when such problems arise. In order to achieve successful equipment relocation, set up parallel installations. Figure 9.27 illustrates one example in which a transceiver can be installed and tested in advance of the actual node move. Other events, too, can be performed with such foresight. Not only will this simplify and speed successful completion of a relocation, but it allows for swift return to the initial configuration if problems appear.

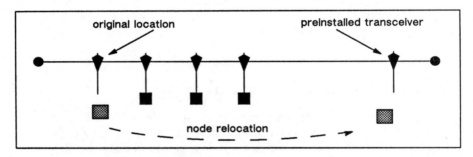

Figure 9.27 Preplanned equipment relocation and parallel setups.

Also, moves may require extra parts, software tapes, extra hands. Plan for all exigencies, any surprises. Be aware that equipment or network configuration changes may have small but significant side effects. A little forethought will preserve that hard-earned respect.

"Squeaky Wheel" versus Problem Resolution

As the squeaky wheel gets the grease, so too, the loudest voice often gets the most response. In many situations, responding to the loudest voice lowers tension, cools tempers, and makes more people happier. As a side effect, however, such attention side-tracks normal planning and problem resolution. It diverts attention from fixing critical failures, performing preventative maintenance, and attending to a controlled agenda. Responding to the squeaky wheel may undermine management initiative, degrade the credibility of network administration, and ultimately strip decision making responsibility from the network administration team. Therefore, the better policy is to plan network needs, assess network resources, determine both short-term and long-term network direction, and last, reach a detailed agreement with users as to network problem prioritization and resolution.

Short-term Versus Long-term Planning

Attention to the squeaky wheel underscores an attention to crisis-level response. While management of a new network or changeovers in management of a problem network may require crisis resolution, long-term success requires a long-term outlook. A manager should seek to maintain his or her job long term, seek to retain the management people on a long-term basis, and plan for long-term network growth, service growth, and technological change. Short-term planning resolves only immediate issues. Long-term planning attends to the configuration of network services over years. Figure 9.28 illustrates why neither of the areas covered by short-term and long-term planning can be overlooked for long.

Short-term Planning	Long-term Planning
Repairs	Preventative maintenance
Upgrades	Performance problems
Equipment relocation	New technology
Labor problems	Strategic application of networking
Performance overloads	Labor and resource concerns

Figure 9.28 Network short-term and long-term planning issues.

Easier Said than Done. . .

Network management is a difficult task. Matrix management impedes easy control of people and resources. It also raises the specter of squeaky wheel problem resolution, a policy apt to undermine network management and divert attention from more pressing problems. The complexity of a network, the sheer size of a network, the number of possible failures and malfunctions, the overloading, and the technical complexity of not only the network, but also the devices accessing that network, create a difficult job. Stress is often the norm. Furthermore, senior management usually is unwilling to allocate sufficient resources to resolve even most of the pressing network problems; resource scarcity is likely.

For these reasons, network management is a difficult task. Respect is won grudgingly and lost easily. Radical changes, unless always successful, will undermine the network manager's authority; management conservatism will erode any authority to fix, change, or improve the network, the communication channels within the organization, or the satisfaction and status due the management team. Work hard for credibility. Maintain that

Do	Don't
Design a segmentable network	Overdesign
Segment coax in short sections	Violate specifications
Pretest new components	Assume component functionality
Define an overall strategy	Mix standards
Define a user "pricing" policy	Take a component for granted
Define a repair policy	Scrimp on technical labor
Install extra wiring	Trust to luck
Identify potential failure points	Mix untested equipment
Experiment before implementing	Ignore user requests
Gain experience	Assume users understand
Search for trouble spots	
Promote preventative repairs	
Build credibility	

Figure 9.29 Network dos and don'ts.

credibility with carefully chosen words, respect, understanding, and accuracy. Promises are easy to make, but they are easier made than kept.

Dos and Don'ts

Figure 9.29 concludes this chapter with a general purpose list of management dos and don'ts. Add to this list as your experience dictates. Copy it and affix it to your wall, if you are so inclined. However, don't regard these few items as all there is to network management; "feel," experience, and other intangibles are learned with time.

Part 4

Network Troubleshooting

When the network fails there are various techniques to identify, locate, and repair problems. Many techniques are time-consuming without specialized tools like a multitester, a time domain reflectometer, a transceiver tester, and a network analyzer. Because each of these tools is indispensable on a large, busy, or very critical network, the knowledge needed to use them and interpret their results is presented in separate chapters complete with photographs, illustrations, and tables.

Chapter 10 suggests practical tools that test, monitor, and analyze network status. When the network fails there are various techniques to identify, locate, and repair problems. Some techniques are time-consuming or expensive and some require specialized tools like a multitester, a time domain reflectometer, a transceiver tester, and a network analyzer. Because each of these tools is indispensable on a large, busy, or critical network, information on to how use them and interpret their results is presented in separate chapters complete with photographs, illustrations, and tables. Chapter 11 details appropriate steps to verify the correct electrical operation of network hardware using a multitester. This tool provides a first pass for testing a network. It is often the one tool available to a network manager to solve serious network failures. Chapter 12 details the usage of a time domain reflectometer and the practical steps to check the conductivity and usability of network cable, connections and cable fittings, and to check for correct installation of taps and repeater hardware. This tool also provides a highly desirable method for benchmark cable installation. Chapter 13 explains the operation of the transceiver tester, including how to operate it, and how to interpret this tool's results.

Chapter 10

Network Monitoring Tools

A network manager who administers a large or growing network is certain to experience slowdowns, bottlenecks, or downtime. In order to combat these common problems, a network manager should have network monitoring tools. Chapter 7 raised the need for certain installation equipment including cable cutters, pliers, screwdrivers, tap set, crimp set, soldering iron, IC extractor, flashlight, hammer, cable ties, and other such tools. After installation, because the network is both a mechanical and software entity, complex analytical tools are needed to evaluate that installation. This network-monitoring tool kit which supplements the normal installation tools should include a multitester, a time domain reflectometer, a transceiver tester, and network traffic-analysis software or a protocol analyzer. Not only are tools needed, but an understanding of how to use these tools and interpret their results is critical to installing and maintaining a network. Ethernet, unlike other "pipes," transmits invisible contents. While a plumber can see current water leaks and the results of past problems and see that a pipe is plugged up or running slowly, Ethernet carries invisible *ether*. Tools make ether leaks and bottlenecks visible.

Functionality of Network Test Equipment

Although functionality of these tools overlaps somewhat, each of these four tools uncovers different types of network problems as follows: the *multitester* tests voltages and resistances to locate critical coaxial measurements that may indicate a break, a short, or faulty network hardware. The time domain reflectometer locates breaks, shorts, and similar cabling anomalies. The *transceiver tester*, sometimes called a *transceiver exerciser* by some vendors, finds badly installed or defective transceivers. The *protocol analyzer* or special network traffic-analysis software monitors network traffic at the software level and detects timing errors, nodes transmitting bad Ethernet packets, traffic overloading, and misrouted packets.

With a sufficient inventory of spare parts, it is possible to maintain a network with nothing except labor. Most network managers do not have the resources to interchange parts and pull new cable when something goes wrong, nor do they have the time or manpower to inspect each and every transceiver connection. Also, the range of possible problems is large but consists of small things; one small speck of metal can short a network and break it. While experience is sufficient for diagnosing most problems—indeed it is possible to function with none of these tools and lots of help—it is a slow process, ineffective when the network is saturated and users can't work. A single hour of downtime prevented can pay for these tools.

Multitester

The multitester is generally available and is inexpensive enough to purchase with petty cash. Figure 10.1 illustrates typical multitesters. The multitester is indispensable. Not only will this tool work on all versions of Ethernet, as well as with 50-ohm and 75-ohm and broadband coaxial cable, the multitester supplementally will indicate network status under all conditions when workstations or a protocol analyzer may not work. Quick tests should show no breaks or shorts in the coax cable, no large fluctuations at low voltages. Chapter 11 explains in detail how to use the multitester to check initial cable and transceiver tap installation, and how to debug a network when it is broken. The binary search method, an efficient method to gradually segment a broken network until a short or break is located, is also explained in Chapter 11.

 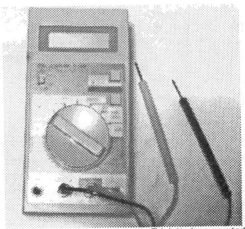

Triplett, Incorporated

Figure 10.1 A digital and an analog multitester.

Time Domain Reflectometer

As previously mentioned, the time domain reflectometer uncovers breaks, shorts, and similar cabling anomalies. Figure 10.2 shows a typical

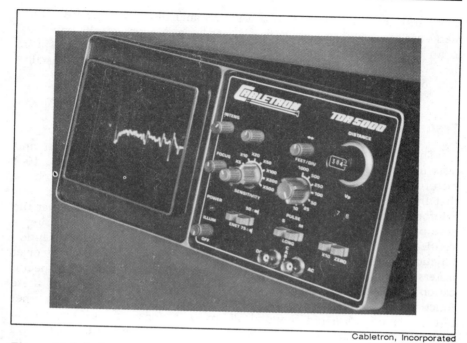

Cabletron, Incorporated

Figure 10.2 A time domain reflectometer with built-in oscilloscope.

time domain reflectometer packaged with a built-in oscilloscope. The oscilloscope graphically displays the electrical properties of a network coaxial cable over its entire length. A rheostat adjusts segment view width (from several hundred meters to several meters, for enlargements of a suspected segment) and a distance display indicates position of the segment view.

Time delay refers to the radar-like process employed to display the electrical properties of the coaxial cable thus eliminating the need for binary searches and the guessing required to locate coax cable problems. While the time domain reflectometer provides approximately the same functionality as the less expensive multitester, it offers a significant refinement: it *precisely* locates shorts, breaks, and other cable problems using the time delay inherent in any electrical radiation emission. The time domain reflectometer works with both 50- and 75-ohm Ethernet coax (and other networks utilizing baseband coaxial, twinaxial cable, or even twisted pair).

Some models of time domain reflectometer offer additional features unavailable with a multitester. For example, while testing with a multitester requires that a terminator be removed or a segment disconnected in order to test a (now) disfunctional network, the time domain reflectometer allows testing without disrupting the network. It acts as a network terminator and can remain connected to a network at all times, and will function concurrently with an operating network with minimal disruption. These refinements are crucial when a network is either large or economically important to an organization; at such times the time domain reflectometer will be perceived as a critical test instrument. Chapter 12 explicitly details installation, operation, and debugging techniques with this tool.

Transceiver Tester

The transceiver tester exercises all the features of a transceiver and tests for proper transceiver installation on the coaxial cable. Figure 10.3 pictures a full-functioned transceiver tester. While a multitester can check that the tap ground probes actually connect into the coaxial shield (this reinforces the need for a multitester), a multitester can't verify that the core probe is properly installed. The transceiver tester provides this simple verification and tests for proper network access, transmission and reception functionality, and heartbeat. Additionally, some models of transceiver testers verify that the transceiver drop cable connectors pin out to specification, and that this cable is correctly installed. While many of these functions could be checked pin for pin, function for function, with other test instruments, it is not economically practical for a network manager to be without a transceiver tester; the tool is accurate and fast. Chapter 13 specifies procedures for using this tool.

The Network Protocol Analyzer

The protocol analyzer verifies correct operation of Ethernet packet broadcast protocols (TCP/IP and vendor-specific network software) and indicates variances from specification. Figure 10.4 shows one such analyzer. A network manager is blind to network software transmission problems without traffic monitoring software. Often, vendors of workstations provide workstation-specific monitoring software. This software may prove adequate if the network is small or if all equipment on the system adheres to the same transmission standards. Otherwise, an analyzer is required.

If a network is fragmented, then few tools can test performance at every single node noninvasively. The inability to test for performance problems at any single node seriously limits the ability to pinpoint Ethernet bottlenecks. UNIX for example, if run over a network, adds many problems because of its basic design, and its stand-alone nature limits accessibility to other machines. Any utilities that capture performance information about single target nodes suffer two serious problems. First, they are invasive and require both network time and target machine time. Second, they change the load on the network by their very presence. Some commercially available stand-alone Ethernet protocol analyzers designed to overcome this inability fail in that they cannot capture and analyze every packet; and an analyzer may capture only every fifth packet whereas other units perform such tasks without requiring global network resources.

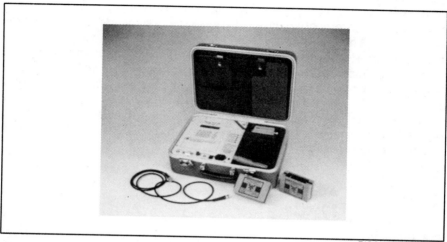

BICC, Incorportated

Figure 10.3 A full-functioned, portable transceiver tester.

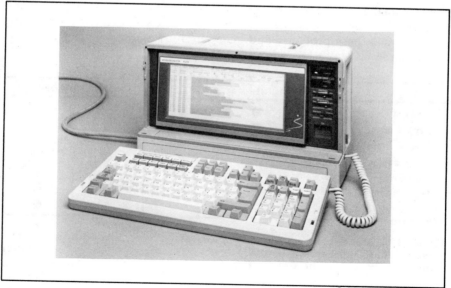

Spider Systems, Limited

Figure 10.4 A typical protocol analyzer.

The analyzer captures global and node-specific traffic-level information. Short, long, mistimed, and corrupted packets, or packets with bad checksums (CRC) are counted and captured for analysis. A full-featured analyzer will also capture all packets, or collect packets filtered by source, destination, and content. Built-in programs will help verify hypothesized problems. The protocol analyzer also operates independently of all other workstations. This yields a significant benefit over vendor-specific software; it is unbiased and shows a view of the network over time. Unlike either a multitester, time domain reflectometer, or transceiver tester, which only provide instantaneous views of the network, the analyzer functions without interruptions 24 hours per day and can indicate intermittent problems that are suspected but difficult to localize without constant supervision. Chapter 14 details the many additional features of a protocol analyzer and explains how to use this tool.

Network Tool Application

The Ethernet network is simple in design and assembly, while complex in actual daily operation as discussed in Chapter 9. The network manager faces hardware, software, and overloading problems. As of yet, no network has been designed free from installation, operational, and mechanical problems. Without these problems, there would be no justification for a network manager. The complexity of these problems and the ability of the network manager to solve them justify the existence of that job. Some problems will be camouflaged. It takes an astute manager and network team to trace these problems and maintain a functioning network. A good tool is surely a "can't be without."

	Multitester	TDR	Tester	Analyzer
Coaxial Cable	●	●		
Drop Cable	●	●	●	
Trans. Installation	•	●	●	
Transceiver	•	•	●	•
Controller				●
Node Level				●
Network Level				●

Figure 10.5 The overlapping functionality of network test equipment. The larger bullets indicates a primary testing function, whereas the smaller bullets indicate that the unit can provide minimal testing functions.

The four network test tools overlap functions. The questions will be, "Which tools do I need?" and "What is the best order in which to use

them?" This section provides some insight into the overlapping functionality and limitations of each tool. The individual chapters for each tool will
address these questions more specifically, and Chapter 21 will address
sequences for troubleshooting common network problems.

The multitester and time domain reflectometer provide approximately
the same information, although the time domain reflectometer additionally
locates exact position of a cabling variance. Some time domain reflectometer units feature a transmission mode to force properly functioning
transceivers to believe that the network is busy, thus by a process of
elimination will reveal defective units. Figure 10.5 shows the overlapping
functionality of the network test equipment.

The multitester shows the existence of global problems, while the time
domain reflectometer locates those problems. The transceiver tester is
node-specific and does not provide global information. Without intuition or
accurate information derived from the time domain reflectometer or protocol analyzer as to the location of a faulty transceiver, each and every node
must be tested with the transceiver tester. The protocol analyzer provides
strictly software information, revealing overloading, saturation, or software
flaws. However, in special cases performance statistics do pinpoint hardware problems. Figure 10.6 demonstrates when each tool is best utilized.

A multitester offers a quick first check when installing new segments of
cable or adding a transceiver unit. It is lightweight, and accurate when the
work window is known. A multitester is unsuitable when there is an annoying but nonfatal network problem, because complete use would require the
network to be segmented, and thus broken. In this case, the time domain
reflectometer is the tool of choice, because it is noninvasive.

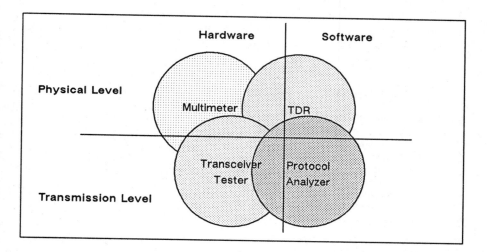

Figure 10.6 Network test equipment utilization.

The transceiver tester fully exercises a transceiver and its connecting drop cable. While a multitester can individually test for integrity each pin-out of the drop cable, each pin-out should be tested for shorting to every other pin-out. This is a factorial test (15*14*13*12...1) and a procedure better accomplished with a transceiver tester. While both a multitester and time domain reflectometer can verify that a transceiver is properly connected to the coax, neither can test full operational transceiver functionality. This includes the seven basic functions of the transceiver—transmission, reception, recognition of collision, test for signal, test for transmission, test for jam sequence, and test for the appropriate heartbeat configuration. This testing could be accomplished with a pair of locally connected test stations, although a transceiver tester is easier and probably less hardware-intensive.

The protocol analyzer duplicates some of the hardware functionality of the time domain reflectometer and transceiver tester. Faulty transmissions, chattering and jabbering transceivers, and transceivers that don't recognize a jam or a busy network would leave particles of packets for the analyzer to capture. Breaks in the cable would show as transmission dead spots if matched with network user complaints. Note the one limitation of the analyzer. Since it operates at the software level, any fatal network problem that prevents normal network transmission will usually render this tool blind. A fatal network problem indicates an electrical problem best uncovered with a time domain reflectometer first (or multitester if the time domain reflectometer is unavailable), and then a transceiver tester. The protocol analyzer monitors the network without constant human supervision; this means that intermittent problems can be observed. A hardware technician would not need to watch the multitester readout or the time domain oscilloscopic display for a 24-hour-period to discover that the evening cleaning crew is rattling the baseboards and shorting a faulty cable connection. The analyzer reveals these problems as time-stamped errors.

- Poor cable connections
- Improperly installed transceivers
- Faulty transceivers
- Faulty Ethernet controllers
- Improperly configured network
- Excessive network traffic
- Overloaded node devices
- Overloaded servers
- Improperly configured software
- Defective software
- Overlapping network addresses

Figure 10.7 Network failures uncovered by network test equipment.

Additionally, the multitester, the time domain reflectometer, and the transceiver tester only provide insight into hardware errors. As the ISO communication model of Chapter 3 indicates, software causes at least half the problems. Network overloading, transmission protocol errors, and transmission broadcast errors could not be perceived without software monitoring, as provided by the protocol analyzer.

Ethernet can fail to perform for a variety of reasons, as shown by the sampling in Figure 10.7. Any single reason can severely effect the overall response time on the network, and a problem with a single node can effect another node on Ethernet, even though the resources they share may be limited to the coaxial cable. An overloaded file server, for example, could request repaging and continuous transmittal of information. These requests require resources that would otherwise be available to others, and therefore effect others on the network. There are a few tools available that allow network performance monitoring; these tools are explored in detail in the next four chapters.

Chapter 11

Debugging with the Multitester

This chapter describes the multitester, its functions, when it should be used, and what alternatives exist to this tool. Furthermore, since the multitester is the simplest and most readily available test instrument, it is indispensable, and becomes the tool of choice for most network managers.

Figure 11.1 A digital multitester (test leads not shown).

Multitester

The multitester is a test instrument that measures voltages, amperages, and resistance. Two probes connect to the component for an electrical test. Figure 11.1 shows a typical digital multitester and the test leads. An analog version is just as effective. Since resistance and voltages are most often tested with this tool, it is often called an *ohmmeter* or *voltmeter*, or even *multimeter*.

Ethernet requires 50-ohm terminators at each end of the network. A network usually fails for less identifiable reasons than a missing terminator, hence the need for network tools, including the multitester. Most Ethernet documentation suggests that you check that terminators are actually installed when the network fails. Because Ethernet will not function without terminators, this type of failure would be an infrequent event, and if it occurs, can be visually confirmed. Once installed, terminators stay in place until purposely removed.

A multitester enables one to see if the network falls within proper electrical bounds. Breaks, shorts, faulty transceivers, and tears and cuts in the cable shield alter coaxial cable resistance and the electrical properties of the network. On installation first test resistance as Figure 11.2 illustrates. Also, if convenient, check the two ends of the core and shield separately for continuity; if there is no resistance, then there is no complete circuit.

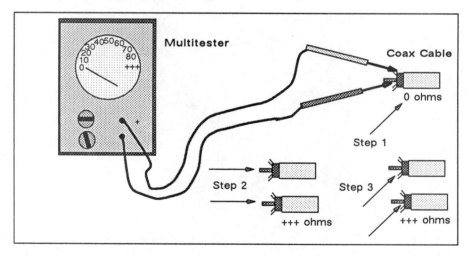

Figure 11.2 Testing the coax cable endpoints with the multitester. Three separate tests should be performed on a raw coaxial cable. The first step is to check the center conductor and the shield. No voltage should pass (the multitester should indicate a discontinuity, that is, no connection). The second step is to check both ends of the center conductor for continuity. The multitester should show no resistance (that is, open circuit). The third step is also a continuity test; check the braided shield from both ends. The multitester should show no resistance (that is, open circuit).

Check the coax cable for shorts and breaks. The next test after the end connectors are installed, a more general test, is pictured in Figure 11.3.

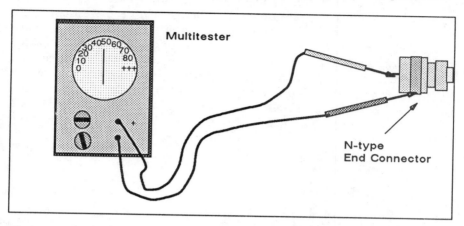

Figure 11.3 Testing the coax cable endpoints with the multitester after the end connector has been installed.

The multitester should show 50 ohms on a transceiver-less network with a terminator installed, less than 50 ohms on a quiet network with transceivers installed because each transceiver in parallel lowers the coaxial cable resistance, and approximately 70 ohms on a functioning network as demonstrated by Figure 11.4. There is little resistance increase or impedance loss on a 500-meter maximum length network. There is, however, signal dissipation over segments as short as 80 meters (260 feet) which, if excessive, will cause poor reception. This signal dissipation is the reason some marginal transceivers may not work correctly, and also why signal repeaters are installed on networks longer than 500 meters.

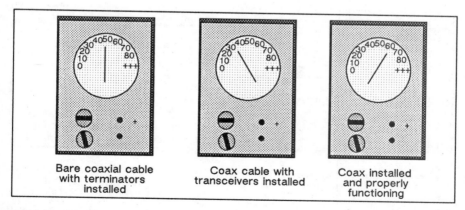

Figure 11.4 The proper parameters for a functioning Ethernet network.

Alternatively, a transceiver tap can be removed or a tap hole drilled for a parallel test of network resistance. Resistance will differ in a parallel test from a check at the end of a cable section; a bare network should exhibit 25 ohms, for example, because of the additive nature of resistance. As Figure 11.5 demonstrates, several garment-type pins can reach the coax shield and access both core conductor and shield grounds without breaking the network. The test probes usually have too large a diameter, and are too bulky to reach. One alternative, if the multitester is used specifically on the Ethernet, is to grind the probe tips thin and sharp. Otherwise, narrow-gauge wire inserted into the tap holes or the pins, as illustrated, is adequate for this type of check. This parallel test obviates the need for breaking the network at a barrel connector or terminator.

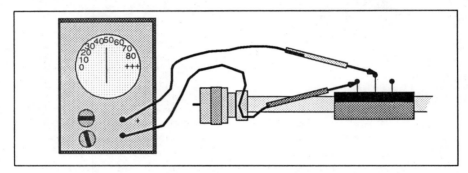

Figure 11.5 Noninvasive check of the network through a transceiver tap.

Note again that when the terminators are removed, the network stops because the Ethernet packet waves are not absorbed by the end terminator and reflect back onto the network causing transceivers to sense a constantly "busy network."

	Minimum	Maximum
Resistance		
Ethernet	17 ohms	72 ohms
Thinnet	17 ohms	72 ohms
Cheapernet	17 ohms	72 ohms
Voltage		
Ethernet 2.or IEEE 802.3	−0.7 volts	0.7 volts
Ethernet 1.0	−0.7 volts	0.0 volts
Thinnet	−0.7 volts	0.7 volts
Cheapernet	−0.7 volts	0.7 volts

Figure 11.6 Correct network electrical values. While there is a wide range of resistance, in practice the range between 30 and 60 ohms is appropriate on an active network. It may be unrealistic to track voltages. There should be no load on a quiescent network, and when the network is active, voltages change in 50 milliseconds, rendering most test instruments useless.

As explained in Chapter 4, the voltages are $\pm$ 0.7 volts and the range is 18–78 ohms. Figure 11.6 summarizes the proper measurements.

Testing Procedures

If resistance is higher than 70 ohms on a functioning network, a transceiver is defective and jabbering. Resistance less than 40 ohms usually implies a cabling short. A short between the copper core and the braided jacket would register as no resistance, 0 ohms as in Figure 11.7. Such a short could be intermittent and phrases like "it's a witch hunt" are not unlikely to be muttered by frustrated network managers.

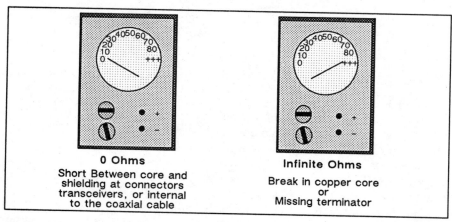

0 Ohms
Short Between core and shielding at connectors transceivers, or internal to the coaxial cable

Infinite Ohms
Break in copper core
or
Missing terminator

Figure 11.7 Ohm values on a malfunctioning network.

Another common multitester procedure is to verify proper installation of a transceiver tap. The shield probes should demonstrate a common connection, whereas the center probe of the tap should be electrically isolated from both shield pins. If core and shield probes show continuity, the center probe is shorting because the tap was improperly drilled.

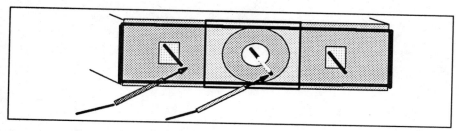

Figure 11.8 Tap installation check. The multitester should show correctly approximately 23 to 28 ohms on a working network. A short at the center tap will yield a reading at 0 ohms, but will show a discontinuity if the tap is not installed deeply enough.

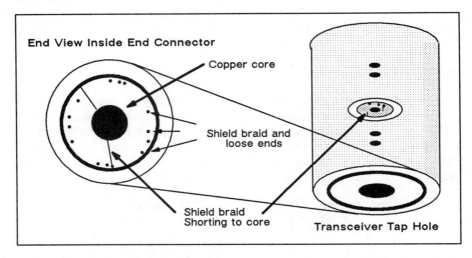

End View Inside End Connector

Copper core

Shield braid and
loose ends

Shield braid
Shorting to core

Transceiver Tap Hole

Figure 11.9 Typical causes for cable shorts are stray wires from the shield.

Another indication of a successful installation is a reading of approximately 25 ohms when the center probe is compared to a shield probe. This reading reflects the two terminators on the network segment; minor variations from this reading indicate other transceivers installed correctly on the cable or Ethernet packets if the network is a functioning network. Figure 11.8 illustrates transceiver tap testing after it has been secured to the cable and the probes inserted through the cable shield and sheath.

Causes of shorts are either kinks in the cable causing breaks through the insulation, or poorly installed taps. Also, a poor tap hole could cause a tap probe to contact both core and shield braid. Another possibility is a poorly installed end connector. If the braided shield is not carefully isolated from the copper core inside the end connector—even one fine strand of braid is enough—the network will fail. Shorts at a poorly installed transceiver or end connector (N-type) occur for the reasons depicted by Figure 11.9.

Intermittent shorts are usually caused by the mechanical fluctuations in the coaxial cable or in the AUI cables. Such stress could be caused by vibrations from a passing elevator, nearby construction work, flexing from a floor or ceiling, cables that are not tied securely, overheating in the wiring plenum, or simply changes in plenum temperature during the course of the workday. Intermittent failures are best isolated with a binary search.

Binary Network Search

The *binary search* method saves time by progressively partitioning the network in a logical and economical pattern until a problem is localized. This *halving* approach is generally undertaken when specialized network test equipment is unavailable. For example, when a protocol analyzer is not available, a transceiver tester and the binary search method can identify faulty components, or when a time domain reflectometer is unavailable, a multitester and the binary search method can be employed to locate a cable break or short. This method is also highly effective with the multitester for tracking down annoying, intermittent shorts and breaks.

The binary search method, like a binary sort routine, is more efficient when there is no a priori information about the job that must be done; if the answer is already known or some intuitive guesses can uncover it, patterned approaches like the binary search become unnecessary. When a network is broken and such first guesses prove inaccurate, the binary search is most efficient. If the network is broken, segment the network at a midpoint. Terminate each segment properly and test each half. One half should now function correctly. The broken half is now segmented in half

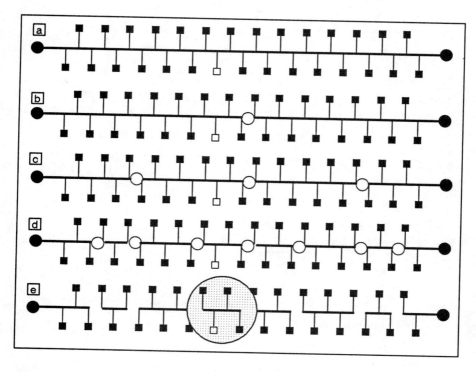

Figure 11.10 The binary search method. Network segment (a) is halved forming two sections (b). This is again halved forming four segments (c). If this process is continued, the network will have eight segments (d). (e) replicates (d), but more clearly shows the individual sections. In actual practice, the network manager would only search those sections that indicate fault, and reconnect all segments still operational. The section with four nodes should be isolated enough for identification of the defect, which in this case is a bad tap.

again, and each quarter is correctly terminated. One of the quarter segments should function correctly. The other, broken quarter contains the problem. If the broken segment of the network is still too large, this process would be continued until the break is effectively isolated. Figure 11.10 demonstrates this technique for intermittent problems; the period might be hours—or extended to days.

If the network is a single continuous cable, this is a good time to cut and reconnect the network into barrel-connected segments. As stated in installation sections of Chapter 7, segment lengths of 23.4 meters (or multiples thereof) are recommended. Cut the coaxial cable, install the end connectors, and terminate the segments. Later, barrel connectors will replace each pair of terminators and recouple the segments. See Figure 11.11 for a description of this resourceful step.

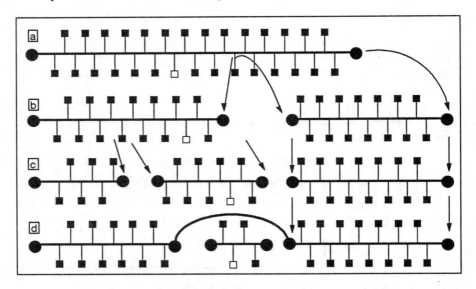

Figure 11.11 Locating and isolating the faulty network component. If the search for a faulty component, a break, or short started from the left end of the Ethernet segment, thirteen electrical tests would be required. Furthermore, if the fault were not a tap unit, sequential testing would not isolate the fault. The halving method reduces this search to three checks to isolate the problem, and two tests position the electrical problem. As (d) shows, the network manager could bypass the defective section to provide partial network service until the fault is isolated.

If a network coax were 500 meters long, were built from a single continuous segment of cable, and had a full complement of transceivers, there would be a minimum of 104 electrical connections (100 transceivers, two end connectors, and two terminators). If screw-in transceivers or Cheapernet drops are installed, there could be 404 electrical connections (100 pairs of end connectors and 100 pairs of transceiver connections, plus two each of the end connectors fitted with terminators). A sequential search implies either a maximum of 104 tests, or a maximum of 404 checks in the more extensive configurations. The search lasts until the problem is solved. An average search could require 52 tests *if* it is certain that a transceiver or connector is the fault. If there is no hint a cable might have been severed, cut, or shorting because the foam insulation has failed, consequently there are no search limits on a sequential search. The binary search minimizes this searching with an efficient algorithm, and solves the problem sooner in the following sequence: 104 connections first suspected are reduced to 52. The 52 connections are halved to 26 connections. These are reduced again to 12, finally to 6, to 3, to 2, and finally to the one unit. Obviously, a power of two could be a more efficient search pattern (from 100 to 64, to 32 to 16 and to 8, and then to 4 to 2 to 1), although the real world may not readily agree on which search pattern is the most efficient. An average search count of 52 is reduced very efficiently to eight tests. That is numerically an 85% reduction, but we assume that this method will yield only a 50% time savings because the network will not always be segmented in a geographically advantageous manner (that is, inaccessible between floors, between buildings, above hallways). This *halving* technique is practical as Figure 11.12 shows.

| | | Required Number of Tests | |
	# connections	Conventional Search	Binary Search
500 Meter Coaxial Cable			
two end connectors	2		
two terminators	2		
100 transceivers	100		
# electrical connections	104	104	8
Average # searches until problem solved		52	6
Average # searches if cable electrical problems		no limits	6

Figure 11.12 The binary search method is time-effective.

The binary search technique is best used when the network is already broken and provides no network service since this technique will halt most (or all) network service. A break in the coaxial cable, or a short between core and shield as in the example used above, chattering transceivers, a network overloaded by one or several nodes, poorly connected taps, or nodes with faulty drop cables, are all network problems that can be solved more efficiently by using the binary search method. Electrical shorts and breaks can be identified with the multitester and located with the binary search method. Hardware problems with more complicated components need to be identified with more sophisticated tools like the time domain reflectometer, the transceiver tester, or protocol analyzer, although faults can be located with this same technique. The next chapters show a methodology for isolating transceiver and network node with software faults.

A multitester is an inexpensive and simple tool for diagnosing a network problem. It is easy to carry in a toolbox given its low cost, compact size, and light weight. It is safe to use, because it will introduce no new problems into the network. The multitester's major disadvantage is that a terminator must be removed or the network must be broken for testing. While the multitester will work even under the most severe network problems, it will not show *where* the problem is located without excessive trial and error. When time is money, the time domain reflectometer is superior to the multitester. Not only will the time domain reflectometer show shorts and breaks, it will show the precise location of the problem. The next chapter enumerates the benefits of the time domain reflectometer.

Chapter 12

Debugging with the Time Domain Reflectometer

This chapter describes the time domain reflectometer, its history, its functions, when it should be used, and what alternatives exist to this tool. The time domain reflectometer (TDR) supersedes the multitester because it can provide the same electrical feedback as the multitester. In addition, it will precisely locate the cabling short or break relative to a cable endpoint. Furthermore, this test instrument when used in conjunction with a camera can blueprint a network. This aids in debugging the all-too-common network failure. The TDR locates coaxial cable perforations, coaxial cable shorts, and can identify an electrically defective transceiver.

Time Domain Reflectometer

Figure 12.1 shows a photograph of a typical unit. This unit contains no oscilloscope display, a TV-like screen which displays a trace curve on a grid, as some units often do. The technique applied by this tool was developed in the early fifties for locating cabling breaks in high-tension wires. The TDR was further refined specifically for use in tracing cable television broadband problems. It was used to locate shorts, breaks, cable impedance variances and overloads on city-wide installations, but has been modified for use in baseband and broadband computer communication environments; the problems encountered are identical.

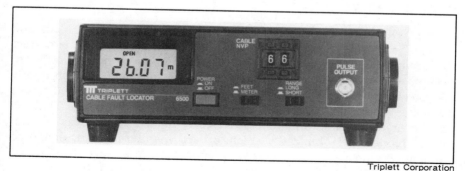

Triplett Corporation

Figure 12.1 A typical time domain reflectometer.

How to Use the TDR

The TDR unit connects onto the network in place of a terminator. A good unit will act as a terminator when disabled or powered off, and thus can remain connected onto the network at all times. It is an important tool in a crisis when a network fails completely. At such times few other tools, especially network software tools which depend on a functioning network, can operate; only noncomputer, nonsoftware tools operate when a network is broken. The TDR operates somewhat like radar. It sends a negative two-volt signal pulse down the network as illustrated in Figure 12.2.

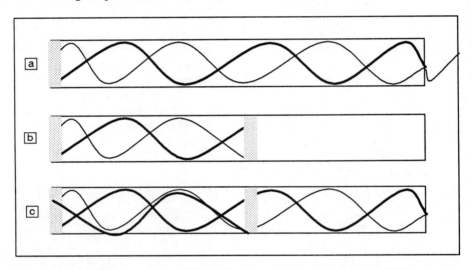

Figure 12.2 Anomalies in the cabling are visible on the TDR. (a)A missing terminator is represented; (b) shows a break in the core, whereas (c) shows a short between the core and the braided shielding.

Propagation Velocity

The TDR must be set for signal propagation velocity, cable ohms and voltage, and signal degradation over distance. Be sure to set the correct propagation velocity for the cable you are testing. Pulses travel at different rates on different cable types, on different ages of cable, and on poorly built networks. Thicknet is approximately 76–78% of light speed where Thinnet is 65–68% of light speed. Measurements displayed by the TDR will be inaccurate if this information is not correctly set. Thicknet is 50-ohm cable, Thinnet is 75-ohm cable which, except when terminated, should be tested at 50 ohms as well. Voltage is DC, and within the ranges of ±2 volts.

Interpreting Results

All obstructions reflect the signal with various signatures which are read from an oscilloscope or numerical display. These signatures must be learned as their interpretation is an art. Transceivers, terminators, end connectors and barrel connections, repeaters, different grades and ages of cable, and, of course, breaks and shorts in the cable are visible in the oscilloscope display. Otherwise, these anomalies are visible as deviations from the normal numerical display. Transceivers show as distinct sine wave patterns, end connectors and barrel connectors show as traffic control bumps, and the terminators show as dead spots and a cessation of signal. See Figures 12.3 through 12.7 for samples of TDR oscilloscope results.

Breaks caused by over-bending cable and cuts through the core, or radio interference from powerful sources (such as transmitters, high-intensity lamps, other electrical cables) show as large bends, spikes, and kinks in the display. Faulty transceivers show up as a wave form different from that of a functioning transceiver—it usually lacks a large spike. If nonstandard or old cable is inserted to replace a defective or damaged section of cable, the TDR will show this with a large pulse deflection. The test pulse wave will reflect with a dramatic difference in height, and with sufficient art one can interpret these deviations.

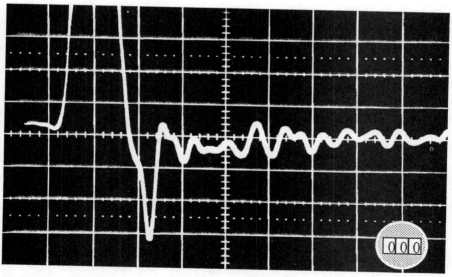

Figure 12.3 TDR display of a quiet network. The reticule grid, the lines that run through the middle of the oscilloscope display vertically and horizontally, is set at 000 meters. Each horizontal grid line is about a meter. The large spike to the left side represents the six-meter (20-foot) test lead. The two small "r–shaped" bumps equidistant from the center grid are transceivers. No problems are shown in this display. Location of transceiver is 6.5 meters (1.8 feet) from the terminator.

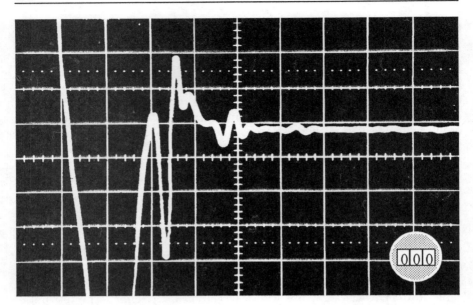

Figure 12.4 TDR display of a break in the cable. The break shows as the "u-shaped" line that runs off the display. Shorts are identical in shape, but appear upside down as "n-shaped" lines.

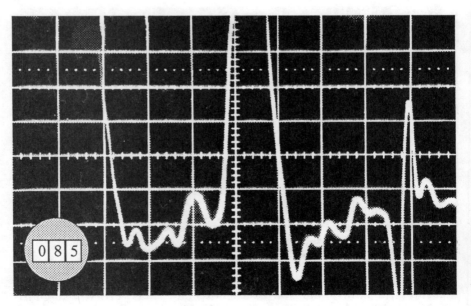

Figure 12.5 TDR display of missing terminator at 85 meters. The spike at the far right is a false reflection caused by the TDR signal striking air. The display would show a flat line to the right of the center scale if the air offered no impedance.

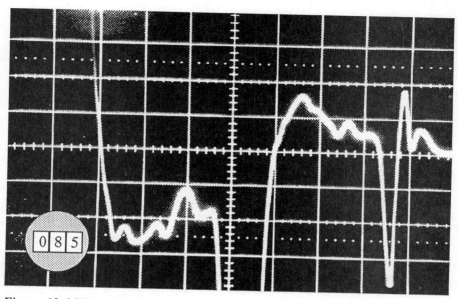

Figure 12.6 TDR display of a short in the vicinity of the distant terminator (at 85 meters). As in Figure 12.5, the spike at the far right is a false reflection and has the same structure as the image in the photograph in this figure. The display would show a flat line to the right of the center reticule, if the air offered no impedance.

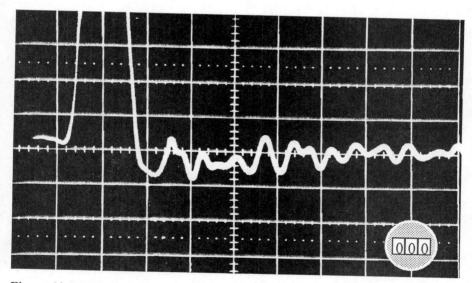

Figure 12.7 TDR display of a missing transceiver (pins could be improperly aligned to edge connector, bent, broken, or missing). Note that this may not be observable via the TDR directly. Instead, a missing transceiver would show up with a deviation from the expected wave pattern.

The oscilloscope CRT also shows distance to the anomaly which is overlaid in the photographic samples. If the cable is measured at installation time and properly blueprinted, any anomaly such as that shown in Figure 12.3 can be quickly dispatched. For example, if the TDR indicated a break at 6 meters (20 feet), it is a safe bet that the end connector was partially unscrewed when the terminator was removed. The TDR lead cable is probably 2 to 10 meters (6 to 30 feet) long, and the display indicates a break at an unlikely location. A short at that distance would imply that an end connector is improperly installed and that shield braids are shorting to the core, or that there is dirt in the fitting itself. Likewise, if the TDR showed a similar problem at 200 meters on a blueprinted 200 meter coaxial cable, this would be another clue that the distant end connector probably was partially unscrewed thus shorting the coaxial cable when the terminator was removed. Figure 12.5 pictures this common installation problem.

As another example, if the display indicated the network length is longer than specified, an end terminator is missing at the end of the network distant from the TDR. A second indication of this situation is a display that is upside down beyond the blueprinted network length as Figure 12.6 indicates. This happens because the wave strikes the end of the cable, finds a medium with a different transmission quality, and reflects back down the cable inversely as shown. This is similar to the transmission characteristics of light when it passes from one medium, like air, through another medium, like glass, and back into air. Depending on the reflective angle of incidence, the image will be deflected. A mirror image occurs at the ninety-degree deflection of an improperly terminated cable.

Figure 12.8 Photograph of the bent probes inside a tap housing.

Figure 12.7 is identical to Figure 12.3 except for a single missing sine wave curve that represents a transceiver that is not physically connected to the network. Transceiver electronics alter the resistance and impedance of the network coaxial cable in a characteristic pattern. This situation will be evident when an older photograph is compared to the current oscilloscope display. Figure 12.8 illustrates how the tap probe could be bent causing just this fault. The tap probe pins, center probe, and ground shield probes are bent and will not align with the connector inside the transceiver casing.

Other shapes produced by the TDR generally fall into a limited number of categories. Figures 12.9 and 12.10 show readouts as generally found on a functioning network. Not only will each type of connecting mechanism and transceiver tap unit appear different, the many different types of coaxial cable problems will yield characteristic properties based upon their affect upon the cable impedance. A short circuit would show a negative pulse, whereas an open circuit would show a positive pulse. Changes in cable impedance do not necessarily imply that the network will not function. The deviations need to be significant enough to exceed the Ethernet limitations. Parallel capacitance (evident at a transceiver tap or a cable connector) is a negative pulse followed by a positive pulse. Series inductance (evident as a scrape or break through the cable shield) shows as a positive pulse followed by a negative pulse. The last common wave form shows that the network cable impedance is out of specification as would happen when improper cable is installed. A series of alternating pulses would suggest this problem.

Figure 12.9

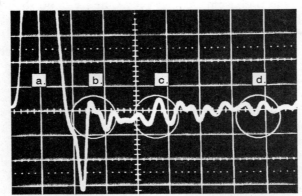

Element (a) is the TDR image caused by coupled coaxial cable with different transmission characteristics. Element (b) is an AMP tap unit and transceiver. Element (c) is a TCL tap and transceiver. Element (d) is the characteristic pattern of two N-type connectors and a barrel connector.

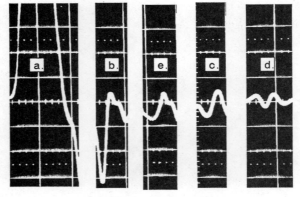

Compare elements (b) and (e). Both are characteristic traces of AMP taps, although (e) is missing a transceiver as shown by the incomplete negative spike.

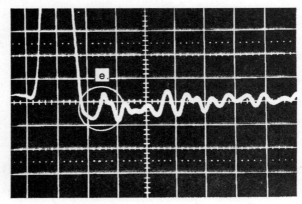

Figure 12.10

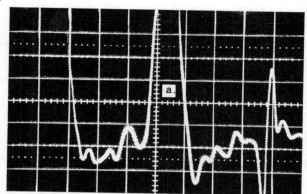

The oscilloscope display above is a coaxial segment 85 meters from the TDR. The missing terminator appears to be similar to a cable break. The trace for the missing terminator appears as a convex spike (a), while the trace for an open break would appear as a double spike (b) if the display were readjusted.

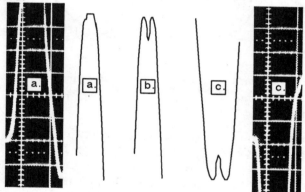

The oscilloscope display below shows a cabling short (c). The concave spike is identical to the cabling break, although flipped vertically. If the trace were centered in the oscilloscope display a double spike would appear.

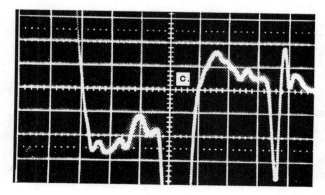

The TDR supersedes the multitester because it accurately positions the problem. There are also certain problems that cannot be diagnosed by just a multitester with any immediacy. These include bad cable, faulty transceivers, radio interference, and poorly specified cable or mismatched sections of cable. While a multitester will identify that one of these problems exists, it will not pinpoint the problem so that it can be categorized and diagnosed. Without a TDR, the course of action would be to segment the network progressively until the problem is localized sufficiently. Unless sections of cable are barrel-connected, the cable would need to be physically cut, and new end connectors and barrel connectors installed to provide access with the multitester and to restore the cable to later operation. Remember that the cable is best segmented in 23.4-meter (76.8-feet) intervals. The time requirement for such a search is excessive and demonstrates why the TDR is the tool of choice.

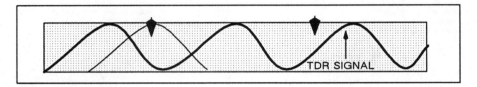

Figure 12.11 The slim line illustrates the faulty operation of a transceiver. The left transceiver broadcast because it has not recognized the carrier sense signal. The right transceiver interprets the TDR signal correctly and acknowledges it as a "busy" signal.

A full featured TDR will also send negative two volt pulses continuously down the network coaxial cable as illustrated in Figure 12.11. This constant pulse will signal to all the transceivers that the network is busy. Each time a transceiver tries to transmit, it will see a network busy signal, and randomly retry. If all transceivers and Ethernet cards (which are installed in the backplane of the workstation, mainframe, or PC) are sound, the TDR will show a picture identical to that of the network with no functioning users; a flooded network will appear identical to a quiescent network.

If the oscilloscope shows a fluttering line as in Figure 12.12, at least one or more transceivers or Ethernet cards are ignoring the busy signal and continuing to transmit. This is indicative of high collision rates (a problem investigated with other tools). A collision rate above 2% is a software indication of a jabbering transceiver or a network exceeding length specifications. A network can function with collision rates above 10%; it is slow and cumbersome at those levels.

While jabber can be diagnosed with the TDR, there is no clever means to locate faulty transceivers or Ethernet cards with the TDR. As with a multitester, more complex problems require more complex tools. In this case, a software/hardware problem requires more than a hardware solution. This is best located with a transceiver tester combined with software tools. When a tester and suitable software tools are unavailable, one approach to locate jabbering transceivers is to shut down nodes one-by-one until the TDR shows no fluttering; the last system removed from the network is jabbering and causing the signal pulses, and is defective. This process will need to be repeated for each defective node. This is an N-Factorial search.* This process will not determine whether the card or the transceiver is the defective element. Replacing them until the problem is fixed is one way to identify the offending component. Software testing and hardware testing of individual elements are more efficient means to ascertain fault.

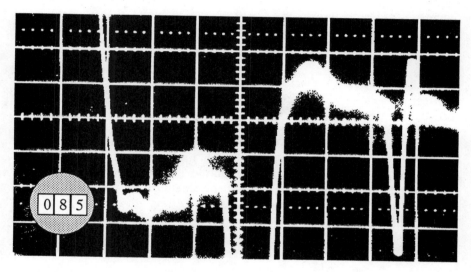

Figure 12.12 The TDR oscilloscope display when a transceiver chatters. Note that the trace line jiggles leaving a blur trace. The TDR will not identify which transceiver unit is at fault, although a binary search as outlined for use with a multitester is effective. A more practical approach to locate the defective transceiver requires a protocol analyzer.

Binary Network Search

The last chapter explained the binary search method when electrical malfunctions disrupt the network coaxial cable. It also alluded to other uses for this technique. The TDR can indicate that a defective transceiver is saturating the network with false signals as explained above; it cannot, unfortunately, position that failed unit. A protocol analyzer could exactly

---

* With 100 nodes and 5 faulty transceivers, the worst case search would require 100*99*98*97*96 steps. If all nodes are shut down and the signal continues to flutter, a node has been overlooked, high-intensity radio is disrupting the network, or there is a hidden guest on the network. Otherwise, as a last resort, suspect the TDR.

locate a failed transceiver by the trail of fragmented Ethernet packets (only if the failed transceiver hasn't broken the network). If a network monitor is unavailable, or that worst case scenario of a broken network occurs, the binary search method is the most effective localizing technique.

The TDR will indicate signal flutter when the network is saturated with a two-volt signal. Break the network into halves and terminate each segment properly. Retest each segment and isolate the problem. Continue halving the network until the transceiver unit can be identified and removed from service. Realistically, the halving procedure may be implemented along separate floors, buildings, or some other geographic division. This is, of course, natural, and while not numerically as efficient as a true binary halving, it will quickly isolate a failed node transmitter.

Blueprinting

The Time Domain Reflectometer is one of the best available instruments to affect physical network blueprinting. The TDR in conjunction with a film recorder or screen camera can illustrate the internal workings of the network coax. All terminators, connectors, and taps and transceivers can be photographed and documented with a relative network location. These photographs form a record against which future problems can be compared, unknown transceivers can be spotted. It is a map of permanence. Figure 12.13 demonstrates the type of information that could be logically included in a careful blueprinting. Figure 12.14 shows a representative cabling blueprint with notations.

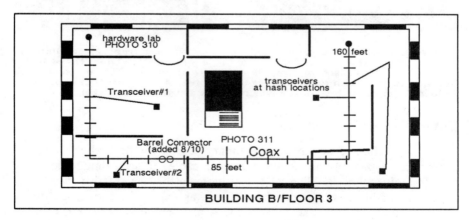

Figure 12.13 Blueprint supplements the TDR photographs.

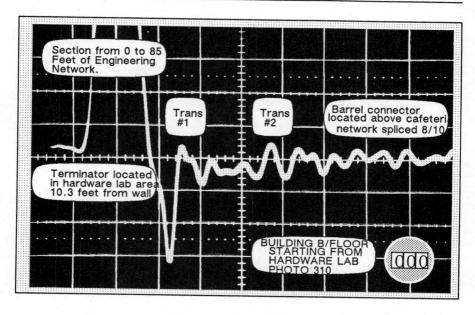

Figure 12.14 This annotated instant photograph shows network documentation appropriate for a careful blueprinting. The photograph is numbered and all hardware is designated. This photograph matches the blueprint in Figure 12.13. If network fails, a current TDR oscilloscope display would be compared to this photograph, and the differences would be apparent.

The TDR locates breaks, shorts, and indicates the occasional chattering transceiver. For more precise hardware verification of faulty transceiver operation, a transceiver tester is the required test instrument. The next chapter details the use of this tool, and how it works. For more precise verification of network software errors, the protocol analyzer is the tool of choice. The workings of this instrument are described fully in Chapter 14.

Chapter 13

Debugging with the Transceiver Tester

This chapter explains the transceiver tester, what it should do, how to use it, and how to integrate this tool into the network tool kit. Unlike the multitester, which is inexpensive and readily available, and the TDR, which is expensive and optional, the transceiver tester is an expensive necessity. This device provides the only practical method for testing a transceiver besides trial and error component replacement.

Transceiver Tester

The transceiver tester is another tool crucial for diagnosing and locating network problems. A transceiver tester will run a transceiver through several tests. There should be several modes of operation to test the transceiver both installed on a network and off-network. A good tester will also test a transceiver drop cable (AUI cable) and verify that pin-out is correct. It checks that the transceiver cable is correctly grounded, something which is often overlooked. This tool is commercially available from a number of sources. It could also be built. Figure 13.1 presents a home-made unit powered by a battery and constructed from a transceiver.

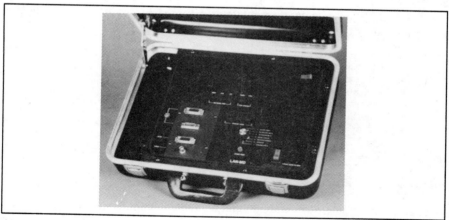

Cabletron Systems, Incorporated

Figure 13.1 A typical Ethernet transceiver tester.

189

The transceiver exerciser is available in many formats. Some are powered from an installed transceiver and access the power from the coaxial cable. Others require small batteries, or plug into a wall socket. The latter variety are very inconvenient in that each test could possibly require correct installation of a transceiver cable *and* the electrical power cable. The battery-powered versions are lightweight and portable, and test full performance of the transceiver. Figure 13.2 outlines the functionality of a transceiver tester.

- Test continuity of AUI cable
- Test correct installation of transceiver:
  - center probe contacting coax cable
  - center probe shorting to braided shield
  - shield ground probes in place
  - AUI cable functioning
  - AUI cable grounded
  - transceiver heartbeat (or no heartbeat)
  - transceiver defers to collisions and busy signals

Figure 13.2 Functionality of a transceiver tester.

A digital or analog readout provides feedback for each test. The transceiver tester will test for proper installation of a transceiver, whether it is shorting out a network or is properly connected to the copper core of the coaxial cable, or whether the drop cable is correctly attached to the transceiver cable connector. While a node may function and provide network access and service for an individual workstation, that node may chatter and jabber on the network, or may function intermittently, consequently increasing the network collision rate for all other workstations. Such a hidden hardware problem becomes visible as a network grows in node count, or as the volume of traffic increases. Figure 13.3 lists the common failures discovered by a transceiver tester.

- Misspecificied hardware
- Bad installation
- Bad transceiver drop cable pinout
- Cross-wired cable
- Jabbering transceivers
- Chattering transceivers
- No SQE
- Voltage level errors

Figure 13.3 A transceiver tester locates these failures.

Rapid network growth may propel a highly acceptable network into the realm of "Why did we ever install Ethernet in the first place?" This type of failure is statistical, and is best solved with information as provided by a test instrument. The coax cable, because of its length, also acts as an antenna. Therefore, an important test performed by the transceiver tester is called the *loop-back* verification, or *self-test*. Such a test effectively verifies proper installation of a transceiver.

Using the Transceiver Tester

The tester attaches to a transceiver or drop cable either on the network or off the network. How the different components actually attach to the tester depends on the design of the unit. Both cable ends attach directly to the tester in order to test the continuity and conductivity and pin-out of the transceiver drop cable. The transceiver attaches to the tester via its transceiver cable connector. Testing encompasses no more than switching on the tester and interpreting the results.

Binary Network Search

The last chapter explained the binary search method with a multitester when a faulty transceiver chattered on the network coaxial cable. It also alluded to other uses for this technique. The transceiver tester can indicate a defective transceiver or misconnected drop cable; it cannot, unfortunately, position that failed unit any more than a TDR can locate a chattering unit. A protocol analyzer could exactly locate a failed transceiver by the trail of fragmented Ethernet packets (provided that the failed transceiver hasn't broken the network). If a network monitor is unavailable, or in that worst case scenario of a broken network, the binary search method is the most effective localizing technique. While the TDR is useful for locating intermittent problems and while it might indicate several potential problems, without this binary method, solving a global network problem might necessitate time-consuming individual testing of each unit on the entire network.

Break the network into halves and terminate each segment properly. Test each segment until the problem is isolated. Continue halving the network until the faulty transceiver unit can be identified and removed from service. Realistically, the halving procedure may be implemented between separate floors, between buildings, or by some other geographic division. This is, of course, natural, and while not numerically as efficient as a true binary halving, it will quickly isolate a failed node transmitter or drop cable for confirmation with the transceiver tester.

As elsewhere, blind interchange of parts, installation of redundant or parallel parts, and the progressive isolation of suspected problems undoubtedly will uncover the specific location of problems. However, traffic monitoring software provides a powerful approach to problem solving.

Chapter 14

Debugging with the Protocol Analyzer

The last three chapters explained how to test the mechanical layers of Ethernet. The multitester and TDR test cable for proper functioning, and the transceiver tester verifies proper operation of transceivers. This bag of tools is limited to resolving hardware problems on single segment Ethernet networks; few tools provide much insight into malfunctions on multi-segment networks. Many network failures can be traced to software that transcends the physical layers of Ethernet, network loading characteristics, and *firmware*, which is software loaded into a specialized hardware processor. Additionally, the process of locating intermittent shorts or failures with hardware testers is a random proposition. Such failures require more analytical techniques and a different network monitoring tool. A generic network monitor, also called a *protocol analyzer*, is the right tool for locating intermittent shorts or failures. It provides information to solve network problems. The protocol analyzer collects network traffic data, reports the status of many different variables and converts them into statistics, and has an analyzer with a sophisticated statistical package that can chart numerical results for visual analysis. The protocol analyzer confirms perceived performance degradation with hard evidence.

Protocol Analyzer

The protocol analyzer is a computer workstation that is a network node. It requires transceiver access through a single tap of a multiport unit. The analyzer can send and receive Ethernet packets just like any other workstation. Figure 14.1 shows one such unit. The analyzer watches the network for all Ethernet packets, not just for signals directed to its node. The protocol analyzer is said to be *promiscuous* because it eavesdrops on all nodes on the network. It is a complicated tool. Commensurate with this complexity, it provides detailed information to trace complicated problems.

A protocol analyzer listens to the signal on the local network and finds a packet with known source and destination. It must also listen and identify jam, collision, and backoff signals on the local network. Furthermore, this tool must be able to identify packets derived from and destined for remote

Hewlett-Packard

Figure 14.1 A protocol analyzer.

gateways. Anonymous packets must be filtered and captured for analysis and eventual problem resolution.

An Ethernet network carries traffic for many different purposes as outlined in Figure 14.2. The consistency of traffic varies by load rate, by source and destination, and by peak characteristics. Control of the network and proper management require an understanding of the flow of information. Since hardware testers only indicate the status of the physical plant, another tool like the protocol analyzer provides input for network use, load, consistency, resources distribution and *implied* resource allocation decisions.

Network Information

A stand-alone protocol analyzer dedicated only to the task of watching the network is an important tool for network maintenance and evaluation. Since Ethernet communications is a statistical process (it is a nondeterministic, and hence probabilistic medium as described in Chapter 5), a tool is required to measure a medium that "usually works." Problems on Ethernet are statistical and usually appear and disappear, or range from bad to worse without anything being "wrong." Also, problems lie dormant until network traffic increases to a statistically critical level before emerging as a crisis. For this reason statistical and software tracking is essential. It is also useful if a protocol analyzer can actively page a person when trouble is noted. To date, this feature is not provided by off-the-shelf solutions.

- Virtual terminal support
- File transfer
- Electronic mail
- Network disk support (i.e. file server)
- Network file system support
- Database access
- Network utilities
- Network programs
- Network output services
- Facsimile integration
- Distributed processing applications
- Phone integration
- Voice mail
- Conferencing
- Image storage and access

Figure 14.2 Typical Ethernet traffic activities.

Network Performance Questions

The network administrator must view the network as a highway carrying data traffic in order to resolve higher level network bottlenecks and Ethernet traffic failures. The network administrator seeks to answer operational questions as outlined in Figure 14.3 in order to evaluate the operational efficiency of any network. Understanding why these questions are relevant is the subject of the next section.

Heisenberg Uncertainty Principle

If the monitoring equipment actively requests and captures information, the process itself skews the results. It is quite likely that file service requests, information probes, and process swap requests performed in the pursuit of network status data will itself generate network loading. The essence of the *Heisenberg Uncertainty Principle* is that the *active* process of observing an event alters the outcome of that event. *Passive* monitoring, on the other hand, watches each broadcast packet without accessing or affecting the network. This eliminates performance losses and potentially obviates any speed limitations that the monitoring actually seeks to chronicle. Unlike most vendor-supplied software tools, most protocol analyzers provide passive monitoring.

Vendor-Specific Limitations

Most vendors of network workstations provide resident software tools to track network access and usage for individual workstations. Some vendors

- What stations transmit on the network?
- Do stations correctly transmit?
- Do stations respond correctly to transmissions?
- Do stations defer to the busy network?
- What is the traffic volume?
- What is the traffic consistency?
- What is the length of messages?
- What is average peak loading?
- What is full capacity?
- What is the average intermessage timing?
- What is the average wait delay?
- Which stations talk to each other?
- Do messages have frame errors?
- Can some stations not reach other stations?
- Which nodes cause problems?
- Which section or segments are overloaded?
- Are gateways and repeaters performing to spec?

Figure 14.3 Questions answered by the protocol analyzer.

even provide software that will measure network usage. If these software tools are accurate and not approximate, an analyzer may be unnecessary.

However, vendor-supplied network monitoring software tools will exhibit the same flaws and faults as their workstations and overlook some types of problems. Often, Ethernet networks are built of many parts from different vendors over a period of time. As a consequence of this typical growth pattern, few types of node equipment can monitor a mongrel network with any accuracy. Therefore, a specialized device is required to capture and parse all types of network packets. The protocol analyzer fills this function because it is *protocol independent*. The analyzer can view all IEEE 802.3 and Ethernet packets that conform to TCP/IP, HPnet, XNS, or DECnet, OSI, or any other "standards." The tool passively captures a burst signal containing an Ethernet frame, then parses this packet to whatever the upper or lower level protocols dictate. Within this framework, TCP information and IP control information, for example, can be viewed without reliance on questionable network-level software.

Some workstation vendors build analyzers as part of their product line. In general, it is a good management practice not to rely on single solutions; backup and alternative methods are reasonable. Therefore, consider purchasing a protocol analyzer from an independent vendor so that any vendor-specific problems or incompatibilities to "standard" Ethernet can be uncovered.

The Role of Network Monitoring

Although Ethernet can be viewed as analogous to a party line telephone network, at other times a highway analogy is more appropriate. Since

Ethernet is a probabilistic medium, certain *traffic* models represent Ethernet's capacity, throughput, and timing attributes with a high degree of accuracy. These statistical models are presented in Chapter 15, but in this chapter the emphasis is placed upon the methodology for analytically tracing network problems by deciphering transmission packets, counts and rates. The mathematical details underpinning Ethernet follow later.

Understanding Network Performance

Ethernet is a purely statistical transmission medium. Network node stations transmit when they see a free line, and collisions occur when two or more nodes see the free line simultaneously. Since Ethernet (versions in common usage) assumes a minimum inter-packet spacing, there can be no "tailgating." Additionally, traffic speed is enforced at 10 Mbits/second. Overloads and traffic problems tend to occur at the nodes themselves barring cable hardware problems. Network problems can be grouped in a hierarchical progression. It is usually worthwhile to check for node hardware problems before searching for network hardware failures. Likewise, it is usually best to search for node software problems before searching for more global network bottlenecks, incompatibilities, or failures.

In order to monitor network performance, it is important to know *how many* nodes there are on the network, and which actually transmit.The first order of network problems occurs when nodes do not transmit correctly. This is usually indicative of improperly specified hardware or network software, or defective components. Likewise, nodes may not respond to transmissions (including collision jam signals). The analyzer gathers measurements to pinpoint these problems.

Once the deterministic network hardware problems are resolved, the second order is the actual traffic load. Each and every piece of equipment may function correctly. Systems may be reliable. Nevertheless, a network may perform slowly and erratically. This is usually indicative of an overloaded transmission channel.

The most significant network measurement is the packet count which tells how many packets, good or bad, have been transmitted on the net-

Good Packets	Bad Packets
Length Type Frequency	Collisions Short Long Misaligned Frame errors FCS errors

Figure 14.4 Network packet measurements. These measurements are also grouped by packet source and destination.

work. This count can be subdivided into good packets and bad packets, by source and destination, by characteristics of packet length, type, frequency, or by error condition. Figure 14.4 groups these items in a matrix framework with practical implications.

Basic network monitoring is the process of capturing packets during a known time frame since problems occur within an interval of time, or can be pegged to a certain event in time. Therefore, packet volume (or throughput) is an important measurement. The consistency of volume is another important unit because inconsistency creates traffic bottlenecks that frequently do not clear; traffic consistency will be discussed in the next chapter. If network problems occur and the assumption is that the network is overloaded, volumes and peak volume statistics may validate this theory. However, it is important to compare observed volume to a theoretical capacity.

Other areas of network transmission problems are the degenerative transmission situations that occur when packets are defective, long, short, misaligned, wrongly addressed, or incompatible with the network standard. The search for the cause of these problems transcends statistical measurements because bad packets have to be retransmitted until they are received correctly. Bad packets can flood a network and halt its effectiveness. In order to expose any sources for bad packets defective packets must be examined for content, and the packet fields should be parsed and viewed as Figure 14.5 illustrates.

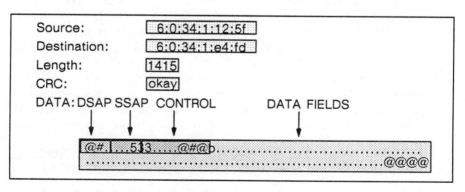

Figure 14.5 View of the parsed Ethernet packet.

In fact, protocol variances usually show in address discrepancies, length or type of field variations, or the LLC and upper-level protocol fields contained within the actual Ethernet data field. If underlying causes for corrupted packets, address discrepancies, or mismatched upper-layer protocols are to be exposed, packets must be captured and dissected.

Collisions

The most meaningful statistic and the one most often provided by resident network Ethernet software is a collision rate. Collisions occur when two or more machines overlap their transmissions. A high collision rate is indicative of many problems including any of the conditions listed in Figure 14.6.

- Overloaded network
- Too many nodes (exceeding specification)
- Too many workstations
- Too many lengthy transmissions
- Chattering or jabbering transceivers
- Defective transceivers
- Defective Ethernet cards
- Defective software
- Mismatched hardware
- Nonspec equipment

Figure 14.6 Typical causes for high collision rates.

Corrupted Packets

Comparisons of rates for short, long, and corrupted packets is another statistic of importance. Damaged packets imply a collision, a defective Ethernet card or transceiver, problems with the coaxial cable, or outside noise. A damaged packet usually has a bad checksum, or cyclic redundancy check (CRC). Short, long, or damaged packets imply faulty software or hardware at a workstation. Statistics on corrupted packets should focus attention on the root causes of problems rather than on some ephemeral "global" problem. Excessive numbers of short, long, or defective packets could imply that transmission from a node transceiver was interrupted or that the transmitting workstation did not realize that the network was busy and incorrectly transmitted information without listening for carrier or other transmissions. There are also a certain number of truncated packets that occur each time there is a collision.

A protocol analyzer with a robust software package (such as Hewlett-Packard's 4797s) eases the difficulty in calculating these items because it will automatically tally packet counts, calculate percentage rates, and graph trends. Graphics display of these items lends more meaning and can show trends not otherwise noticeable. However, even with a less satisfactory software package, the basic information can be collected and downloaded or rekeyed to a spreadsheet program for the same results.

Packet Counts

At a minimum, some metrics are required to compare network perform-ance over different time frames. Another network status indicator, in addition to the collision rate and the error rate, is a packet count. This number can be compared against a count from another day to see if unusually heavy traffic is the reason for perceived performance problems. For example, if there were 15,000,000 packets today versus 12,000,000 packets yesterday—a 20% increase—the magnitude of this difference would explain why performance has suffered, assuming no significant change in the collision level. An even more useful statistic would be a packet trans-mission rate per hour called a "traffic" rate. While packets per day is a useful comparison, more immediate packet counts are useful. Counts per second, per minute, or per hour constitute a traffic rate. These counts allow comparisons during shorter intervals within which most Ethernet problems occur.

Statistics for Network Planning

The number of good packets is irrelevant until correlated with other information. By combining the number of good packets transmitted (rather than the total packet count) with either the lengths of each packet or average length of transmitted packets, a transmission-level count is gener-ated. This is a *bps* (bits per second) figure. Every manager needs an indication of how much work is actually accomplished for planning growth, managing new tasks, and maintaining a functioning network. Collision levels are not practical for this because they increase nonlinearly; add a new workstation and the collision rate is liable to double or triple, or even break the network. Usage rates aid planning by providing a nearly inde-pendent statistic. It is *nearly* independent because as the network grows and the load increases, response time decreases and less work can be completed within any interval. Consequently, usage rates are apt to be lower per node on a saturated network than on a non-saturated network. Usage rates are more consistent.

The usage rates also show type and quantity of work by node. They provide the necessary data to make informed network planning decisions. Chapter 16 presents many options to tune network performance. The problem remains to identify what should be tuned.

Network Traffic Composition

A subset of nodes will have higher rates of usage than other nodes as a consequence of the work performed, or as a result of those nodes' need to access network resources. Different users work different hours, perform various duties that load a network differently, and generate different consistencies of Ethernet packets. Also, too many users and nodes clearly can overload a network and create bottlenecks and slow network response. Indicators of node-specific overloads are outlined in Figure 14.7.

- High density of packet count (high-level load)
- Lengthy transmissions (high peak demand)
- Minimum (or less) interarrival times (saturation)
- Slow user response (overloads)
- Packet corruptions (overloads)

Figure 14.7 Indicators of traffic problems.

To understand the root cause of uneven traffic problems, it is important to understand the composition of that network traffic. The pie chart in Figure 14.8 summarizes data from captured packets. Of 3300 packets, 500 were mail messages, 300 were follow-on packets for mail messages, and 2400 were applied to other uses. Only 100 packets were identified as collision fragments. The graphs imply that 25% of all network traffic in this sample is mail. Because there were follow-on mail packets, 60% of all mail messages average longer than a kilobyte. Note that 40% of all messages are brief. It is possible that one message is .3 megabytes long (and requires all 300 follow-on packets). This would skew the statistics and is one hypothesis to investigate.

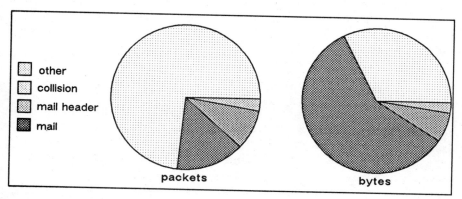

Figure 14.8 Indicators of network traffic composition problems. The pie charts detail the percentage of network traffic allocated to a particular function. In this example, most of the packets are small, but a few large mail packets correspond to most of the network utilization.

The analysis does show that most mail messages are fairly brief, and 500 messages are a fairly significant number. If they come from a single node, it may imply that one user is broadcasting globally and this may be unacceptable. Perhaps this type of transmission should be restricted to certain hours. If most messages are transmitted to a single node, perhaps this transmission level may imply the need for a bulletin board system rather than a mail broadcast. These are courses of action that packet content may suggest. Packet header information could be correlated with each mail message to indicate the actual length since the packet header does contain the length of the actual information it contains.

Some processes may demand a significant portion of network traffic. Electronic mail, for example, may be a *hidden* use of network resources. The implication in this example is that mail is disproportionately overloading the network; while packet counts for mail are not large, the effect of actual traffic is skewed toward servicing mail requests. Likewise, data file uploading and downloading may be a significant load; this can be verified by examining the contents of the long trains of packets sent between specific pairs of nodes. Time-stamping of packets would aid in this type of investigation. Perhaps, like mail, this type of transmission should be restricted to certain hours too.

A solution, if usage-specific traffic is deemed a problem, may be to identify the need for electronic mail. Another similar source of network traffic is graphic paging, sometimes known as screen refresh. This condition may imply that large blocks of high-density graphic information are being transferred with frequency from one machine to another. Several solutions to these types of problems are possible. First, transfer could be accomplished by tape or floppy disk rather than by the network. Second, a special link might be constructed to remove the burden from the main network, for example another Ethernet cable or RS-232 line, solely to support this transfer channel. Third, mail could be posted on a passive bulletin board rather than broadcast on the network.

Global and Node-Specific Data Collection

Network software tools are sometimes available on the workstations, network servers, or PCs that are connected to the Ethernet network. Network software tools may count packets, packet collisions, and sometimes identify source and destinations with packet counts. Most often this software provides only single node information and not global information about all nodes. Both node-specific and global information is required for the best results in network maintenance. This information must be *accurately* acquired and displayed in useful formats. Figure 14.9 presents the minimum functionality for monitoring transmission level network operations required to answer the network manager's questions.

- Count packets:
    all packets
    short packets
    long packets
    corrupted packets
    good packets
- Display length of each packet
- Display average size of packet
- Count collisions
- Store packets to memory (and/or disk)
- Monitor traffic levels
- Monitor individual nodes, look for:
    high levels of traffic
    high rates of collision
    high rates of retransmission
    type of traffic
    corrupted packets

Figure 14.9 Statistical information required for network analysis.

A global collision rate indicates a global problem such as overloading or network configuration violations. Although a global rate may indicate individual component failure, it is more effective for diagnostic analysis to compare global rates against individual rates at the node level. Node level collision rates should be uniform unless there is a node-specific problem. Collision rates above the average indicate nodes which are prime causes of collisions. Collisions may also occur specifically among a subset of nodes. Collision statistics for specific nodes allow the network manager to focus attention on root causes of collisions. For example, one subset of nodes may have transceivers or Ethernet cards from the same manufacturer. Problems may have developed (or, more likely, have not appeared until the network became critically saturated) with this hardware. Or, to take another example, collisions may only occur between two different types of workstations. In such cases, it's likely that the workstations are having difficulty intercommunicating. Problems at this level are common but uncommonly difficult to diagnose without node-specific correlation.

Unless single node statistics can be captured inexpensively and analyzed globally, network software tools are only transient indicators of network problems. Single node statistics *may* pinpoint a problem with a particular node without indicating a specific node as the source of problems. Global counts may indicate a local or global problem, but rarely will pinpoint the cause. Unless global information with node specific corroboration is available, problems cannot be isolated to a specific node. Even a problem as common as chattering transceivers cannot be resolved without such corroboration. Without the specific node information *correlated* to the global information, excessive transmissions of meaningless packets cannot be traced to their hardware sources except by trial and error or a binary search with physical test equipment.

The network statistics in Figure 14.10 show a high rate of collisions. This global statistic would lead one to believe a problem exists everywhere. Node analysis from simple node-specific software would suggest that both nodes 1 and 3 are faulty, whereas in fact only a single node may be causing problems since both a 20 and a 25% collision rate are significant. One node may be demonstrating that it is having difficulty communicating with the other node. More specific information corroborating that all collisions at node 3 were caused by transmission to node 1 would confirm that only node 1 is a problem. The discrepancy of 400 packets could be associated with runt or oversized frames (bad packets) that would occur if node 1 had a faulty transceiver.

	Node 1	Node 2	Node 3	Network
Output packets	12400	15000	15000	42400
Input packets	6000	22000	9000	37000
Collisions	3000	0	2000	5000

Figure 14.10 Node-specific data bring global analysis into perspective.

If usage rates seem localized to certain groups of nodes, or localized to a certain manufacturer's parts, or certain types of users, then it might be desirable to localize those groups on subnets, or allocate special resources to the groups. Often, those groups may not warrant the extra costs associated with the additional resources, or it may be politically unfeasible. It is important to note that Ethernet is a public resource without locks or accounting statistics. The added resources may be applied to improve the global performance incidentally in the attempt to improve performance for a selected group of nodes and users. Capacity is a *global constraint*, not a controlled resource.

General Purpose Network Flow Information

Figure 14.11 lists some typical questions and corresponding important network statistics by name. The listing, by no means complete, is representative of the most expedient manner to answer each question posed.

Typical Network Questions	Statistics of Relevance
What stations transmit on the network?	source and destination costs
Do stations correctly transmit?	eliminate all packets with error and analyze
Do stations respond correctly to transmissions?	node simulation; utilization and collision rate
Do stations defer to the busy network?	collision rate
What is the traffic volume?	counts, rates and utilization rate
What is the traffic consistency?	capture packets; source and destination
What is the length of messages?	size distribution
What is average peak loading?	utilization rate; capacity rate
What is full capacity?	track collision vs. packet counts or rates
What is the average intermessage timing?	interarrival times
What is the average wait delay?	latency distribution
Which nodes talk to each other?	source/destination matrix
Do messages have frame errors?	analyze and sort packet errors
Can some stations not reach other stations?	analyze pattern of lost packets; simulatation
Which nodes cause problems?	packet counts, error counts; collision rate
Which section or segments are overloaded?	rates, collisions, interarrival times
Are gateways and repeaters performing to spec?	rates, collisions, interarrival times

Figure 14.11 Typical management questions and corresponding statistics.

Figure 14.12 lists some important counts, rates, and calculated statistics by name. This is not by any means a complete listing, just representative of that network monitoring information generally provided by protocol analyzers. The equations for these or the methodology to generate them are explained in detail in the next chapter. This list is included here in order to annotate several of the next charts and detail the applicable uses for the individual counts and rates.

Packet counts:
    packets transmitted
    packets received
    packets transmitted with collisions
    packets deferred
    packets per node
    by source
    by destination
    by source to destination
    size distribution (-, 64, 128, 256, 512, 1024, 1518, +)
    network period peaks
    node period peaks

Packet errors:
    alignment errors
    CRC errors
    short packets
    long packets
    invisible packets
    incompatible packets
    misaddressed packets

Channel utilization:
    throughput
    peak rate
    utilization as a percent of capacity

Capture:
    all packets
    packets during an interval
    packets with errors
    packets with specific errors
    packets with certain data types
    packets from specific source node(s)
    packets directed to specific destination node(s)
    packets with specific source/destination pairs
    packets with a certain size

Statistics:
    interarrival times (0-100 microseconds)
    latency distribution
    packet size distribution
    node usage as a percent of capacity
    node usage as a percent of network utilization
    packet rate per second
    bit rate per second

Figure 14.12 The protocol analyzer collects these common counts and rates, filters packets for specialized content, and calculates statistics useful for network analysis.

Network Performance Data

Having identified statistics of interest, a measurement methodology needs to be developed. Although the troubleshooting chapter at the conclusion of *Keeping the Link* outlines some ranges for common network indicators, the worksheet in Figure 14.13 includes sample data for a large, complicated network, and the necessary steps to convert the collected data into applicable information. In this sample, the users experienced a network that is slow and unresponsive; they have complained to the network manager who must validate or discount the users' claims. As a consequence of a thorough analysis with a protocol analyzer several unrelated problems are uncovered.

node	input	error	output	error	coll	i%nput	%output	%coll	%tot	%Ncoll
A	89897	261	37307	5	4719	0.29	0.01	12.65	0.18	0.68
B	2492034	0	6116816	5	67413	0.00	0.00	1.10	29.53	9.65
C	192212	251	129838	11	7926	0.13	0.01	6.10	0.63	1.13
D	561151	0	415580	10	13108	0.00	0.00	3.15	2.01	1.88
E	15987246	0	10022484	169	362252	0.00	0.00	3.61	48.39	51.85
F	812002	446	747493	25	43555	0.06	0.00	5.83	3.61	6.23
G	42862	0	44130	2	21	0.00	0.00	0.05	0.21	0.00
H	611480	1923	42840	14	7231	0.31	0.03	16.88	0.21	1.03
I	115363	38	64289	1	1661	0.03	0.00	2.58	0.31	0.24
J	103	0	84478	867	9872	0.00	1.03	11.69	0.41	1.41
K	82097	234	40996	14	6665	0.29	0.03	16.26	0.20	0.95
L	65316	346	10880	2	863	0.53	0.02	7.93	0.05	0.12
M	153256	0	120172	94	52406	0.00	0.08	43.61	0.58	7.50
N	618	452	3140	3	338	73.14	0.10	10.76	0.02	0.05
O	1040322	1824	604794	48	36172	0.18	0.01	5.98	2.92	5.18
P	1334398	347	1315634	9	48097	0.03	0.00	3.66	6.35	6.88
Q	44748	0	53752	0	0	0.00	0.00	0.00	0.26	0.00
R	91380	0	32778	4	3748	0.00	0.01	11.43	0.16	0.54
S	476121	266	483599	59	26625	0.06	0.01	5.51	2.33	3.81
T	80594	0	72483	4	24	0.00	0.01	0.03	0.35	0.00
U	79780	0	71956	4	24	0.00	0.01	0.03	0.35	0.00
V	92126	0	21619	1	1490	0.00	0.00	6.89	0.10	0.21
W	141428	0	108958	0	0	0.00	0.00	0.00	0.53	0.00
X	6018	0	501	3	450	0.00	0.60	89.82	0.00	0.06
Y	116901	150	66893	9	4043	0.13	0.01	6.04	0.00	0.06
Z	33	2	59	7	1	6.06	11.86	1.69	0.32	0.58
TOTAL	24709488	6540	20713472	1370	698704	0.03	0.01	3.37	0.00	0.00

Indicator	Nodes	Solution
Busy Nodes:	B, E	sub-net or filter
Collision Nodes	A, H, K, M, X	check out cables, electronics or software
Bad Hardware	N, Z	check out the hardware
Network Collisions	E	no problem!

Figure 14.13 Statistical worksheet. Although node E shows a moderate collision rate on its own packets, it dominates the network collision rate. This "red herring" is immaterial since the network collision rate is reasonably low at 3%.

In this example, information has been captured during a twenty-four-hour period on a network with twenty six nodes. The column headings represent each node, the number of packets input (i.e. received), the number of errors at the transport layer for these input packets, the number of packets output (that is, transmitted), the number of errors at the transport layer for these output packets, the collision count for output packets, and five columns for rates. The first column shows input errors as a percentage of packets received. The second column shows output errors as a percentage of packets transmitted, and the third column is the rate of collision for packets transmitted from that node. The last two columns cannot be calculated until all the other information has been completed since these rates require network totals. These two right hand columns show a method to compare node usage against network usage: *%tot* calculates packets transmitted from each node as a factor of all packets transmitted on the network, and *%Tcoll* calculates collisions for each node as a factor of the collisions on the entire network.

The following eight graphs compress a large number of network statistics into a clear picture. The network represented is a complex network with one main segment interconnecting four lesser segments; it has 172 nodes in total. The rate of utilization reaches saturation levels so that typical problems are presented to the reader.

Figure 14.14 subdivides the network load by source machine type. In this sample, a conclusion to be made is that the Xerox equipment is providing a baseline activity during the course of the day, perhaps data backup, co-processing, global modem, or mail services. The load on the IBM equipment is counter-cyclic to the normal workday suggesting some planned off-peak process, whereas the Apple and DEC equipment appear to be servicing users during the normal workday. Such assumptions could be verified by packet capture techniques or learning about the specific processes on the network.

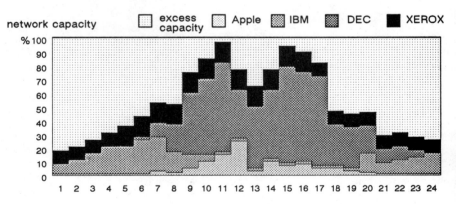

Figure 14.14 Peak load by source computer during a 24-hour period.

This same information is displayed in a different format by network service usage in Figure 14.15. Most of the peak load is created by user demands during the normal work hours.

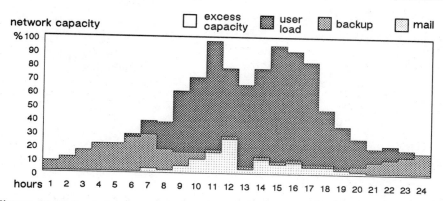

Figure 14.15 Peak load capacity by usage during a 24-hour period.

The graph in Figure 14.16 presents loading on the main network segment that interconnects with four *other* segments. This traffic is identical to that represented in the above figure as the overlay implies, although some of the load is localized on the subnets and therefore does not appear on the main net.

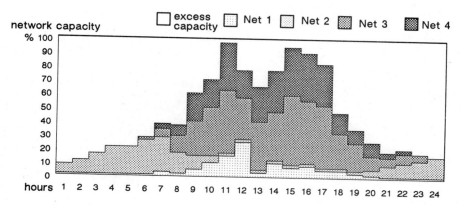

Figure 14.16 Peak load by network source during a 24-hour period.

The data used to construct the graph in Figure 14.16 are repeated by the histogram in Figure 14.17 which displays traffic by packet size. Several upper-level protocols and errors are overlaid to indicate the common packet sizes. In this sample, TCP/IP is the upper–layer protocol. Errors are represented by packets that are less than the 64 bytes minimum which represent collision fragments, or those packets that exceed 1518 bytes which represent transceiver chatter.

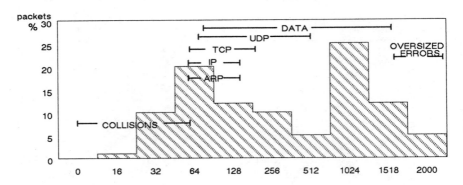

Figure 14.17 Distribution of packets by size. Each different size represents a different type of purpose.

The network collision rate correlates to the peak load in the last time period charts. Because the collision rate is nonlinear, it jumps when traffic builds above 40% of network capacity. This loading is obvious during peak business hours, and drops off during lunch and afternoon slack times as Figure 14.18 illustrates.

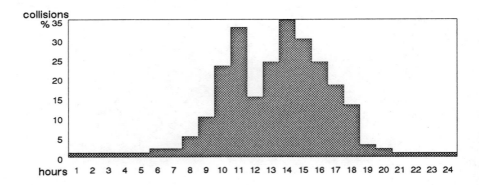

Figure 14.18 Collision rate during a 24-hour period.

Interarrival times should be a minimum of 96 milliseconds. Interpacket spacing of less than 96 milliseconds represents collisions or signs of hardware defects. The network interarrival time in Figure 14.19 implies a 35% collision rate, thus duplicating information in Figure 14.18 converted to another format.

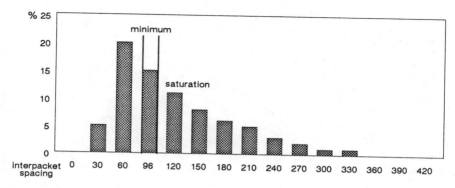

Figure 14.19 Histogram of interarrival times in milliseconds.

Network access latency as shown in Figure 14.20 is the time required for a request to be filled. The information is superimposed on the interarrival time for comparison. Latency times provide less important information than collision rates or error rates, although they can confirm whether the problem is overload or hardware. In this case, since the latency shows a bell curve, the implication is that the network functions correctly except when the traffic load is too high, and latency shifts outward.

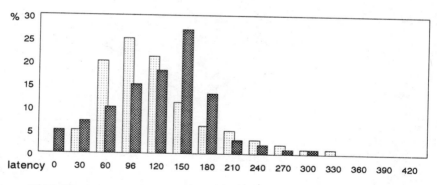

Figure 14.20 Histogram of network access latency.

Another informative pictogram is an internode matrix. The two representations contrast traffic, as in Figure 14.21, or collisions, as in Figure 14.22, between various sets of nodes. This information indicates rational places to break a network into separate segments if required. Additionally, this two-dimensional information compresses the many earlier graphs into clearer pictures. When traffic rates are compared to collision rates, anomalies like node 3 show as nonfunctioning, and node 6 and node 172 show extraordinary collision rates. Nodes 4, 5, and 6 show as busy nodes with five- and six-fold increases in traffic levels over the other nodes.

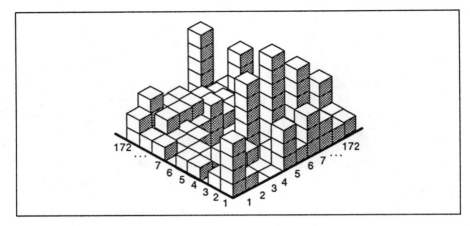

Figure 14.21 Internode traffic rate matrix.

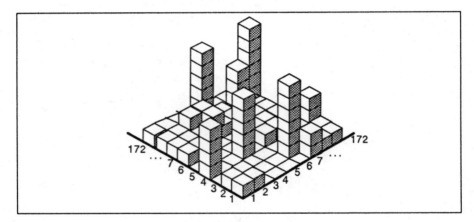

Figure 14.22 Internode collision matrix.

Node Simulation

When statistics fail to identify network problems, node simulation on a protocol analyzer is a powerful methodology. Specialized software constructs packets of any length and content. A packet could thus contain any combination of errors, sources and destinations, and actual data content. Furthermore, network loading could be artificially increased to saturation levels to exercise the node software or develop statistics otherwise unavailable within a specific network situation. Figure 14.23 suggests the types of packets that can be built and the types of tests possible with node simulation. The delay and utilization characteristics of a network under *various* load conditions is important consideration in design and planning stages.

Simulation	Anticipated Test Indications
short packets	software error handling
long packets	software error handling
corrupted packets	software and hardware error handling
forced collision packets	transceivers and TCP/IP
percentage network loading	network performance/growth capacity
misaligned packets	controller hardware
specified sources	node functionality
specified destinations	node functionality

Figure 14.23 Network simulation for preconceived theories.

Network Usage Assessments

While an analyzer can chart network performance, it also performs other esoteric duties with some imagination. Its functions might include preparing usage statistics for accounting and billing purposes. These statistics could then be used as a basis for charging users and groups for network utilization. Take as an example the information in Figure 14.24.

User f in *group B* is the major user of network resources. Although it may be politically unfeasible to charge *group B* for his utilization, it might be important to demonstrate demand for network resources. It is certainly the case that should the network become saturated and unable to meet the demand for services, network access for *user f* may need to be changed.

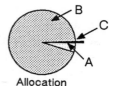

Public Network Support Costs: $100,000		
group	allocation rate	prorated share
A	.047	$4700
B	.947	$94,700
C	.0047	$470

Allocation

group	user	daily average packets		percent utilization	
A	a	10000		10	
A	b	40000		40	
A	c	50000		50	
			100000		4.7%
B	d	400000		20	
B	e	700000		35	
B	f	900000		45	
			2000000		94.7%
C	g	1000		10	
C	h	2000		20	
C	i	7000		70	
			10000		0.47%

Figure 14.24 Budgetary allocation by prorate network usage. Packets were captured and collated by source address in order to generate the utilization percentages.

Group C might, for example, be the accounting department that provides the paychecks, payables, and receivables. Network utilization is minimal; however, relative value of this work is certainly maximum. This example indicates an implicit resource allocation decision.

Capture and Store

Another key feature of a network analyzer is the tool's ability to intercept and retain packets. It should be able to capture every packet, although on a busy network available buffer space may prevent more than seconds or minutes of data to be stored. Some analyzers are too slow to capture every packet; they may capture one in five packets. This is statistically sound if the tool is capable of identifying and tracking each and every packet without storing the packet's contents. Some analyzers are too slow to recognize all packets. This means that packet counts do not accurately represent traffic; this is not sufficient. At a minimum, the statistics must be collected accurately. Node workstations often provide resident software to track this information for that node. Some node workstations provide software for global tracking. If this information is accurate and not just approximate, a protocol analyzer may be unnecessary. The ability to filter selected packets or extract only header information is a powerful tool for statistical compilation, usually only available with a protocol analyzer. Also, time stamping of packets is a desirable feature for matching individual packets with function as demonstrated in the mail example. It also provides latency and interarrival statistics and a reality check on the accuracy of these statistics.

Several analyzers store from half a megabyte to four megabytes of packets. They take a photograph of the network activity. On a saturated network, four megabytes may represent only three seconds of activity. Captured packets can be stored on disk and analyzed later with word processing tools. For example, four megabytes of network traffic could be stored to disk. A quick view might indicate many mail packets as in the earlier example. Electronic mail seems to require considerable disk space (confirmed by other tools) and now it seems to require a large portion of the network. How large is a matter for estimate unless the four megabytes can be analyzed and measured by content. If the file can be edited and parsed, an accurate percentage figure can be compiled. Unix tools like *grep, wc,* and *awk* are especially competent for this analysis; otherwise edits and sorts with line counts are appropriate.

Snooping with the Analyzer

A protocol analyzer allows anyone who understands the use of this tool to monitor transparently and unobtrusively. By capturing and parsing packets, it is possible to decipher what users are doing on the network, who is doing things illegally, unethically, or against policy. One use is to see who is using what resources on the network. While this seems Machiavellian, it can prevent unwarranted use of organization resources. It can uncover thefts, breaches in security, or hidden intrusions via unauthorized transceiver taps. Another use of the protocol analyzer, if it has the ability to build specified packets at the bit and byte level, is to falsify packet designs and break whatever security is in place. If this tool can break security, this would indicate that others could undermine the security systems as well. Chapter 17 details these and other security issues.

The ability to capture and view packets adds a level of sophistication to network performance tuning. It also promotes spying. Collision counts, packet counts, defective packet counts, any counts by spawning node are information of value and useful to tuning a network. However, at higher levels of sophistication—when all other problems have been identified and resolved—it becomes important to understand the mix of information actually transmitted. Informed guesses may indicate a particular set of nodes are used for long-haul uploading and downloading of large files. Other nodes with heavy but sporadic network loads may indicate large electronic mail requirements. By visually inspecting selected packets, it is possible to confirm these hypotheses.

This chapter explained the workings of a protocol analyzer, the types of information it can collect, and how to analyze and apply those data. The next chapter derives the mathematical underpinnings for traffic analysis with an emphasis on degenerate network performances. Chapter 16 will apply this practical understanding to the logic of tuning networks.

Part 5

Management Planning and Strategic Analysis

This section explores the management and strategic issues of Ethernet networking. Performance tuning, security, backup and human aspects are covered since these are critical management concerns. As network technology evolves, competition and the usage of networks for strategic advantage is increasingly an organizational concern. This chapter provides the reader with an understanding of Ethernet technology and operations, and Parts 6 and 7 conclude *Keeping the Link*.

Chapter 15 calculates the statistics of Ethernet. This means that the Ethernet transmission is a random process and inherently statistical in nature. Chapter 16 builds upon the knowledge from the chapters on installation, configurations, network traffic, and statistics for the purpose of tuning network performance. Chapter 17 discusses security issues, addresses why the networking model contains no reference to either data or physical security, discusses why Ethernet is not secure, and explains precautions that can be taken to protect a network from outside prying and unauthorized access. Chapter 18 explains backup procedures, and suggests what hardware, software, or operational procedures can be implemented to produce a nearly fault-tolerant network whereas Chapter 19 illustrates why qualified people are an important resource for network administration.

Chapter 15

Statistics for a Network

The last chapter detailed the workings of the protocol analyzer. This chapter derives the mathematics and reveals further insights into Ethernet mechanics by confirming rules of thumb with statistics. The assumptions are that Ethernet networks perform poorly when overloaded, that collisions are a proxy indicator for poor performance, and that these problems can somehow be solved. Additionally, a manager of a busy network may assume that there are better protocols than the chaotic talk-at-the-same-time Ethernet. The statistics will show that collisions do impair efficiency, but that Ethernet is efficient when understood.

Network Traffic

Ethernet relies on a probabilitistic transmission process with no priority enforcement. Packets from the sending node are broadcast in all directions on the network. It is the responsibility of the receiving node to accept, acknowledge, and reply to those transmissions. Simultaneous transmission is actually allowed, although such simultaneous transmission creates a colli-

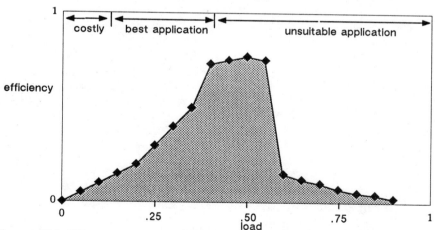

Figure 15.1 Ethernet network model plotting efficiency as a function of traffic load. The best application is in the range of 10–35% channel utilization. Ethernet is too expensive for minimal applications and unsuitable for chronic overloading applications.

sion. A collision is an indication of a network conflict which is resolved on a first-come, first-served basis on Ethernet. This CSMA/CD method of resolving collisions is why Ethernet is considered stochastic. It is a very efficient and very fast process for low loads, but increasingly inefficient as network traffic load increases. In fact, calculations (based upon the mathematics presented later in this chapter) yield a peak capacity around 55% of rated Ethernet capacity. Capacity drops precipitously around 60% loading as shown by Figure 15.1.

Saturation

Ethernet has no built-in overload protection circuitry. When Ethernet is overloaded, there is no mechanism to curtail traffic, dissuade nodes from transmitting, or suggest that users relax and slow down. This is particularly noticeable when a network jams. When traffic loading is above 60%, the requests for transmission are so dense that they collide. The network is reset after each collision, but immediately upon conclusion of the jam signal, all the colliding machines again vie for slot time and create new collisions. This impasse, if it continues without reprieve, is *network saturation*. Often, the only solution to this condition—it may not be a problem that needs to be solved if infrequent—is to power down all the nodes on the network or halt them for a period of time to reset and settle the crush. By analogy, it is a traffic accident that must be cleared from the roadway before traffic can safely resume. If saturation is a continuous, it may be advisable to reconfigure the network or check for hardware malfunctions.

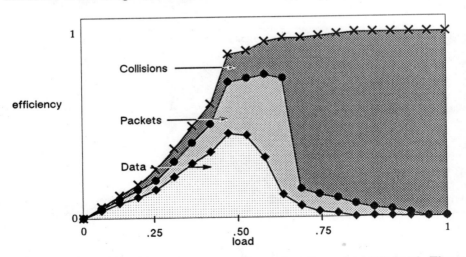

Figure 15.2 Ethernet network efficiency as a function of traffic load. The black region to the right of the 55% threshold represents a traffic jam precipitated by "network saturation."

Conceptually, as Ethernet is loaded, the probability of collision increases and the probability of data correctly delivered to the destination decreases. Collisions increase exponentially because collision resolution is random and because network traffic itself is not random. Additionally, a 55% loading factor means that the network is transmitting at least one packet 55% of the time; it also means the network is saturated at a far higher rate because the chance of two or more nodes transmitting at the same time is disproportionately high. Consider also that every TCP/IP application-layer transmission will request an IP acknowledgment. This implies that every TCP/IP transmission is doubling the packet count. At levels of traffic higher than 55% the network will *saturate* with collisions and fragmentary packets, providing no data throughput. Figure 15.2 illustrates the mathematical structure of throughput in an eye-opening presentation. The mathematical theory used to construct this graph is developed throughout this chapter, and its implications are explored.

Synchronized Transmission

Over time, a network reaches an equilibrium state. Overnight, for example, when bulk jobs like remote file backups are processed, traffic often synchronizes. Jobs that initially compete for slot time often line up in an orderly queue because the traffic must be processed upon receipt. This initializes a send→process→reply→send→process sequence that oscillates with the other processes. Synchronized transmission is unlikely on user-spawned tasks, or during normal working hours when many processes may periodically flood the network and unsettle any bulk jobs. No manager should plan for synchronized network loading because it is a chance event subject to background noise, loading factors, packet sizes, and burst rates. It is an anomaly of Ethernet and blind spots in the upper-layer software.

Ethernet Blind Spots

In some implementations of Ethernet the transceivers and controllers, or even the upper-layer software like TCP/IP, often exhibit *blind spots*. These software or hardware design bugs perpetuate certain types of network problems such as sporadic network saturation, abnormal preambles, or inability to see certain Ethernet addresses or packet types. This is most prevalent when different types of hardware and software utilize the same network bus. A typical blind spot is caused by various implementations of the vendors of different systems of the collision backup algorithm, which is likely to exhibit less than perfect performance or compatibility with the renderings of other vendors.

Simple Error Rate Statistics

Some simple statistics decode the operating efficiency and status of an Ethernet. This information is generally collected from node-layer software or the protocol analyzer. The most applicable information is rates. Rates are the counts of a specific type of event during a fixed time interval and are the most useful statistics for determining efficiency. For example, three types of rates to look for are the packet rate, sometimes called a *transmission* or *traffic rate,* a collision rate, and error rates. Figure 15.3 lists some tracking formulae. Error rates represent transmission errors as a percentage of total packets transmitted, and these rates should be calculated this way for uniformity.

Transmission rate	= "TRAFFIC"	(1)
	= # packets sent / time period	
Transmission rate / sec	= # packets sent / second	(2)
rate / minute	= # packets sent during a minute	(3)
rate / hour	= # packets send during an hour	(4)
Runt frame rate	= # runts / # packets sent	(5)
Oversized frame rate	= # oversized packets / # packets sent	(6)
CRC error rate	= # CRC errors / # packets sent	(7)
Collision rate	= # of collisions / # packets transmitted	(8)
Collision rate per hour	= # of collisions in one hour /	(9)
	# of packets transmitted in one hour	
Collision rate per hour	= collision rate * one hour /	(10)
	length of collection time (in hours)	

Figure 15.3 Formulae for basic network statistical calculations.

The count for packets transmitted generally differs from the count for packets received because collision requires a retransmission of all involved packets. The collided packet will have been transmitted twice, but received only once. The disparity between these two numbers, number of packets output, and the number of packets received, should approximate the collision count. If the difference substantially varies from this some packets are under- or over-sized, or have faulty addresses and this is indicative of a software problem.

Definition of Abnormal States

Ethernet statistics are not necessary on a network where all works well. Compulsive managers may collect such information just as a matter of course. However, the information pays dividends when a problem does occur and benchmarks, just like cable blueprinting, are valuable as measuring sticks. The equations in Figure 15.3 will provide useful results in suboptimal networks. There are also other situations indicative of malfunctioning hardware that can be tracked through statistics.

Packet counts:	
packets transmitted per node	Count outgoing packets
packets received per node	count iincoming packets
packets transmitted with collisions	count collisions on outgoing packets
packets deferred	— requires special node resident software —
packets per node	Count of outgoing and incoming packets
by source	Count incoming packets and filter by source
by destination	Count incoming packets and filter by dest.
by source to destination	Filt by source and destinations at global level
size distribution	Extract length and count by size
network period peaks	track highest transient load for network
node period peaks	Track highest transient load for node
Packet errors:	
alignment errors	Filter and count
CRC errors	Filter and count
short packets	Filter and count
long packets	Filter and count
invisible packets	Capture packets and sort
incompatible packets	Capture packets and sort
misaddressed packets	Capture packets and sort
Channel utilization:	
throughput	Summation of packets by packet size
peak rate	Highest transient load of throughput
utilization as a percent of capacity	Throughput (bps) / 10,000,000 bps
Capture:	
all packets	Filter by specific parameters
packets during an interval	"
packets with errors	"
packets with specific errors	"
packets with certain data types	"
packets from specific source node(s)	"
packets directed to specific destination node(s)	"
packets with specific source/destination pairs	"
packets with a certain size	"
Statistics:	
interarrival times (0–100 microseconds)	Subtraction between clock times of arrivals
latency distribution	Average waiting time to transmit
packet size distribution	Sort sizes and count
node usage as a percent of capacity	Packets/node/10,000,000 * ave packet size
node usage as a percent of network utilization	Packets/node/throughput
packet rate per second	Packets transmitted/time period
bit rate per second	packet rate * ave packet size * 8 (bits)

Figure 15.4 Common statistics applied to network analysis.

Transmission errors are classified as Cyclic Redundancy Check (CRC) errors, alignment errors, under- or over-sized packets. A CRC error is a checksum error on the Ethernet packet and is usually discovered in conjunction with other types of errors. An alignment error occurs when a packet is not a multiple of eight bits and is usually indicative of a framing error. A short packet contains less than 64 bytes including address, length, and CRC fields whereas a long packet exceeds 1518 bytes including address, length, and CRC fields. A network should experience no forced collisions, no abnormal preambles, and no backoff errors. Forced collision means a packet is transmitted even if traffic (carrier sense) is detected on the network; that is, if the packet will collide with other packets already on the network it is still transmitted. Forced collisions are generated by defective hardware, unsynchronized software, or on networks with mixed vendor equipment. When a packet is transmitted and collides, it is received at the destination node with either a CRC or an alignment error, if it is received at all. Abnormal preamble occurs when the preamble doesn't match the legal eight-byte Ethernet synchronization pattern. No backoff error means a transceiver transmitted when there was no carrier, but also that a transceiver did not wait for the necessary 9.6-microsecond interpacket spacing. Figure 15.4 lists additional statistics.

The normal Ethernet network experiences minimal collision rates, approximately 1–2%, and a negligible number of CRC, alignment, or packet size errors. Errors for these items should be insignificant; significant error rates imply malfunctioning hardware, software, or network overloads.

Theoretical and Obtainable Capacity

Another useful statistic measures obtainable performance against a capacity. See Figure 15.5 for theoretical and attainable transmission rates. The theoretical capacity of Ethernet is 10 megabits per second, or 1.25 megabytes per second since a byte contains 8 bits. Sustained burst rate on Ethernet, really an attainable rate as determined empirically, is 2.5 megabits per second, or approximately 300,000 bytes per second, and this can be represented as a rate. This yields a difference between the theoretical rate and actual throughput. Calculated and plotted graphs detail this later in the chapter.

Note that in most computer nomenclature megabits and megabytes are usually octal numbers and are rounded for convenience. A megabit is actually 1,048,576 bits (2^{100}), a kilobit is 1024 bits (2^{10}), and these numbers are *not* pertinent here. Ethernet is an exception to this generic computer nomenclature as all of its numerical calculations are based on a decimal count; transmission rates are based upon 20 megahertz, or 20 million clock cycles per second. Since this clock timing drives a Manchester encoding scheme as outlined in Chapter 4, this cycle yields 10,000,000 bits per second in communications terms. Packet size is averaged at 1024 bytes for these calculations.

rates of transmission		bits	bytes	packets
specified rate	per second	10 Mb	1.25 MB	1280
attainable rate	per second	2.5 Mb	.312 KB	160
specified rate	per minute	500 Mb	75 MB	76800
attainable rate	per minute	150 Mb	19.25 MB	19200
specified rate	per hour	36000 Mb	4500 MB	4,608,000
attainable rate	per hour	9000 Mb	1125 MB	1,152,000
specified rate	per shift	288,000 Mb	36000 MB	38,864,000
attainable rate	per shift	67,000 Mb	9000 MB	9,716,000

Figure 15.5 Ethernet transmission rates for two-node networks.

These statistics pertain to two machines talking only to each other without the interference from other machines trying to communicate simultaneously. Ethernet is a collision detection medium which means that a transceiver begins to talk in order to see if the network actually is busy and the 96-millisecond delay time creates a window for collision. When a collision occurs all transceivers must now reset their transmissions and the interrupted packet must be retransmitted. Because the rate of collisions and throughput are exponential, actual throughput is not so directly calculable for a busy network. More involved mathematics are required to model the Ethernet mechanisms and estimate this information. Two models are presented later in this chapter, although the next two figures summarize the mathematics pictorially. A model of throughput for a tuned two-node network is represented by Figure 15.6. The slope of the curve reflects the interdependence that is apt to occur between two nodes at higher transmission rates and a condition called "synchronization."

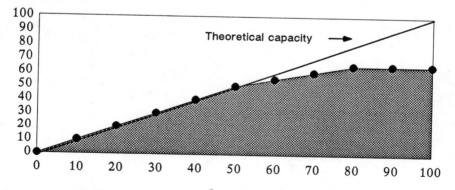

Figure 15.6 Empirical Ethernet throughput on a two-node network.

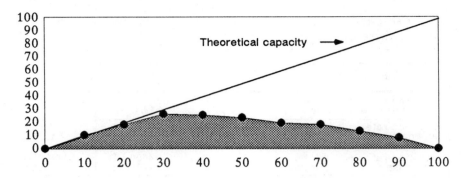

Figure 15.7 Empirical Ethernet throughput on a fully populated network.

A similar model of a multinode network is represented by Figure 15.7. These statistics were empirically generated on a tuned 100-node network, of which 10 nodes supported fully populated eight-port fan-out units and no synchronization of transmission. Total workstation count is therefore 172. There were no repeaters on this network. The cost of collision on network performance is obvious when comparing Figures 15.6 and 15.7, although this loss is still not calculable. This differs from Figure 15.1 because the network is not saturating completely except above 90% loading levels. One explanation is that the user-level software is failing, or that users are deterred from accessing the network.

Efficiency would read 100% if Ethernet were deterministic, if Ethernet were used solely for long haul transmissions between two nodes, or if two channels were established for two nodes, one outbound, one inbound much like a two-lane highway versus a single lane country road. As the number of machines and nodes increases, the probability of collision statistically increases and throughput falls. Benchmarks of collision avoid-

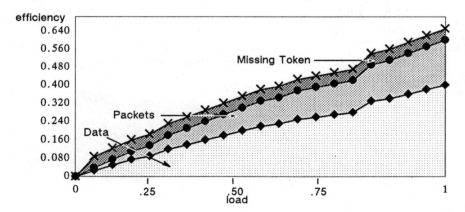

Figure 15.8 Token ring protocol efficiency as a function of traffic load.

ance in token ring networks imply that token passing schemes are more efficient above 35 to 40% network loading. This empirical benchmark matches the shape in Figure 15.7 and the token throughput graph presented in Figure 15.8. Packet size also effects transmission throughput by changing latency time and the time between successive transmissions, and by potentially forcing latency to the 96-millisecond minimum.

Transmission Efficiency

Packet size limits packet rates as Figure 15.9 indicates. The false implication is that Ethernet is more efficient with smaller packets. However, each packet requires a fixed-cost overhead that detracts from "efficiency."

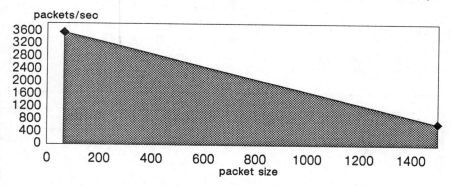

Figure 15.9 Throughput as a function of packet size.

While gross transmission efficiency is a linear function of packet size as Figure 15.10 displays, other events alter efficiency. For example, data messages that are less than the minimum 46-byte frame are padded to that full length, thus yielding a greater inefficiency.

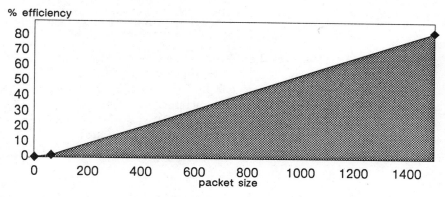

Figure 15.10 Ethernet channel efficiency as a function of packet size.

Likewise, transmissions that exceed maximum packet length are parsed and broadcast in multiple packets with the toll of multiple packets. While the gross evaluation suggests reasonable efficiency, the internal and external control information often demanded by TCP/IP, XNS, or DECnet lowers these figures. If the reader recalls, the IP protocol requires a confirmation. Ethernet is, however, more efficient than token passing mechanisms because there is no overhead for transmission control and permission other than what has been illustrated in chapter 5.

Transmission efficiency is defined by Shannon[7] as the percentage of data actually transmitted to the effort applied. Ethernet packet sizes vary from the 64-byte minimum to the 1518-byte maximum. While the packet does contain data, anywhere from 1 byte to 1500 bytes, each packet also contains a minimum of 18 bytes of address and accounting information. Additionally, TCP/IP demands its control information fields, and these reserve the first few positions of the Ethernet data field. Transmission preamble and separation delay subtract from the maximum transmission capacity as well, and because these items are fixed sizes for each packet transmitted, efficiency is higher for larger packets as Figure 15.11 charts.

	Minimum Packet Size	Maximum Packet Size
Preamble	64 bytes	64 bytes
Address fields and overhead	144 bytes	144 bytes
Data frame	46 bytes	1500 bytes
Separation delay	96 bytes	96 bytes
	350 bytes	1804 bytes
Packets/second	3571	692
Preamble	1,828,544	354,753
Address fields and overhead	4,114,224	798,192
Data frame	1,314,266	8,314,500
Separation delay	2,742,816	532,128
Efficiency	0.02%	83%

Figure 15.11 Ethernet transmission efficiency by packet size. The data frame is the variable-sized element with a minimum of 46 bytes to a maximum of 1500 bytes, although actual data may contain just a single byte.

Figure 15.12 summarizes the overhead costs for different packet sizes in a single chart. Obviously, this information represents theoretical capacity. In actual usage, average packet size and the distribution of packet sizes affect network performance, data throughput, and data transmission efficiency. The capacity and the detrimental effects of collisions must be developed with a completely different type of mathematics.

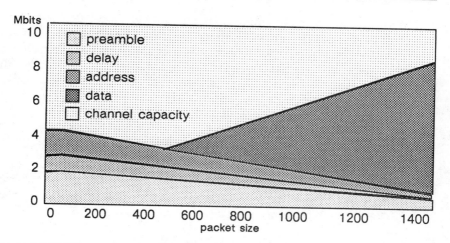

Figure 15.12 Ethernet channel efficiency as a function of packet size.

Ethernet Modeling

Since Ethernet collisions are the major limitation to channel capacity and network utilization, it is important to model them. Because collisions are statistical and interdependent with many factors like packet size, node count, or average transmission rate, nonlinear methods are required to understand the transmission mechanics. An area of applied mathematics called *combinatorics* is useful for defining collision probabilities.

Combinatorics defines the mechanisms for counting correlated events and was explored mainly by the 17th century French mathematician Descartes to explain the probabilities of a then popular card game called Whist. Ethernet, like 52-card Whist, is a finite set of events. This includes transmission, reception, collision, and idle time. In Ethernet, the probability of a single-node network experiencing a collision is nil. The probability of a two-node network experiencing a collision is the probability that both nodes will transmit at the same time. Mathematically, this is reflected by the "negative" of that situation because it is more useful and mathematically expedient to explore the probability of not experiencing a collision due to the complex interrelationship of these events. The probability of *not* experiencing a collision is the chance that the first node does not transmit *and* the chance that the second node does not transmit. Subtract this equation from 1 to derive the probabilities of experiencing a collision. Figure 15.13 presents this for one, two, and many nodes.

The probability of a node actually transmitting is difficult to determine. First, a load level must be determined for each and every node. Second, that load must be applied *independently* for each node despite the possible correlation between events and the nonuniform loading often experienced on a network. This is often impossible since node transmission is dependent on what the network or other nodes are doing, and transmission often synchronizes due to the packet waiting times and processing times required on each transmitted packet at the destination node. Additionally, the mathematics assumes node and traffic independence which is not usually provided. For example, users work during the hours of 9 am through 5 pm, attend meetings, and work in parallel, therefore requesting the same services. Also TCP/IP confirmations are not processed independently. While combinatorics could estimate the cost of collisions, for these reasons combinatorics is usually superseded by more involved modeling techniques.

for 2 nodes:	P(collision) =	$1- (1-n_1)(1-n_2)$	(1)
for 3 nodes:	P(collision) =	$1- (1-n_1)(1-n_2-n_3)+$	(2)
		$(1-n_2)(1-n_1-n_3)+$	
		$(1-n_3)(1-n_1-n_2)$	
for N nodes:	P(collision) =	$1- (1-n_1)(1-n_2-n_3- \ldots - n_N)+$	(3)
		$(1-n_2)(1-n_1-n_3- \ldots -n_N)+$	
		$(1-n_N)(1-n_1-n_2- \ldots -n_{N-1})$	

where n_i = probability of node i transmitting

Figure 15.13 Combinatorics allows computation of collision probabilities.

Operations Research and Ethernet Modeling

More complex branches of mathematics are required in order to accurately describe the cost of collisions on Ethernet. This includes *Operations Research,* which encompasses probability theory, simplex reduction techniques, and heuristic modeling. These models have been developed and amplified since the 1950s as an outgrowth of formalized Operations Research. This is a fertile field for new findings, further research, and new applications. The mathematics are, however, practical enough to apply to Ethernet network service modeling. In fact, the graphs in this chapter were prepared using operations research models and equations. From this science two mathematical models accurately represent the transmission operations of Ethernet. The first is called a *Queuing Model,* and the other is called a *Markov chain.*

The Queue Model

The queuing model describes waiting lines (hence *queues),* service response times, and throughput. It is appropriate to apply to Ethernet because nodes wait in line for slot time to transmit. Queuing theory provides a large number of alternative mathematical models for predicting different real-world events such as airplane arrivals, gas station servicing time, and metropolitan traffic jams. The traffic jam analogy is appropriate here. The queuing model defines process steps, waiting times, service times, service fulfillments, and service request denials (e.g. collisions).

The three features of the Ethernet mechanism are the arrival process, the waiting queue, and the service mechanism as shown by Figure 15.14. This waiting line design illustrates the major mathematical groupings which include the source distribution, the waiting queue, and throughput as represented by serviced requests.

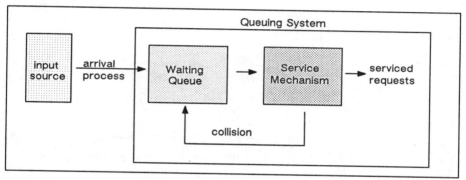

Figure 15.14 The queue service model.

The Markov Model

The Markov chain defines *transition states* for an environment. In the case of Ethernet, a transition is the change from a quiet network to a network in collision, or from a network in the state of transmission to a network in the state of idle. There are many more transition states. Markov modeling, sometimes used as part of *Monte Carlo* calculations, is particularly effective at representing games of chance. In fact, most of these algorithms were developed to increase the personal odds at the card tables of Europe in the 18th and 19th centuries as the Monte Carlo designation implies. Gambling provided the major impetus to the development of mathematics and calculus as we know it. Markovian models are appropriate tools to describe the behavior of CSMA/CD LANs because part of the Ethernet transmittal process includes the random arrival of transmission service requests. The fact that collisions are not random is not pertinent at this stage in the model definition because the collision mechanism itself does not define the model; the collision mechanism is an outgrowth of this model.

The state transitions described by the Markov model are presented by the flow Figure 15.15. The three states in Ethernet are Idle, Collision, and

Successful transmission. This yields nine transitional phases that include the change from idle to transmission, from idle to collision, and from collision to idle. The Markov model designates a probability for each state change, and these nine factors can be solved in the steady-state equilibrium.

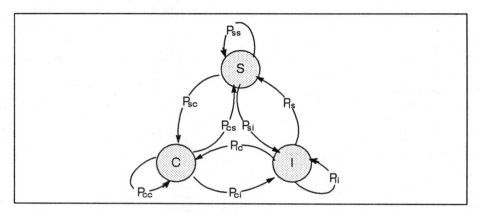

Figure 15.15 The classic Markovian state transition model as illustrated for Ethernet. The nodes represent event states which are transmission, collision, and channel idle. The arrows illustrate transitions between states.

The Ethernet Model

Figure 15.16 shows the single server mechanisms of Ethernet transmission fulfillment. Ethernet is a single server—one mechanism services all requests for transmission throughout a network—and this designation is independent of the node or machine count, or the actual network configuration. Only one packet request can be serviced at a time. The alternative is a collision. This illustration is a Markovian model because it represents the process rather than the waiting times, lines, and throughput as in Figure 15.14

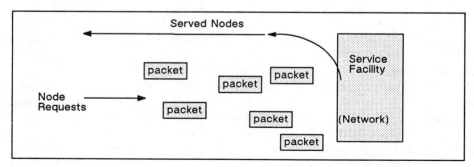

Figure 15.16 The classic Markovian model for Ethernet.

The next representation in Figure 15.17 condenses the many nodes into an organized and elegant model with a single server. This design simplifies the mathematical rendering into a queuing model architecture where the three basic statistics are introduced: successful throughput, collision, and traffic which is the sum of throughput and collisions.

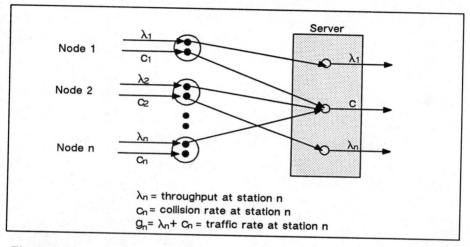

Figure 15.17 The classic queuing model architecture for Ethernet.

The Poisson Model

The classic queuing model assumes an infinite number of nodes and a fixed arrival time. This needs to be modified to model the mechanisms of Ethernet. Because Ethernet has a finite number of nodes (maximum 1024) the transmission request arrivals can be estimated with the *Poisson process*.

The Poisson process which defines λ_n, the mean arrival time, is described in Figure 15.18. The Poisson process models the *inter-arrival time*, the time between consecutive requests, and describes a phenomenon involving events which occur "rarely" in small time intervals. It is frequently applied when event distributions are studied, as in the case of Ethernet transmissions service requests. Transmission requests are fulfilled based upon a *birth-and-death* process in queuing theory. Births refer to requests for network service and deaths refer to the fulfillment of the communication request. Births and deaths occur *randomly* where the rates only depend upon the current state of the system. The crucial assumption for a Poisson distribution is that only one birth or death can occur at a time. Ethernet is a special case that is called a *limited source model* because the calling population is finite.

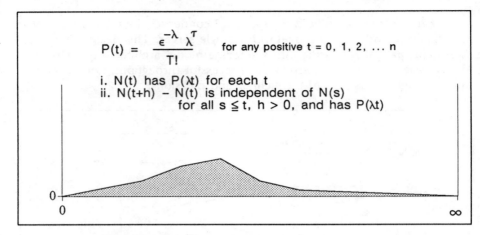

$$P(t) = \frac{\epsilon^{-\lambda} \lambda^{\tau}}{T!} \quad \text{for any positive } t = 0, 1, 2, \ldots n$$

i. $N(t)$ has $P(\lambda t)$ for each t
ii. $N(t+h) - N(t)$ is independent of $N(s)$
    for all $s \leq t$, $h > 0$, and has $P(\lambda t)$

Figure 15.18 The Poisson model for random Ethernet transmissions.

With these arrival (birth) and service (death) times assumptions, the mathematical architecture can be reduced to a set of queuing equations. In fact, the equations are necessary to answer questions posed at the beginning of this chapter; as a byproduct, other important statistics can be derived. The waiting queue itself is a quasi-random process that is not useful to model independently since the queue is determined by the Ethernet controller. Standard queuing equations [4] are listed in Figure 15.19.

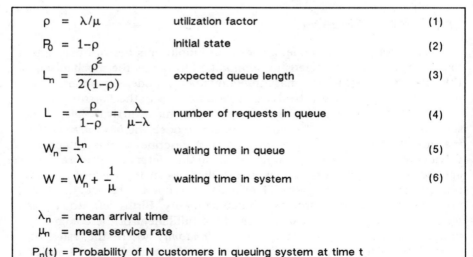

$\rho = \lambda/\mu$	utilization factor	(1)
$P_0 = 1-\rho$	initial state	(2)
$L_n = \dfrac{\rho^2}{2(1-\rho)}$	expected queue length	(3)
$L = \dfrac{\rho}{1-\rho} = \dfrac{\lambda}{\mu-\lambda}$	number of requests in queue	(4)
$W_n = \dfrac{L_n}{\lambda}$	waiting time in queue	(5)
$W = W_n + \dfrac{1}{\mu}$	waiting time in system	(6)

λ_n = mean arrival time
μ_n = mean service rate
$P_n(t)$ = Probability of N customers in queuing system at time t

Figure 15.19 The Pollaczek-Khintchne equations for steady-state solution of the Ethernet model. Many solutions are available due to the large number of mathematical interrelationships.

For example, if packets arrive every 16000μs and contain 1024 bytes (or 8192 bits), the utilization level will approximate 50% by equation (1). Likewise, the length of the queue will be .25 packet requests by equation (3) and (4), and wait time will average a 16000μs by equation (5); this is solved by plugging the resulting values of .25 and 16000μs into the formula. The total system time will logically include the 16000μs wait time plus the transmission time of 8192μs by equation (6). Despite the appearance of simplicity and linearity (and some very logical equations) many nonlinear assumptions support these estimates.

It is interesting that as service times increase, *all* waiting times increase. Therefore, the key conclusion is that *consistency* of node service has as important a bearing on network performance as average service speed. In other words, if the network is erratic, performance will be that much worse. Also, it is interesting to note that the queuing model does not predict collision frequency; the Markov model does.

The reader is spared the tedious steps in reaching the equations for collision costs. The transition between events must be explored to solve the collision costs. Logically, the probabilities for all nine transitional stages must sum to unity since only one stage can occur during a given interval. The times associated with each stage can be solved as a series of linear equations as shown by Figure 15.20.

$$
\begin{bmatrix}
P_s * P_{ss} + P_c * P_{cs} + P_i * P_{is} = P_s \\
P_s * P_{ss} + P_c * P_{cc} + P_i * P_{ic} = P_c \\
P_s * P_{si} + P_c * P_{ci} + P_i * P_{ii} = P_i \\
P_s * 1 \ \ + P_c * 1 \ \ + P_i * 1 \ \ = 1
\end{bmatrix}
$$

$$s = P_s / (P_s * L_s + P_c * L_c + P_i * L_i) \qquad \text{Throughput} \qquad (1)$$

$$U = s * L_s \qquad\qquad\qquad\qquad\qquad \text{Utilization} \qquad (2)$$

Figure 15.20 Equilibrium probabilities for the Markov state transition model.

Each state change probability is reduced to simplest form in Figure 15.21, and these entities are substituted into the four preceding linear equations and reduced. The results also yield utilization and throughput factors based upon these same equilibrium values.

	Representation	Mathematical Reduction
P_{ii}	$P_0(\infty)$	0
P_{is}	$P_0(a)$	e^{-ag}
P_{ic}	$1 - P_{is}$	$1 - e^{-ag}$
P_{si}	$P_0(1)$	e^{-g}
P_{ss}	$P_1(0)\, P_0(a)$	$ge^{-(1+a)g}$
P_{sc}	$1 - P_{si} - P_{ss}$	$1 - e^{-g} - ge^{-(1+a)g}$
P_{ci}	$P_0(\bar{y})$	$\bar{e}^{Yg}$
P_{cs}	$P_1(\bar{y})\, P_0(a)$	$ge^{-(\bar{Y}+a)g}$
P_{cc}	$1 - P_{ci} - P_{cs}$	$1 - e^{-\bar{Y}g} - ge^{-(\bar{Y}+a)g}$

$$P_k(t) = \frac{(gt)^k}{k!}e^{-gt} \qquad \bar{Y} = \left(\frac{1}{1-e^{-ag}}\right)\left[a - \frac{1}{g}\left(1 - e^{-ag}\right)\right]$$

Figure 15.21 Reduction of the steady-state transition probabilities. See [6].

However, these do not show the collision statistic without other steps. $\bar{Y}$ represents the expected collision count and P_k is the probability of collision; Figure 15.22 lists the state and reduction equations. Unfortunately, predicting either the number of collisions or the probability of collision remains a complicated nonlinear equation.

State	Mathematical Representation
L_s = successful transmission	1
L_c = collision	$\left(\dfrac{1}{1-e^{-ag}}\right)\left[a - \dfrac{1}{g}\left(1 - e^{-ag}\right)\right]$
L_I = idle	$1/g$

g = packet rate given average transmission time
a = propagation delay (transmission slot time)
$$\bar{Y} = \int_0^a (1 - F(y))\,dy = \int_0^a \left[1 - P_0(a-t)(1 - P_0(t))/(1 - P_0(a))\right]\,dt$$

Figure 15.22 State times for each Ethernet event. A is the propagation delay, or the transmission slot time.

The sets of equations in Figure 15.23 generate statistics on network efficiency, success of channel capture, and the contention interval. Efficiency in this definition implies the rate at which a node can capture the Ethernet channel and transmit. The *contention interval* is described as the time period when collision can occur. Because each node listens before transmitting the slot time, or network propagation time, is defined as the contention interval.

$$A = na(1-a)^{n-1} \qquad \text{This is maximized for the ratio} \quad A = \frac{1}{k} \qquad (1)$$

$$P_j = A(1-A)^{j-1} \qquad \text{The probability that a contention interval is length j} \qquad (2)$$

$$\bar{j} = \sum_{j=1}^{\infty} jP_j = \frac{1}{A} = (1 - \frac{1}{n})^{1-n} \quad \text{average contention interval length} \qquad (3)$$

$$\text{Efficiency}_{CSMA-CD} = \frac{T}{T + \bar{j}} \qquad (4)$$

average wait time: k < n nodes

Figure 15.23 Ethernet collision and efficiency equations. Equation (1) calculates the probability that a node will successfully acquire the channel. This holds for k transmitting stations on a network with a total of n nodes. "a" represents the equal probability that each station transmits. Equation (2) expresses the probability that the collision contention interval is length "j." Equation (3) is derived from the first two equations. Because each transmission will have an equal probability of collision, this can be described by equation (4).

Dissimilar Arrivals

A Markovian model modified to handle a finite number of nodes can explain how peak load periods generate dissimilar arrival rates. *Random* has a special meaning in probability mathematics. It refers to a process with a predictable outcome but stochastic events. Random does not mean "erratic." There is rarely a micro-scale pattern to network loading, and thus a very "random" and erratic transmission arrival process. In keeping with the practical bent of this book, the reader will be spared the tediousness of this mathematical expansion. However, the preceding solutions assumed a Poisson arrival rate of uniform distribution. In point of fact, arrival rates are not mathematically random but erratic and because of the coordinated nature of most transaction processing, arrival rates correlate. Figure 15.24 lists the reasons.

- Process coordination
- A standard workday
- Transmission and receipt
- Nonstochastic load demands
- Queue pressure from incompleted transactions

Figure 15.24 Reasons for nonrandom service request distribution.

Two major Poisson distribution assumptions fail with Ethernet because there are variations in service times and requests are not random. Packets clearly have different lengths and require varying transmission service times. Protocols remove the randomness of transmissions from the system by providing resolution of transmission contentions and failures. Additionally, a minimum interarrival time is imposed at 96 milliseconds. Interarrival time is the transmission slot time, or the time between consecutive transmissions. Poisson's limited source distribution is not heuristically matched and for these reasons an Erhlang distribution is sometimes used to approximate collision statistics despite its assumption of random interarrival times. The Erhlang distribution is useful because it approximates empirical observations more readily. Figure 15.25 illustrates utilization rates for different *skew* values of the Erhlang distribution.Notice that it shows the same traffic features that were first presented in Figures 15.1 and 15.2; this completes the mathematical modeling.

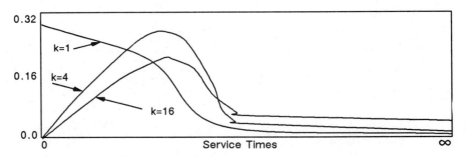

Figure 15.25 The family of Erhlang probability density functions. Service times are presented along the horizontal axis. The variable k is proxy for packet lengths and frequency of transmissions.

Figure 15.26 illustrates the network utilization factor for different packet lengths and higher levels of transmission. These statistics show that higher utilization rates will saturate Ethernet, but in the end, larger numbers of nodes will halt efficient use of the network as the sheer number of transmitting nodes raises the probability (and actuality) of collisions to unacceptable levels. Performance degrades as the channel saturates. Despite the fact that the channel is a single server and the multiple node requests from a single node appear to correspond to single requests from multiple nodes, multiple nodes more readily degrade performance. This is akin to the familiar highway crawl not merely because too many cars use the highway during the day, but because there is too much traffic during selected intervals and the bottleneck never clears; every automobile is different and can't be likened to a bus even though a bus logically provides a similar distribution service.

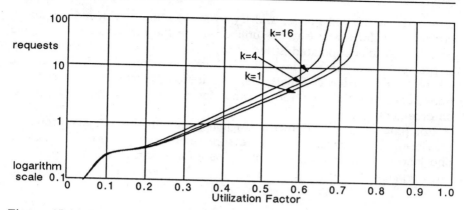

Figure 15.26 Channel utilization factor charted against steady-state node requests. The variable k is proxy for packet length and frequency of transmissions.

Multiplexer Filters

There is a tradeoff between node queuing time and the collision times both at the node and at the cable media. Local concentration units (via a multiplexing fan-out or smart repeater) will increase node queuing time, although they reduce the probability of a collision on the cable media. The mathematical equations on the previous pages can be modified to reflect the local concentrating effect of the multiplexer. For additional information on this subject, see references [4] and [5]. In simple words, the multiplexer filters collisions from a clustered grouping, thus lowering the chance that collisions will even reach the network. Subdivision of an overloaded network into small gatewayed subnets provides similar gains by lowering traffic load and stabilizing traffic flow. Traffic problems may recur if sub-net traffic backs onto the main network. The analogy is that traffic can be isolated into "high speed" and "local" lanes just as on certain high-volume automobile freeways, therefore reducing "traffic sheer." This implication explains why the multiplexer and subnets are the most effective method for solving network bottlenecks.

Conclusion

In conclusion, when all is said and calculated, it is clear that Ethernet is a very efficient and effective medium. Protocols such as token ring which are deterministic just are not as powerful as this random and chaotic collision mechanism. The realization is interesting when considering other protocol alternatives. Additionally, the statistics and modeling confirm the practical limits network designers and managers have learned by trial and error. Plan for a maximum of 30% channel capacity. Limit single networks to a maximum of 60 nodes, and try to avoid subnets with more than 30 nodes particularly where nodes utilize remote file service or frequent file transfers. A fully populated Ethernet with 1024 nodes is fine if the network is sparsely used, or provides only minimal functionality. Last, provide adequate alternative channels when saturation is imminent, or clear all nonessential traffic from the channel for a manually employed priority enforcement.

For practical application, the original graphs in this chapter provide a measuring stick against which to measure a network's performance, health, and load. The next chapter applies this information to network performance repairs.

Chapter 16

Tuning Performance

While the last chapter detailed the mathematics of Ethernet in terms of queuing models, state transitions, and the expanded algebra, this chapter explores methods to rechannel overloaded networks, improve throughput, increase network speed, and improve network reliability. Most network managers eventually experience network performance degradation as network software functionality or workload increases. Improving performance usually implies increasing the packet throughput and managing the consistency of the transmission rate. Performance also encompasses network reliability and efficiency.

There are several ways to solve network problems, including observance of specification, rechanneling, installing gateways, smart repeaters, and fan-outs, as well as more exotic technologies. A very sophisticated software solution requires an increase in the interpacket delay for establishing *priority enforcement*. Unfortunately, TCP/IP does not support priority transmissions. Best solutions are usually based on a clear understanding of the network problems and the available, simple, and relevant technologies.

This chapter details the techniques necessary to tune an Ethernet network. These techniques include monitoring system performance, analyzing network statistics, and understanding the condition of that network. Figure 16.1 outlines performance tuning methods in a time-saving list.

- Monitor network load
- Monitor network performance
- Analyze network statistics
- Verify that the network matches Ethernet specifications
- Insure component consistency
- Install alternative channels for specialized needs
- Install multiple channels to balance loads
- Isolate segments with gateways
- Remove network repeaters
- Install "smart" repeaters
- Provide fan-out units to improve configuration
- Buffer messages with store and forward devices

Figure 16.1 Performance tuning methodology.

Network Load and Performance Monitoring

Network management is responsible for knowing what happens on the network. Ideally, the management will see the load approach unacceptable levels and take the necessary precautions to maintain high quality service before users are aware of traffic overloads. Few tools other than a protocol analyzer or specialized packet-counting software tools provide sufficient services to monitor network performance with any accuracy. Small networks supporting limited file transfers, mainframe to personal computer downloading and uploading usually avoid capacity problems. Larger or more utilized networks often demonstrate a creeping traffic growth, and eventual and sudden network capacity constraints. While it is possible to localize and resolve network overloads without understanding the composition of the network traffic, network load and performance monitoring pinpoint locations of problems and provide the network manager with information necessary to correctly implement network repairs.

Network Statistic Analysis

The mathematics are a curiosity unless understood and applied. Proper network load and performance analysis is most efficient with an understanding of the basic equations. Traffic rates (relative and absolute), collision rates, and request resolution time (internode timing) are some of these important equations. Any rates that exceed a "normal" load imply a possible problem situation. If all rates vary, but do not vary logically, this too can be a clue to network performance problems. Chapter 22 includes statistical evaluations for different states of network performance to aid in comprehension and troubleshooting.

Verify Configuration to Ethernet Specification

On small networks, the prevalent cause of network performance problems are misspecification problems. The network segment could exceed the 200/500-meter length limitations, the node count could exceed the 100-unit maximum, or the transceiver drop cables could exceed the 40/50 meter maximum. Also, transceivers could be spaced too close together, or be simultaneously configured for 1.0, 2.0, and 802.3 standards. Figure 16.2 reviews common network misspecification problems. Other root causes include sloppy installation that results in faulty cables, loose connections, poorly configured software, or mismatched cable components. Cables often "work" on Ethernet until the network becomes overloaded; mismatched cable raise the impedance above acceptable levels. If you suspect one of these problems, consult Chapters 4 and 5 for configuration information, or review Chapter 7 for installation suggestions.

- Maximum segment cable length exceeded
- Maximum segment node count exceeded
- Too many segments/repeaters
- Maximum transceiver drop cable length exceeded
- Transceiver drop cable grounding incomplete
- Poor electrical connections
- Low quality components
- Mismatched components
- Sloppy installation
- Transceiver spacing not multiples of 2.5 meters

Figure 16.2 Critical parameter violations.

Component Consistency

Another common cause for degraded network performance is noncompliance with a single Ethernet standard. Ethernet 1.0 does not work well in conjunction with Ethernet 2.0 because of collision detection differences, nor will IEEE 802.3 standard systems work efficiently with either Ethernet. All are similar. Timing differences are the primary cause of traffic inconsistency. The same argument can be made with XNS, DECnet, and HPnet TCP/IP derivatives. When multiple system software architectures must interface on the same network, the different systems can be isolated on separate network segments as Chapter 7 suggested. At a minimum, monitor mixed networks specifically for transmission deficiencies. Other specialized interfacing equipment such as repeaters, gateways, or bridges can adequately protect network users from performance degradation due to mismatched standards and minor operational or component variations.

Ethernet components, too, can create difficult-to-uncover problems. Different vendors may supply transceivers or Ethernet controllers with transmission rate clocks with subtle timing differences, or marginal signal quality. This equipment, while tuned for incestuous usage, may communicate with other vendors' equipment unpredictably. Therefore, maintain consistent network node configurations for best performance.

Network Saturation Solutions

Most Ethernet networks experience performance degradation when the traffic level is too high. The last chapter developed the mathematics and explored the methods to track and confirm this problem. If the traffic level is too high, and it cannot be reduced through user incentives (like peak time toll charges), there are several other methods to divert traffic for better performance including off-loading, installation of "local disks," additional or alternative channel installation, and specialized repeaters. Load, traffic consistency, peak volumes, capacity, node location, recabling, and network extension techniques are a few of the issues covered within the next few sections to aid in resolving performance problems.

Distribute Load

The most economically available method to lower network usage is to charge for network service at graduated rates and offer users incentives to avoid prime-time network access. This is what the telephone utility does to reduce day time traffic and encourage off-peak usage. Since any network is built to handle a peak load, and since a peak load may be several times larger than off-hour usage, there is a built-in network excess capacity. Unfortunately, that extra capacity is available during non-prime working hours. Figure 16.3 illustrates this principle by graphing the network load during the progress of a normal day. Harried users often implicitly understand this principle and re-orient their work schedules to reduce the impact on the overloaded network. Publish a graph of daily network loads to encourage off-peak usage if financial incentives are impractical.

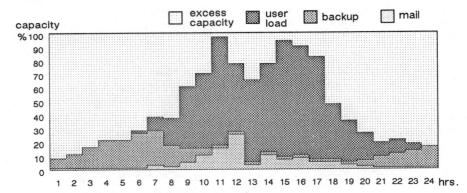

Figure 16.3 Peak network load capacity.

When this last option is unavailable, the next easiest method to reduce traffic levels is to filter the traffic and not allow certain vehicles on the network during peak usage. The network administration group, for example, doesn't need to perform data backups when the network is overloaded. Electronic mail can be stored and forwarded when the network shows a lull, or else saved for distribution during non-peak hours. Other processes may be hogs of network resources. Curtail such processes. Figure 16.4 illustrates a typical distribution of network traffic. Note that this display represents volume percentages each hour of the typical day. Collision traffic parallels the peaks of the last figure, but most traffic is disk access. Mail and graphics paging is a minor component in this sample.

Electronic mail often starts as a ten-line memo containing 1000 characters, but then is directed to 150 users. Since each user receives a separate

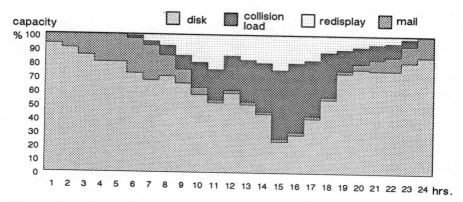

Figure 16.4 Traffic composition.

copy, 150,000 characters plus the mail addressing information and Ethernet packet information must be included. That simple mail message therefore requires upwards of 300,000 characters of network transmission. A bulletin board with a single posting reduces this "junk mail" load almost fully. Side benefits include a reduction of "temporary" mail disk storage, temporary because each day's new mail will require that old space.

Data backup could be banned from the network and performed exclusively from the node bus. Such a policy may entail additional backup devices; it shifts financial costs from network communication channel improvements (infrastructure) to node-specific upgrades (depreciable usage-specific equipment).

Provide Local Resources

Since network traffic often consists of paging information, graphic display, or mail transmissions throughout a facility, a solution is to install local resources. Network printing can be relegated to local nodes, as can file storage. Determine the composition of the network traffic and rebuild the network to optimize for local solutions. Local disks and segregated backup channels might be an appropriate step to improve the performance of the sample networks illustrated in Figures 16.3 and 16.4. This type of analysis is ideal before embarking on any network reconfiguration. The down side to partitioning a network into clusters of local resources is that the concentration of resources originally available through networking is reversed and shifts financial costs. Management load increases, costs increase with the addition of local resources because local units are generally more expensive than the public "bulk" versions. This reverses the economies of scale available through network resources. While this alternative may be more expensive, or take too long a time to install, it is an option.

Install Specialty Controller Hardware

There are more sophisticated and expensive methods to resolve Ethernet bottlenecks. It is possible—but unlikely for most network users—to modify TCP/IP or build a new operating system to provide for priority transmissions. There are also specialized hardware implementations that can improve Ethernet performance. Controllers with more buffer space increase throughput for slow workstations by caching large transmissions. Specifically, Ethernet controllers are a growing tuning option. As an example, the *interphase controller* provides better node performance at the link level by providing three times the normal Ethernet clock rate and by timing transmissions to overlap. Other controllers that compress data achieve more efficient network utilization, while some vendors are designing hardware that will provide optimized protocol translations faster than software.

Optimize Node Bottlenecks

Unloading overburdened nodes is another simple method to improve network performance. A common example is a workstation connected between two networks that provides gateway service. If this workstation is heavily used for processing, it will not have enough power to provide protocol translation and data rebroadcasting. Note, too, that the Ethernet controllers are usually bound to the node workstation's bus speed or to the disk I/O speed. Solutions include installing a faster CPU, or dedicating a workstation to gateway service, or adding a specialized gateway to supplement the workstation, as illustrated in Figure 16.5.

There are three possible performance gains from substituting specialty gateway or bridge units for dual-ported nodes. First, there is better individual node performance. Second, there is faster throughput by off loading suspect node controller hardware or constrained bus configurations. Third,

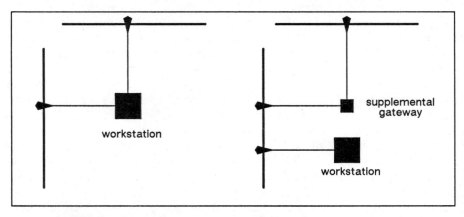

Figure 16.5 Supplemental gateway provides dedicated service to reduce a bottleneck.

there is better signal quality and interconnectivity for multivendor installations and Thicknet/Thinnet crossovers; the workstation providing multivendor gateway service is likely to perform better for its native information than for other vendors' information.

One performance bottleneck may actually be a bridge, gateway, or smart repeater. If a unit is rated at 12,000 packets per second, it will handle about 6000 packets per side under optimal conditions. Do not overlook this as a potential bottleneck on extended topologies. Also, consider that the interpretation of a higher-level protocols slows the repeating process. As a consequence, a fan-out unit is faster than a repeater. A simple repeater in turn is faster than a smart repeater. Routers are slower than bridges.

Provide Alternative Channels

When a network carries a traffic volume in excess of design capacity, performance deteriorates nonlinearly. If performance is already degraded, new loads degrade performance disproportionately as illustrated mathematically in Chapter 15. This is true for Ethernet, since Ethernet is a statistical process, but not true for token passing networks which are *non-stochastic*. Vendors are now introducing token networks specifically designed as Ethernet bridges to provide a better load distribution. Alternative channels provide additional communication paths, much as side roads relieve a highway bottleneck after a traffic accident. Alternative channels lower the demand on the network much the same way that local devices lessen the number of requests for network access. An alternative channel might provide specialized high-speed disk-to-disk file transfers, imaging information transfer, or terminal services.

Terminals (DTE) require full packet transmission for each key stroke and are an overlooked Ethernet resource hog. Terminal equipment transmissions reveal efficiencies of less than 2% when most network traffic may experience 60% efficiencies or higher. RS-232 lines, twisted-pair for example, yield a better match than Ethernet for such low speed transmission. Conversely, an imaging camera or scanner often digitizes upwards of a megabyte of information from a single picture. At Ethernet speeds, 1000 or more packets will need to be built and transmitted. Such a load could jam an unloaded network for four complete seconds, or a network at capacity for several minutes. An Ethernet in a constant bottleneck may be unable to complete the data transfer in a suitable time frame, and thus "time out." Direct device-to-node bus connection improves transfer rates and transfer success rates. Figure 16.6 represents several variations of alternative data communications channels. Many managers recommend hybrid networks and tune performance in just this manner.

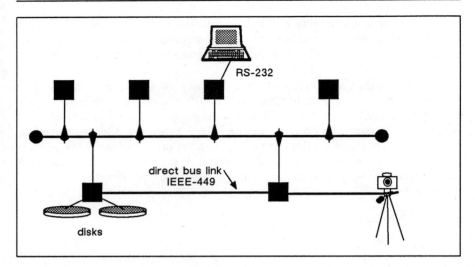

Figure 16.6 Alternative channel provides dedicated service to reduce a bottleneck.

Install Fan-out Units

Multitaps, the multiport Ethernet taps, also yield a performance boost for saturated networks. The fan-out unit filters each of its clients and resolves potential collisions before those collisions even reach the network node. Figure 16.7 depicts this process with five simultaneous requests negotiated to a single network access. Heavy users are best concentrated together on the same fan-outs since each fan-out unit in effect acts as a small network before traffic is committed to the network coax.

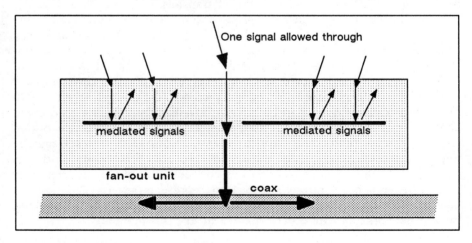

Figure 16.7 Fan-out units reduce network collisions.

In fact, fan-out units provide network service without a coax cable which is useful for shows and other temporary needs. Because the fan-out also negotiates potential collisions from the workstations connected to it, its usage lends the fan-out to construction of *concentrated local area networks* (CLANs). Note that the fan-out does not intercept packets like the smart repeater and prevent their dissemination. It only filters potential collisions from among the workstations it services before these collisions reach the coax; all packets are passed to the coax. If correctly planned, such concentration can substantially lower the network traffic, as Figure 16.8 explains, by facilitating precollision mediation.

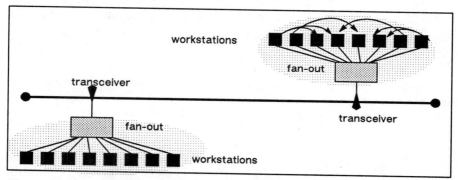

Figure 16.8 Fan-out units can be applied to create a *concentrated* LAN.

In a clever and subtle variation of the CLAN configuration, a fan-out unit would service eight stations (a common number of ports supported by a multiport), although one station would also interface to the network as an additional valid network node and mediate the traffic. Since the marketed aim of the unit is to provide eight ports for each transceiver, this next configuration contradicts the usual application of the fan-out units.

Figure 16.9 contrasts these two uses of the fan-out unit pictorially. The normal application is to provide eight ports with a single transceiver for eight workstations, whereas in this optimal performance configuration, one node location services the same eight parts, but with the addition of an additional Ethernet controller and transceiver cable in one of the eight workstations.

This is not as hardware efficient, but it does yield significant improvement for concentrated high-density nodes. This adaptation of off-the-shelf parts creates a surprising and inexpensive alternative to the smart repeater which is explained in the next section. It differs from the general application because the fan-out offers a *restricted* local area network. Such a design could appropriately service file servers and busy data backup equipment without perceptively increasing the network traffic load since it is a completely isolated LAN. In an analogous configuration, a workstation that is performing as a software gateway can act as a smart repeater too.

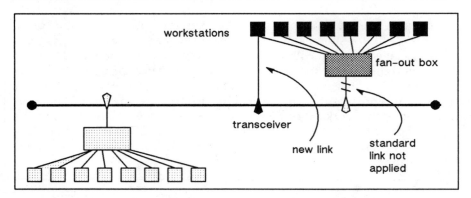

Figure 16.9 Nonstandard application of a fan-out to decrease load.

Remove Repeaters

Repeaters generally *create* performance problems by extending the transmission slot time. This increases the likelihood of collisions on the network. A repeater simply increases the potential for too large, too busy network configurations by extending the network architecture to the statistical breaking point. In situations where a network is grossly overloaded, disconnection of repeater units may solve the traffic bottleneck as shown in Figure 16.10. This obviously defeats the purpose of the network by cutting intercommunication channels. There are other alternatives, but this iconoclastic solution is quickly implemented to solve short term overloading until more reasonable (and expensive) options can be implemented.

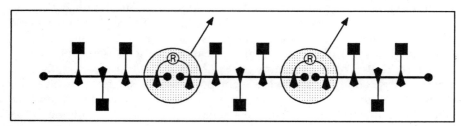

Figure 16.10 Unlink segments on an overloaded network.

Substitute Smart Repeaters

Repeaters fall into two categories. The simple repeater as described above just repeats a transmission signal onto another network segment. If the new segment is in the state of collision, the originating segment will also experience that collision and both segments will need to transmit the packets again.

The other category of repeater, the smart repeater, filters packets for retransmission. While the smart repeater does not avoid the inherent collision conflicts, the smart repeater can isolate and section a network for better performance. The smart repeater transmits only those packets with a destination on another segment. It traps local packets just as the fan-out CLAN configuration traps local packets. Figure 16.11 illustrates the function of a smart repeater.

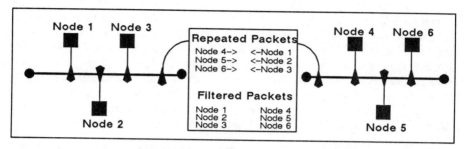

Figure 16.11 Install smart repeaters on an overloaded network. Only packets sourced from nodes 4, 5, or 6 destined for nodes 1, 2, or 3 are repeated across this gateway. Likewise, only packets sourced from nodes 1, 2, or 3 destined for nodes 4, 5, or 6 are repeated. Traffic thus is reduced.

While a network of 100 nodes may generate, for example, 100 units of global traffic, a network segmented in three sections with two repeaters (the maximum configuration) will generate the same volume of traffic because the repeaters will be forwarding the complete 100 units of traffic. If the network is correctly designed, the load originating on each section is perhaps as low as 33 units (the average). If smart repeaters are installed

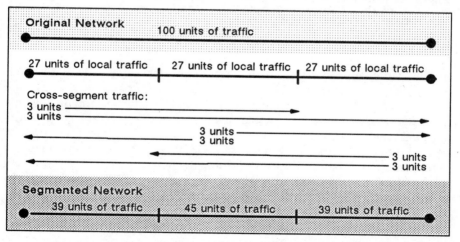

Figure 16.12 Smart repeaters reduce network load by isolating traffic to the necessary sections. Three sections of a single segment have an average of 33 units of traffic, of which 27 are local and 6 are destined for other segments. When these segments are subdivided with smart repeaters, traffic volume decreases by 55–61%.

instead, the result is a possible reduction in network load of 66%, although a more reasonable expectation would be about 50%. End sections will experience a lower traffic level, while the mid section will often be forced to repeat traffic bound for the other end section. This economy is illustrated in Figure 16.12.

The Ethernet specifications limit the number of segments a packet can travel to a maximum of three. Large and efficient network configurations that adhere to this limitation can be designed. For better performance, an unlimited number of segments can join one (or more) backbone segments for network sectioning, as shown in Figure 16.13. However, the smart repeater will not lower the load unless each network segment is carefully planned to concentrate loads within its boundaries. If each segment, or a grouping of segments, has individual overloading problems, the smart repeater will only provide a short-lived performance improvement.

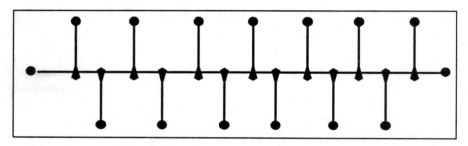

Figure 16.13 Network configuration linked with smart repeaters. This design echoes the gateway design and is a standard tactic to extend the bus topology.

Buffer Networks with Store and Forward Gateways

The store and forward mechanism duplicates some of the filtration functionality of the smart repeater. It also understands the concept of the collision and will store a message packet for an unlimited amount of time until network slot time is available; it might save the message packet until off-peak hours. This store and forward technology is used for long-haul optical fiber networks and microwave links to overcome the inherent weaknesses of the collision detection technology, because long-haul connections cannot function efficiently in realtime at Ethernet speeds. In effect, the CSMA/CD packet is converted to an orderly, token transmission as outlined by Figure 16.14.

This is an expensive technology usually installed as an ISO gateway. It is, however, suitable for low volume, low priority transmission. It is dependent upon the robustness of the network software, since the typical TCP/IP transmission confirmation is not supported in real time. In fact, receipt confirmation may not be supported except at the mechanical level of the store and forward gateway. The concept is akin to a receptionist taking a message when the telephoned party is already busy; no message receipt confirmation is provided to the caller and the intended recipient of the call never knows he was wanted until a message is received, or until a follow-up call is accepted.

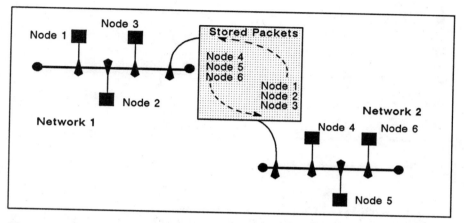

Figure 16.14 Store and forward buffering relieves bottlenecks by holding nonessential packets until the network is less loaded.

Rechannel with Additional Ethernet Segments

When network bottlenecks are endemic the best solution is additional Ethernet channels. This implies that new cable and additional Ethernet access hardware will be installed. There are at least two distinct options. The first requires a duplication of the existing baseband network. The second alternative requires the installation of a multichannel broadband network. Both options are costly, and the decision making process will contrast the financial costs, maintenance issues, and the risk of acquiring a new technology. It is important to realize that multichanneling is no panacea; sufficient capacity must exist on each channel to provide transmission for local traffic and the detoured traffic.

Expand Conservatively

Figure 16.15 presents a conservative expansion process. When other expansion options have been applied as deemed appropriate, the actual recabling should be planned in stages to minimize downtime and disruption. In this example, the overloaded original network is left intact until a new channel is designed, built, and tested. Changes proceed in simple stages until operation is assured. If subtle problems arise in the early stages of the transformation, the changeover can be reversed until resolved. This philosophy is useful for new installations, and also for revisions and repairs to existing networks. A preplanned move is best, as suggested in Chapter 9.

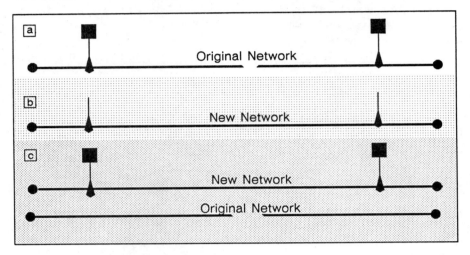

Figure 16.15 The expansion process is best achieved by a phased installation in case of installation problems. Figure 16.15(a) shows two nodes on an overloaded network. These nodes will be relocated to a new network. The intermediate step, shown in (b), illustrates the installation of a parallel coax and tested target transceiver and cable installations. The last step is the relocation of the node equipment and removal of the old transceiver and cable setups as shown in (c).

Pros and Cons for Baseband

Baseband channel installation is a known quantity. It is understood by the organization. Its use as the expansion medium allows for the recycling of existing parts, tools, and equipment; this is particularly true for transceivers and controllers. It is physically simple to install except when large bundles of cable are necessary. Broadband cable is an easier addition when many channels are required because one cable carries a signal width sufficient for many channels. While "transceiver" access is mechanically similar for broadband, the actual electronics vary from the baseband. Although certain vendors market broadband conversion kits that interface with existing baseband controllers, this conversion may require justification on more than economic grounds. Wider or faster bandwidths only alleviate *certain* types of limitation. Observe that all aspects of a network must be tuned in synchronization for balanced solutions including software performance, bus speed, node concentrations, transmission rate consistency, and traffic composition. As an example of this holistic view, consider what would happen if a highway were widened when the bottlenecks were really at the entrance ramps, or if only hilly sections required a climbing lane for trucks. Chapter 3, in part, addressed these issues.

Tuning Performance

There are three basic conditions requiring tuning. These are a high-density clustering of nodes, an extended network bus topology, and network overloading, conditions which are encountered by the network manager on all but the simplest networks. Even a network with five personal computer nodes could create performance issues. For example, all five units might be within the same office and require a long, coiled coax cable in order to install the transceiver taps at the minimum distances. As another example, these five personal computers could be sited 1500 meters apart requiring special repeater hardware. While such design problems are possible on the minimal network, traffic overloading is a more common network constraint. Network extension options for Ethernet include adding coaxial cable to the maximum permissible length (500 meters), installing repeater hardware to yield a maximum contiguous length of 1500 meters, or installing gateways which can arbitrarily extend the length and *width* of the network topology. More esoteric hardware like T-1, fiber or broadband cable, and microwave extensions can expand the network topology for distant multisite facilities. Fan-out units, sectioned networks, or smart repeaters can isolate traffic to avoid collision saturation. Longer networks tend to increase the loading and strain on Ethernet and therefore any extensions require careful analysis as part of the design phase.

Provide High-Density Service

The easiest solution to high concentration nodes is the fan-out unit as presented in Chapter 8. This multiport tap provides more than a single station access from each transceiver. This unit overcomes two explicit Ethernet limitations, that of minimum tap spacing, and that of maximum node count per segment. A single fan-out will provide eight taps; it could be used for a tightly clustered office to ease the pressure of threading cable a long distance for clustered needs.

Expand Reach with Wider Area Networks

As technology advances, most organizations discover that information becomes a critical component to their success. Information gathered from distant and occasional sources assumes a transmission technology different from local area networking. Modem telephony, satellite, infrared or microwave transmission, T-1, and PBX are viable options to service those wide area networks. These technologies connect into Ethernet LANs via ISO bridging.

Recable

In addition to major questions of baseband versus multiple channel broadband, there are secondary concerns of thick versus thin coax cable, brand/type considerations that deserve discussion. As stated in Chapter 3, while the thick cable has better signal isolation properties for longer segment lengths, it requires more care to install, tap, and protect than the thin cable. The N-type fittings fail with marginal installation, while the BNC Thinnet connectors are more secure. Coaxial cable cannot sustain a tight bend, and it is stiff with its fragile copper center conductor. Thinnet cable offers better economic performance, although it is not physically as durable as the heftier cable.

Cable extensions are best implemented with cable from the same manufacturer and the *same lot* to minimize signal reflection. Since it is unusual to have purchased spare cable specifically for extending a network at a later time, it is wise to build cable from 23.4 meter length multiples as explained in Chapter 6. This is an expedient solution. Do not mix manufacturers. While this seems a small point, consider that traffic is rated at 10,000,000 characters per second on Ethernet at a maximum network length of 1500 meters. At a signal failure rate of 0.01% per 100 feet, the error rate will grow to 15%, or 1500 characters each second, at an *average* Ethernet load.

Solve Traffic Overloading Problems

On a saturated network, the immediate problem is to lower network demands, or rechannel that load. Figure 16.16 outlines the steps necessary to alleviate this problem.

- Reschedule peak loads
- Remove repeaters
- Install fan-out units
- Segment network with smart repeaters
- Install alternative channels
- Gateway busy sections
- Install more channels
- Install a high-speed backbone
- Install faster controllers
- Replace dual-purpose nodes with gateways or bridges

Figure 16.16 Steps to relieve a saturated network.

Tune for Peak Volume

Peak volume traffic levels are only a problem when traffic reaches saturation levels. At that critical breaking point, the network may not transmit *any* traffic during that peak period and for a period after the traffic level has subsided. If there are no installation problems—which is the most frequent cause for network bottlenecks, two common causes of network saturation are statistically high loads or blind spots in the Ethernet software. The blind spots must be programmed around with modifications to higher-level processes or explicit bug fixes. Software should back off when the process is delayed by the network, and TCP/IP or other "Ethernet" software should recognize this gridlock and ease it.

Tuning Recommendations

Network tuning encompasses more than remedial repairs. Your Ethernet should be designed to service current loads with expansion points for future growth. Chapters 8 and 9 detailed many of the planning and operational concerns. Another of those concerns is building a network with enough foresight to meet the user community's future communication needs. The last figure in this chapter, Figure 16.16, lists tuning recommendations.

- Plan for capacity
- Plan for overloads
- Set options to resolve in short term
- Set options to resolve in long term
- Provide the network with automatic "fuse" mechanisms
- Provide local access only when the network is saturating
- Educate users

Figure 16.17 Tuning recommendations.

Chapter 17

Network Security

This chapter confronts the issues of physical and data network security. Approaches that combat threats, strengthen vulnerabilities, and lessen risk are exposed to the reader. It is critical to differentiate computer system security from network security because computer security is possible without network security. LANs in general complicate security issues by extending the computer architecture to a physically distributed area and undermining the basic textbook data security procedures. As a consequence, the need for networks should be carefully investigated in light of security concerns. For any network installation, the ramifications of open network architecture should be understood, and the many alternatives to network security should be learned. The chapter outlines security vulnerabilities, and offers security measures for the reader's evaluation.

Security Overview

Attitudes about computer security are changing, not because theft and abuse are so common, but because the stakes have become so high. Computer processing and networking technology are no longer simply business tools; they are the lifeblood of many organizations. For these reasons, a concerted effort is required to divert attacks on networks.

Literature and movies have long had a special fascination with computer crime and abuse. Reports of yet another clever intrusion or massive "white collar" theft is the grist of good reading. Like everyday burglaries, breaks in security are something that happen to someone else. In general, only minimum protection measures are applied, although such steps provide a false sense of security.

Security is hard to define. What one software or hardware designer invents, another can crack—given enough incentive. Computer system and network users invent new problems because they hit upon novel methods to attack the protection mechanisms, just as viruses adapt to new protection measures. Hardware security has been the traditional route for control because it has been possible to limit physical access to equipment. Yet, with the increasing distribution of equipment onto the factory floor, or into individual offices, and with remote links via networks, the cost and difficulty of applying security has increased significantly. Traditional security is

- Inadequate physical security
- Inadequate indication of "sensitive" material
- Lack of locks on workstations
- Lack of organizational security policy
- Inadequate password systems
- No access logs or journals
- No records kept of efforts to penetrate security
- Lack of end-user security education

Figure 17.1 Common security breaches.

a secluded room; but that is no longer possible with networks. The acceptance of networks raises the organizational cost and significance of a careless, dishonest, or disgruntled employee damaging the machinery and information, or stealing information. Figure 17.1 cites common reasons for security breaches.

Ethernet Lacks Inherent Security

Ethernet itself provides no security—neither network security nor data security. Ethernet is designed as a simple and open physical medium for data transmission. Furthermore, Ethernet is not immune to snooping and spying, nor diversion of information. Figure 17.2 outlines these basic vulnerabilities. This startling limitation may surprise some; how could a network exist and succeed where security is either virtually impossible, or comes at very high cost? However, Ethernet transmission protocols are straightforward, and thus allow for transparent transmission of encrypted data.

Ethernet, like Unix, has prospered because of its simple elegance and wide range of uses. While some specialized networks succeed solely because they meet strict government security criteria, or enforced contract bidding specifications, other networks have succeeded because they are simple enough to promote equipment interconnection and a generic platform. Ethernet fills this description admirably. Ethernet is simple and consequently, robust. It does, however, face security threats.

- Open architecture
- Broadcast communication
- Easily tapped
- No hardware security measures
- Easily jammed transmissions

Figure 17.2 Ethernet security vulnerabilities.

Threats to the Network

There are four categories of network security threats. There are internal and external vulnerabilities, and physical and data related risks. Externally, an organization is at risk from events that might compromise the physical integrity of the network. An organization is at risk from external threats posed by modems, network and microwave, or PBX telephone-tapping performed by computer "hackers," the occasional career crook, and motivated competitors.

Internally, the organization is vulnerable to profiteering employees and contractors, disgruntled employees, and the random disaster. Unless the network is perceived as a toy and data never have value and all users perceive that work accomplished on the network is totally exposed and expendable and agree to this, then and only then is security an unnecessary constituent of network design and administration. Figure 17.3 illustrates those items at risk in a simple matrix.

	External	Internal
Physical	power lines data lines network facilities	power supplies data lines and coax network facilities access units
Data	dial-up lines microwave links data line links wastepaper	network nodes file servers output devices wastepaper

Figure 17.3 Network items at risk and vulnerable to attack.

External Threats

A network is exposed to external threats from physical attacks, and to a significantly greater degree, from data tapping. Most local area networks are contained within a single building, and as a result are usually secure from physical affronts. A saboteur cannot cut cable if it is locked away, nor disrupt power if power lines are underground and not differentiable from many other lines. While this issue is often overlooked by many organizations, computers, in particular mainframes, have been attacked by terrorists and competitors. A destroyed mainframe or severed network is not only an expensive item to repair or replace, the data or time lost can bankrupt a business, especially when data are the lifeblood of the business. Last, do not discount the possibility of catastrophe: computer damage from chance events such as fire, flood, explosion, lightning and power surges or power deficits, or a collapsed building could set the organization back more than need be under such extreme circumstances.

While extrinsic damage to a network might occur—it is best not over-looked—dial-up modem and remote connections are the more frequent avenues of assault onto a network. Most networks, even Ethernet, often see the external world through telephone connections. There is no reason to prohibit such contact although there are many reasons to *control* it. Most organizations have local offices, satellite facilities, and communicate professionally and academically with others off-site. The problem is to prevent unauthorized entry onto the network that would allow a "user" to delete files, modify files, power down the network, access privileged information, copy information for profit, or disseminate information to the public to discredit or supplant the organization. Figure 17.4 lists the potential dangers that must be guarded against.

Physical	Data
catastrophe power disruption terrorism network jamming	network jamming network tapping theft of information data diddling data tampering misappropriation of data

Figure 17.4 External network threats in need of protection.

Internal Threats

A network is under scrutiny from the inside. Once the basic physical security of the network is breached, as often is the case, the network equipment is at risk. Unauthorized access to information is simplified, and prevention and detection are progressively more difficult to achieve when it is an amorphous "intrusion." The simplest security flaw is caused by users not logging off their machines. This is akin to leaving a door ajar, so that anyone can enter. While remote network links can be tapped between buildings if they are radio or microwave signals, internally the network can be physically tapped like a common telephone eavesdrop. Ethernet, as explained above, expands the horizon for eavesdropping since Ethernet broadcasts the transmission packet globally to all network nodes. An intruder with a means to promiscuously read packets can intercept information without anyone being much the wiser. Note the connotation of the word *tap* being used in conjunction with "Ethernet transceiver" and that it is the common reference to a node attachment unit interface (AUI).

A highly sophisticated user can override *any* software protection by directing falsified Ethernet packets to a target node; this scheme progressively modifies those software protection schemes for an eventual intrusion. The source and destination addresses could both indicate the target node, and few protection schemes are designed to protect a user from harm. This level of power is possible because Ethernet is open, and most operating systems key upon packet address information. As a consequence, protection stops far short of top security.

While eavesdropping has its many risks—breach of organizational secrets and theft of information—modification of data can be more devastating because it can remain hidden indefinitely, or be propagated and disseminated before errors are detected. Money can be siphoned from a payroll and redirected to other pockets, trade secrets can be tampered with, private files can be read, development efforts can be hindered, and "ironclad" results can be scrambled, discrediting the innocent. Figure 17.5 lists ways that security can be breached internally.

Physical	Data
power disruption network sabotage equipment damage network jamming network tapping	network jamming network tapping theft of information data diddling data tampering misappropriation of data

Figure 17.5 Internal network threats in need of protection.

Physical access to the network equipment raises the possibility of sabotage from a disgruntled employee or an authorized visitor. The physical network, the node equipment, and the data residing thereon are at risk. Most organizations assume no need to protect the equipment from employees. This is often an expensive assumption.

Protection Countermeasures

There are some straightforward measures which will protect the network. These include physical network isolation, standard password protection, limits applied to outside access, occasional changeovers in network operating policies, data encryption, and last, the monitoring of access channels, both physical and logical. Loss limiting measures include fall-back provisions, and a good network backup policy. Figure 17.6 indicates these progressive countermeasures.

Physical Network Isolation

The most effective network protection is simply to lock up the network and make it unavailable. Obviously, this severely curtails its usefulness. However, when more emphasis is placed upon physical security, and when access to the network is controlled, the network is more secure. This holds

- Physical network isolation
- Password protection
- Limited external access
- Sub-network isolation
- Occasional policy changeovers
- Data encryption
- Access control for network monitoring devices
- Application of monitoring devices to detect intrusions
- Vandal detection
- Hierarchy of access
- Fall-back countermeasures
- Network backup

Figure 17.6 Security measures applicable to Ethernet.

true for both physical and logical devices. Therefore, the best medicine is to limit access to the network where feasible. Unfortunately, most networks provide a necessary communication channel for business usually as electronic mail, change notices, meeting announcements, and other normal messages, and such draconian measures are inappropriate.

However, the concept of physical security through access limitation can be extended as far as necessary to meet requirements. The rule is to lock up as much as possible. Mainframe and network file servers should have limited and *controlled* access. If printed or drafted output (fighter plane plans, for example) is confidential, then certainly lock up the printers and delegate one person to burst, collate, and distribute all network output. For additional confidence, bond that person and shred paper and magnetic trash. Since data storage mechanisms often use removable media like tapes, disks, punched output, or removable magnetic or optical platters, a cautious approach is to restrict access to these classes of devices and their active media. Log all mountings, and catalog all purchases, uses, disposals, and distributions of storage media.

If more security is required, lock up the coaxial cables and other transmission channels. Place cables beyond reach, in a plenum, in locked corridors or restricted areas. Position multiplexing fan-out units beyond occasional reach and protect the Ethernet transceiver and transceiver drop cable connection. If this is unfeasible or impractical, then at the minimum, restrict access to as much of the physical network as possible. The node equipment is always vulnerable, although on a broadcast transmission medium like Ethernet, each node provides a window of vulnerability onto all other network node equipment, including file servers.

Fan-out boxes not fully populated because some ports or slots are not utilized offer a ripe invitation. The transceiver is already in place, and the additional fan-out box is invisible to the network monitoring tools. Therefore, it is wise to disable the extra unused fan-out slots where security is an issue, and periodically inspect all transceivers for unauthorized tinkering. A transceiver drop cable could be diverted from a single station node via a fan-out box without anyone being wiser unless the a periodic physical inspection is actually performed as shown in Figure 17.7.

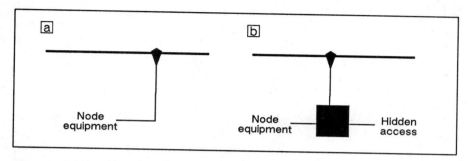

Figure 17.7 Fan-out ports provide a hidden opportunity to spy. Figure 17.7(a) illustrates a common node with transceiver and transceiver drop cable. Figure 17.7(b) demonstrates how a cable can be intercepted with a hidden fan-out unit.

Password Protection

At the software level, password authentication protection is the most effective mechanism for network protection. Passwords prevent unauthorized access to files and network devices, and protect information from diddling and tampering. Unix is one (of many) operating systems where security can be breached when physical access is granted to the equipment. However, for most novice users, passwords keep prying eyes out. Most serious data thefts have been perpetrated by novices who exploit a hole in the system. Password protection limits software access to a node, thus limiting access to the network. Additionally, contingent upon the network operating system and support services, password protection may lock individual files. In situations where security is of utmost concern, tools that analyze files at the bit and byte levels can be entirely removed from the system or locked away from the casual user. Such tools can invalidate bit-level protection mechanisms.

Password protection is only as strong as the weakest link. Login names and passwords that are freely disseminated ease access to the system. Common passwords that everybody knows breach the security. Hired consultants with external dial-in privileges can be a serious security problem. Prudent management of security requires that passwords be changed regularly, and that when an intrusion is indicated, passwords be deleted from the log until ownership of a login is re-requested. Good policy also requires that when people leave a company, their passwords be removed from the log, especially when a person has left under questionable circumstances.

This is the most readily available network protection. Most networks provide password protection as a minimum security measure. It is also the most easily applied countermeasure, although it requires vigilance.

Limited External Access

Most published security breaches have occurred through phone access modems. The most often perpetrated breaches occur through trusted employees or careless procedure and password controls. A phone line is a doorway into the network, the modem a lock, and the password is the final key. Therefore, the best protection is no protection and no phone lines. When phone lines are necessary, several precautions are relevant. Do not publish the phone number. Change the phone number frequently. Use modems that wait for a tone from the caller. This has the advantage of not accidentally informing a dialer that a computer exists at the number dialed. Install call-back modems that do not accept calls without verifying the caller, the phone number, and the password. Install specialized modems that are difficult to use (many modems talk only to others identical to themselves), or that scramble transmission. Figure 17.8 outlines these crucial procedures.

```
• Avoid dial-up connections
• Don't publish the dial-up phone numbers
• Change the phone numbers frequently.
• Use modems that don't supply a carrier tone
• Install call-back equipment
• Control distribution of logins and passwords
• Change passwords frequently
• Install specialty modems
```

Figure 17.8 Limit dial-up access.

Where a network runs between buildings, lock up the cable, or install optical fiber which at least for the present is difficult and expensive to tap. If these possibilities are unfeasible, inspect the connections daily for signs of possible intrusion. If microwave or a radio frequency is used, scramble those transmissions. Be aware of the possible security leakages at time of installation, understand the need for organizational security, and weigh the benefits of applying the necessary security countermeasures. Figure 17.9 outlines these items.

```
• Lock up access to cable
• Check for intrusions
• Install optical fiber
• Alter transmission frequencies
• Scramble/encode transmissions
• Root out anomalies
• Remain vigilant
```

Figure 17.9 Limit physical access.

Subnetwork Isolation

Networks isolated by bridges, gateways, or smart repeaters provide additional surety. Every step taken to isolate a network from public access increases the inherent security. While internetwork access is frequently required, subnets add a buffer. All transmissions destined for nodes on the originating network are not globally broadcast beyond that originating network. A bridge, gateway, or smart repeater filters only that traffic which must be transferred to the other networks; this effectively retains sensitive material. As noted previously, this does not preclude the conveyance of "doctored" packets unless transmission is a one-way process.* In this way, a network could be constructed with a centralized and rigorously secured network facility as illustrated by Figure 17.10. This secured network would lock out all remote links and dial-up access. On the other hand, the central secured network could reach out and remotely access the other networks and their resources including *dial-out* telephone communication lines. Many such secured subnets could be constructed with access to a general purpose network backbone.

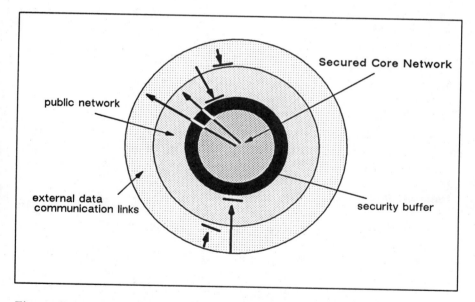

Figure 17.10 Map for securing subnetworks.

---

* Once one-way transmission is established from the core area, a vulnerability is nevertheless established.

Occasional Policy Changeovers

The best security relies upon sudden change. The most complete physical security systems, the best password and encryption systems depend upon new people, new passwords, new keys. You cannot bribe someone who is new and cannot break what you do not know; any security system is improved by constant and unpredictable variety.

Computer network security can implement such changeovers. Access codes, passwords, sign-in procedures, front desk guards can be revised with frequency. Change upsets best laid plans, and improves the odds that a trail of evidence will remain if an intruder actually breaches the network. Figure 17.11 outlines security measures that should be changed frequently.

```
• Sign-in procedures
• Access process
• Guard personnel
• Location of computer
• Door keys
• Passwords
• Codes
• Network links
• Remote login access
• Locations and names of files
```

Figure 17.11 Security measures that should be changed frequently.

Data Encryption

Ethernet transmits anything placed in the data fields. Ethernet easily supports data encryption. As stated in Chapter 4, Ethernet, like the party telephone system, is blind to the nature of the conversations. Anyone who wants to listen to a party line conversation is welcome, but unless the listener understands the key, the conversation is privileged. Just as a telephone will handle foreign languages, Ethernet will transmit "foreign" data. Even promiscuous capture of packets will prove valueless if the data are properly encrypted. Data encryption is the most easily implemented security measure. It is, however, expensive in terms of computer time to encrypt and decrypt data, and should be applied judiciously. Furthermore, a motivated intruder could break almost any encryption scheme. Therefore, in those situations requiring encoded data transmissions and encoded data storage, other security measures should also be applied.

Access Control for Network Monitoring Devices

Certain monitoring devices like the protocol analyzer allow promiscuous access to all Ethernet traffic. With such a device mail, file transfers, in fact all network traffic, can be passively, selectively and silently captured. All mail, all data, all files can be cracked, read, and understood (unless encrypted). While the traffic may provide only a glimpse into the full information desired by an intruder, such a device clearly can unlock private secrets. Hidden taps and transceivers that are not authorized are more difficult to spot, but once noticed are obvious for what they are. Not only is such a monitoring device highly effective at uncovering secrets, it is easy to hide its presence. It is a suitable piece of network equipment—and it belongs.

An analyzer, or network software with certain features, will allow anyone with enough skill to capture and analyze Ethernet packets transparently and unobtrusively. This promiscuous data capture technique raises a first line security issue. Additionally, many protocol analyzers will allow a sophisticated intruder to build falsified packets that could crack security locks by forging valid keys. However, if a network administration removes, limits, or monitors usage of all such tools, a minimal measure of security can be achieved. Other measures are required for more certain protection.

A protocol analyzer is so obvious for its inherent danger that it is overlooked. While there is a clear need for it, unauthorized usage constitutes an invasion of privacy and breach of network security. Therefore, lock up such devices, and when they are in use, monitor their usage.

Application of Monitoring Devices to Detect Intrusions

While the protocol analyzer can actually intrude on private communications, the analyzer can uncover unauthorized network access. Nodes that shouldn't be on the network will appear as unknown Ethernet addresses, or will transmit at unusual or unauthorized times. Furthermore, access to unauthorized devices, supposedly prevented but actually achieved, can indicate vandalism, and so be disclosed.

If transmission facilities on the analyzer were disabled to prevent such inadvertent data diddling, the snooper still needs network access. This is most often provided through a transceiver and tap. The TDR would show an extra tap where none should be. When security is an issue, precise network blueprinting becomes critical. Furthermore, a detailed impedance chart should indicate any present or *past* unauthorized tapping. The vampire clamps leave marks and increase the parallel impedance, and end-connectors or cuts into the network coaxial cable are impossible to hide, becoming clues of tampering if detailed blueprinting is maintained.

Although data encryption will foil some vandals, time works against data encryption. The key can be lost, passed around the office as passwords often are, broken with enough time and poor key recycling procedures, or broken by a clever person. There are additional techniques to thwart data theft. While the network monitor allows a sophisticated user to capture and read packets, it also can indicate who is utilizing network resources and thus indicate a possible spy. While the promiscuous mode of data capture is invisible to the network because the Ethernet signal is a global broadcast, certain clues can correlate excessive CPU load with limited network access. Other mismatched clues may indicate snooping. The network monitor can also uncover unauthorized users as described in Chapter 14. Unauthorized users may inadvertently expose themselves with unknown Ethernet addresses, since all addresses are unique. Sooner or later, an unauthorized node is bound to request a retransmission. This, however, requires good detective skills to uncover.

Vandal Detection

A crook does not play by the rules. This is the prime danger. In order to counter such danger it is important to understand the value of the data on the network and the damage that can be perpetrated; knowing this will point to the possible danger and to the people who will benefit from such intrusion or damage. The information resident on a network has no value except to certain parties. There are usually warning signs in security breaches. Train the network operators to spot anomalies since they often monitor all network traffic and could uncover problems as they happen.

- Network login times
- Network login names
- Packet traces
- Node impedance differences
- Network transmission interference
- Network server problems
- Missing output
- Missing or altered data files
- Unusual network activity

Figure 17.12 Clues to network intrusion.

Most of the administrative emphasis should be applied to prevent vandalism. The original network design should factor in security as a basic configuration constraint. Daily operations should be altered occasionally to disrupt the norm. Such strategies protect the network in anticipation of vandalism and snooping, but in no way completely preclude them. After most intrusions, there will be traces that can be analyzed to prevent further access. These traces include log files, packet traces, time stamps, improper network impedances, unusual network interference, computer server problems, and missing or changed data files. The traces are outlined in Figure 17.12. The TDR in conjunction with network blueprints, administrative information, and good detective work can reveal electrical improprieties, while the network analyzer can indicate other software and traffic disparities as explained above.

Hierarchy of Access

There are several categories of security access created to clarify and evaluate the growing number of protection methods and escalating "secure" operating systems. As users acknowledge the need for security as an integral part of the operating system and network landscape, vendors are listening. However, confusion reigns with this proliferation of user requests (primarily Department of Defense, aka DoD) and vendor offerings. To address this problem the National Security Decisions Directive lists a framework for evaluation [see 11]. This framework is in Figure 17.13. The highest level is the verified sub-category under the verified protection level. To date, these exotic systems are merely in the design stages. Previous attempts at complete security fail either through excessively slow response time or under the concerted efforts of expert system crackers. Unix, for example, is C_2 although with a little effort can meet C_1. Multics, CMS, VMS, and other like systems also fail at C_2. CP/M and PC–DOS are clearly minimally protected.

A   Verified Protection
   A_1 Verified design

B   Mandatory Protection
   B_1 Labeled protection
   B_2 Structured protection
   B_3 Security domain

C   Discretionary Protection
   C_1 Discretionary security protection
   C_2 Controlled access

D   Minimal Protection

Figure 17.13 Hierarchy of access.

Fall-Back Countermeasures

Network access audit trails and network security audits are standard procedures when security is an important network concern. Often, the logs will indicate an anomaly suggesting an intrusion. If an intrusion has been detected, it is necessary to act. If the intruder is known and the access point revealed, the problem is solved although damage may already have been done. If the intruder is unknown, there are two courses of action. The first is to watch and wait, and trap the intruder. The second is to lock up the network without hope of catching the intruder. Which course of action appears best depends upon the costs of continued damage and repair to that damage and the vindictiveness of the affected organization.

There are clear detective methods for trapping an intruder. The TDR and network analyzer provide one method of electronically locating snooping. Sherlock Holmes' style of observation is likely to reveal more cautious intruders. However, when the danger is clear and acute, and the identity of the intruder is less important than protecting the network, a staged shutdown of network doors is the best course of action.

There are elements of both hardware and software that can be shut down. These steps are outlined in Figure 17.14. From the hardware viewpoint, change as much as possible and disconnect as much as possible while retaining the required minimum functionality.

The procedure is as follows: disconnect all dial-in lines and change the access numbers to prevent future intrusions. Power down all remote transmitters and alter the transmitter frequencies. Inspect all coaxial cables, fiber optic cables, and wire connections for signs of tampering, splicing, and all other indications of line tapping. If the intruder may have discovered information derived from waste paper, or from stolen printed material, make rapid plans to alter paper disposal methods and output distribution. Lock up the printers and hand-deliver printed output. Shred waste paper. Certainly, data storage media hold the entirety of the organization's secrets. Lock up those media, that which is online and also that which is on backup tapes. Furthermore, log the disposition of the data storage media. Change keys, codes, and access procedures.

```
• Disconnect modems
• Change dial-in telephone numbers
• Shut down remote transmitters
• Alter radio or microwave frequencies
• Inspect cables and links for tapping or intrusion
• Inspect network software and files for tampering
• Change password file and purge outdated entries
• Alter executive code file ownerships
• Relocate and/or rename critical data files
• Disconnect bridges and gateways
• Cut hardwired connections
• Lock up printed output and storage media
• Reduce network user access
• Restore physical or data damage
• Limit access to remote devices
• Change door keys
• Alter entrance codes
• Change guards
```

Figure 17.14 Security fall-back countermeasures.

Many steps can be taken in software to locate signs of tampering. It may appear as missing or altered data files, or unusual log entries. Restore whatever damage is discovered. Additionally, change the password access. Purge outdated password entries. Limit remote access to other network nodes and network devices. Change the access to network software that might allow data tampering and data snooping. This includes programs that read "protected" disks or files at the bit and byte levels and programs overriding disk or file-level protection schemes. Restricted access is possible to security-sensitive materials by moving them or changing their names.

These are generic techniques. The techniques work equally well when initially installing a network or at any time the organization suspects a problem. If the network is insecure, it is prudent not to tarry and wait until a problem is revealed before applying such countermeasures. Security entails a cost in time, materials, labor and aggravation.

It is important to have adequate protection mechanisms; tight security could mean that it will be forever unnecessary to repair damage or prevent damage from happening again. Security is a series of applied techniques that are disruptive, inconvenient, and rarely transparent. The hope is that such techniques will never be required, but they are instituted purely on a prophylactic basis.

Network Backup

The network is hardware, software, and the data. If the hardware were damaged, it could be replaced more easily than the information it contained. Despite this relative ease of restoring hardware, do not overlook the need to have spare parts on hand. Fan-out units, file servers, keyboard-level components are good candidates for the spare inventory. Assess the damage that would be done to the organization if a key component failed and were irreplaceable for a period of time. Keep spares of those units that could create a crisis if broken and irreplaceable. Do not limit backup procedures solely to the data and software.

Many organizations are critically dependent upon data. Either they are the organization's product, or they provide records of funds payable and receivable. Data also can explain critical production or operational techniques. Network backup procedures provide a means to repair software and data damage. If a catastrophe occurrs, backup media may change a *catastrophe* to merely a major *inconvenience*. As trite as that sounds, backups are a standard policy for most organizations with mainframe computer facilities. *Mainframe computer facilities* is referenced here mainly as an example of what has developed the attitudes and policies bred from the experiences now effecting the new network technologies. Many networks, however, developed from small components and therefore the organization and its managers lack the realization of the network's crucial importance. As a result, backups are nonexistent, infrequent, or applied to that minimum of personally owned files deemed important.

A good portion of any network is resident in unique files that define the relationship of nodes on the network, the operations of the network itself, and quite possibly scripts that have been programmed to automate many arcane processes that have become complicated over time. This information, as well as the actual data files, has special value to the organization.

The software too may be a critical component. The vendors may have gone out of business and new copies might not be obtainable. Network backup is therefore a crucial procedure to insure network integrity and security.

In the final statement, braggarts will often reveal their activities and indicate problems and a security breach. Listen well, be vigilant, and evaluate the level of security required. Cleverness will undermine all security systems, and ruthlessness will sway the most secure. Note well that the strongest security program will fail if the network operators and network users who are assigned to protect the resources are compromised.

This chapter has presented the issues surrounding network security. Threats and real dangers have been outlined, and practical and effective countermeasures have been proposed. Additionally, fall-back measures including backup procedures were prescribed for when the preventative measures failed. These backup measures are detailed in Chapter 18.

Chapter 18

Backup and Redundancy

The last chapter introduced the subject of file backup and network component redundancy within the context of network security. Backup and redundancy are also operational concerns since users' work, organizational information or product may reside on network equipment. Prophylactic concern is warranted; only in those situations where the network is a toy, simply a communications backbone, or where network users are responsible for their own work will such backup concerns be moot. Therefore, most network managers will discover that backup and redundancy are crucial aspects to their success and continued employment, thus best resolved in a concise and clearly communicated policy.

Network Backup

The Ethernet network is an amalgamation of hardware, software and network data. The hardware is more easily replaced than the information contained within. Despite this relative ease of restoring hardware, do not overlook the need to have backup spare parts on hand. Assess damage to the organization should a key component fail and remain unavailable for an indefinite period; fan-out units, file servers, keyboard-level components are good candidates for the spare inventory. Do not limit backup procedures solely to the data and software aspects; also, consider the human aspect.

As explained in the preceding chapter, data diddling and tampering can disrupt operations and cause manifold problems. Backups and the network redundancy procedures explained in this chapter provide a time limit for the propagation of damage. If an intruder deletes or alters a file and this is discovered, backups provide recovery. Very few problems can be created that cannot be repaired from backup. Backups have value for the data they contain.

Since media are very portable, they should be tightly controlled and protected; damaged media may prevent restoration. Because catastrophe may strike a site, or sabotage may be very extensive and thoughtfully planned, backups should be removed off-site for additional security.

Backup and redundancy are necessary processes to insure continued and consistent network operations. Backup and redundancy encompass more than tape or disk duplication of critical files; it implies duplication of critical data files, configuration files, software, password keys and access codes, physical coaxial cables, transceivers, node equipment, and network servers. When a network provides the unique infrastructure to link different departments and functions within an organization, the network assumes an importance far in excess of its real value. The network's ability to disrupt the normal ebb and flow when it breaks justifies expensive procedures to maintain that network. A network may be indispensable; for those short periods of time when it cannot be used, it must be preserved. To this end backup and redundant procedures are the corrective action.

Backup and redundancy exceed duplication of data. Any component with the power to disrupt operation should be duplicated. This includes software, hardware, data, *and* human labor. Figure 18.1 illustrates the elements warranting this attention.

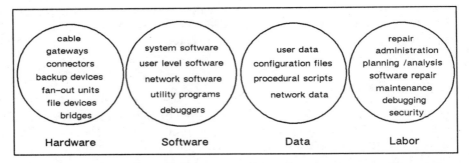

Figure 18.1 Network components require periodic backup, both in terms of physical media backup and in terms of replacements in case of problems.

The Value of Information

Many organizations depend upon electronic filing. It either is the organization's product, or it provides records of funds payable and receivable. Data in the form of lists of detailed instructional sets (CAD/CAM programs) may direct production or operational process. Network backup provides one of the few available and certain means to repair software and data damage. Should disaster strike, the backup may change a *catastrophe* to merely an *inconvenience*, as trite as that phrase may seem. Backups are a standard policy for most organizations with mainframe computer facilities. Many networks, however, are outgrowths of the free-form and independent personal computer environments and therefore the organization and its managers lack experience with the cost of a network shutdown. As a result, backups are non-existent, infrequent, or personally performed without clear or detailed instructions and without a fixed interval between backups. Network backup is a crucial procedure to insure the continued operations of the network.

Media Backup

Most networking organizations create, modify, or disseminate software or data. The network provides the conduit for information. Since this information is easily damaged or lost, and not easily recovered if lost, much attention is given to preserving its integrity. Media backup is the usual form for duplicating and saving data. Magnetic media—floppy disks, cartridge tapes, cassette tapes, disk packs, reel tape, VCR—and paper copies or punch cards are the usual format for backups. The data and software are copied from the source hierarchy to this archival media for long-term storage. Figure 18.2 presents a sampling of stable data storage media.

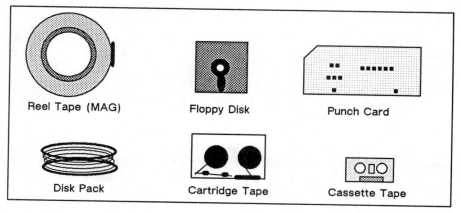

Figure 18.2 Data storage media.

There are many issues to address about media backup. Figure 18.3 outlines some of these. Questions often asked include what data should be saved, and on what media should they be saved. It is also common to weigh how frequently data should be backed up, and during what time of the day, or before and after what operations information should be duplicated. Because there are security concerns, where the information is stored is a pressing issue. Since backup media is both expensive and, eventually, bulky, the media are often recycled. How media are reused could have long term ramifications if they are prematurely recycled.

Not infrequently, customer commitments, venture-capital development agreements, and other legal agreements require media backup, storage of software releases, and research data sets to be stored in escrow and financially insured. The IRS requires that financial records be retained for a number of years. Backups that fail to restore damaged or lost information are obviously worthless. This raises the issue of verifying backup media for content and accuracy.

- What should be saved?
- How often should data be saved?
- Where medium should be used?
- How should the media be stored?
- Where should the media be stored?
- What access precautions be applied?
- How should data recoveries be instituted?
- What happens when the media are incompatibile?
- At what frequency should data be saved?
- How long should data be saved?
- What legal requirements must be fulfilled?

Figure 18.3 Data storage questions.

What to Save

The simple answer is to back up all information that the organization cannot afford to lose. Software and network information that can't be replaced easily, or is expensive to replace, should be duplicated. Data and financial records should be saved. System software rarely changes and can be saved infrequently. Purchased software is often provided on media that are in their own right suitable as the backup, and a working copy should be made from the original while the vendor's master becomes the backup.

A backup procedure has costs too. Media are expensive. The labor required to duplicate the information on a periodic basis is expensive. The backup process itself requires computer time, and often increases the level of network traffic, slowing other operations. These costs, which would be incurred for each and every backup, can be quantified as Figure 18.4 demonstrates. One way to determine how much should be saved is to calculate the costs of a backup strategy against the replacement value of what can be lost. Lost data can be recreated at some cost in time. This cost can be calculated. The work lost while the data are reconstructed can be assigned cost. These costs, which would be averted by a backup, can be aggregated and valued.

Tangible	Intangible	Long Term
Media	Network time	Storage costs
Labor	Network traffic load	Security risk
Storage costs	Network downtime	Media degradataion

Figure 18.4 Network backup costs.

A direct comparison between averted costs and periodic backup costs is not necessarily correct. The backup procedure is an insurance policy. Direct comparison between averted costs and incurred costs implies a need for 100% coverage; however, an organization must determine an appropriate level of risk [of potential data loss] which it is willing to assume. This risk may be 0% (no risk) or 100% (all the risk). Generally speaking, daily, semi-weekly, or weekly backups are adequate. Even a daily backup does not avert all risk since there is a window of risk. A daily backup might imply a 5% risk, whereas a weekly backup may imply a 10% risk. Risk is difficult to assess because it factors such items as the probability of a data storage device failing and a data loss, and also the probability that recovery will take a certain amount of time. Since any backup scheme can fail—backup tapes could be corrupt, for example—risk is always inherent. Even "fault-tolerant" networks still exhibit a likelihood of failure.

Last, how much risk the organization is willing to assume must be considered. Some organizations will bet that the computers and the network will never fail, whereas others recognize that the business livelihood could be jeopardized by data loss. This simple mathematical relationship will determine the frequency of backup and the type of information to backup that is best suited to an organization's needs.

Who Provides Backup Services

Once a backup policy is determined—how often and how much—it is necessary to determine who actually provides the backup service. The network manager or network administration group provides these services if global network resources exist for network backup, if few other events disrupt the routine of the administration group, and if time is not an issue.

Personal information could be saved globally, or saved by the individuals to whom it has value. Most mainframe environments perform global data backups since the data are stored in a single, concentrated location. This may be the case on a network which has centralized file servers. Where a network is distributed, as in the example of a personal computer network, and few facilities exist for global data backup, individuals are responsible for personal backup. Where users provide their own network service, users often are exhorted to provide their own backups. Impress upon users that doing their own housekeeping is in their best interests, but the network administration group will help as needed.

What Media

The media that are regularly available to the network machines should be the backup media of choice. PC networks generally have floppy disk drives. This is adequate. Where storage of local fixed disks exceeds the size of the floppy disks, cartridge disks or streamer tapes are suitable devices for data redundancy. Also, data can be easily copied to another machine. It is less probable that both fixed disks will fail at the same time. (Probabilities of dual failures are generally factors of individual failures plus any correlated risks such as power surges, overheating, or sabotage.)

When data backup is a frequent and disruptive event floppy disks or streamer tapes may have insufficient capacity and speed. Reel units with 8-inch or 11-inch reels provide higher density and larger storage capacities. Cache space for backups also moves the process off-line. Convenience and capacity are usually the most important criteria for selecting backup media.

The media should also be long-lived. When the computer is powered off, the information should not be lost. Therefore, electronic memory is not appropriate. Cartridge or reel tape, floppy or cartridge drives, punch tape or cards, and disk packs are common backup media. Furthermore, the medium chosen should be stable in the environment in which it will be stored. Do not choose paper or cards if they are liable to be eaten by insects or mold. A sealed disk pack is more secure for such a hostile environment. In addition, if electrical or magnetic interference is apt to erase data, paper stock is more appropriate as a medium. Most media will endure if care is exercised.

The media should be selected for compatibility with other machines. If a catastrophe does occur, destroying the entire facility, overspecialized media may complicate data and network recovery, or force network hardware replacement decisions that are not completely forward thinking. Technology does change; do not allow a disaster to have ramifications for the network restoration. Also, make sure that if a backup unit fails for any reason, the organization will not be exposed to unnecessary risk. For example, if a tape drive fails, another unit should provide continued backup procedures and lost data recovery.

Last, obscure media provide both benefits and potential problems as suggested above. Obscure media add a level of security to the network by making external data recovery more difficult. Unusual disk or tape formats raise the cost of information theft. Likewise, the selection of a large tape reel or a disk pack instead of a disk or tape cartridge makes it less likely that information will be removed from the building. However, obscure formats may increase the risk of losing information should equipment fail and be difficult to repair.

How Frequently and When to Back Up

A frequent question is how often should backups be made. The answer is two-fold. First, back up as frequently as necessary to protect the work and data you are unwilling to lose. Vendor software may not need backup ince it is available on the original installation media, although site specific installation information does. Network configurations change infrequently and can be duplicated whenever a change is made. Data files that change with regularity such as personal workspaces and account information, might be backed up once a week, once a day, or even two or three times a day. Networks that provide commercial transactions, such as air traffic control, real time manufacturing control, or financial transfers might need support in parallel with an entire duplicated network and file spaces. Again, the cost of loss must be balanced against the cost of providing protection. Backup frequency depends on an organization's view of risk.

Second, perform a cost-benefit analysis. Determine the cost of providing the backups: include media (which can be recycled after a time), time, network degradation and downtime, labor, and storage costs. Compare those costs against the value of the lost work, or the value of re-creating the lost work. Include the social, publicity, and aggravation damage wrought by loss. Choose whichever is least. Note that backup is an *insurance* cost, and the comparison between backup costs and *possible* material loss should be a fractional factor. In other words, if the possible loss is X, it is appropriate to apply only $X*n$ where $n<1$ to reflect only the probability of loss. It is too expensive to insure the actuality of loss except when deemed necessary. If you think that data loss costs customers, respect, and other intangibles, and that it is necessary to completely insure against the loss, consider that the value of X should include the value of such soft costs. Figure 18.5 outlines the mathematics for such a calculation.

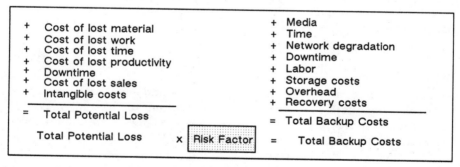

Figure 18.5 Network backup insurance analysis.

Where to Store

Backup media should be stored in a "safe" place. This means that the media should not deteriorate from elements, nor should it be subject to theft, misuse, or loss; it would be a serious management concern if backups were missing or corrupted. Backups should also be conveniently located. To insure security in the event of a far-reaching disaster such as a fire, flood, or theft, backups might also be stored off-site. Consider as possibilities a bank vault or a warehouse that specializes in storage of computer media. Generally, a locked off-site room with restricted access and an entry log provides an adequate location. Note that precautions for safe media storage should be followed. Figure 18.6 lists these precautions.

- Dry
- Cool
- Upright
- Static-free
- No magnetic fields
- No electrical fields
- Easy access
- Timely access
- Secured

Figure 18.6 Precautions for safe media storage.

Recycling Policy

Generally, backup media are recycled after a time. Backup media are expensive and when information has been superseded, the media can be used again. Also, the media are bulky, and require adequate storage space. Over time, this can be expensive and can precipitate a decision to recycle. Figure 18.7 depicts a recycling policy where media storing monthly backups are recycled after two months and media storing daily backups are recycled after each month. Note that quarterly media storing backups are not recycled until a year has passed.

Value of Stored Information

Stored data have value to the organization and potentially to others, such as competitors. Thus, it may be important to take all measures necessary to insure their safety and usability. Many organizations cover the value of their data with an insurance policy. While many media storage service companies do insure readability and safety of the physical media,

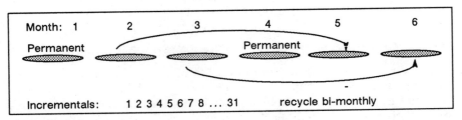

Figure 18.7 "Leap-frog" media recycling policy.

they may not insure the data on the tapes. In fact, without reading the tapes to verify that information actually exists, the service company could not know what exists on the tapes it stores. It guarantees the physical safety of the media only, not the logical content. Therefore, when information is a key constituent of a business it is important to evaluate and insure the monetary worth of that information. As elsewhere, insurance costs are high. Most organizations only insure what they cannot afford to lose. Assess the level of risk your organization is willing to assume and insure the remainder. Decrease risk with insurance on the media.

The caveat is that media dependability may fade over time as the media are used over. This can be checked, but note that wear on the media and the equipment tends to degrade performance and longevity.

Verification of Backup

Once a data backup and media recycling policy is implemented, the process should be tested occasionally to verify that it is effective and working as anticipated. It is appropriate to audit the library and ensure that the inventory of backups matches expectations. It is prudent to verify that the policy governing access to the information is actually enforced so that backups are not lost, corrupted or stolen. Those who should have access should know how to locate pertinent media and perform the necessary tasks. Those without access privileges should be denied access to the media. The data backup should be usable. A crisis can be compounded unnecessarily when lost information is discovered after the fact to be irretrievable. A lot of trust rides upon the network management when the team establishes a *disaster recovery plan*. That trust may be forever broken if the recovery plan is flawed. A periodic audit of the backup media and their accuracy is a simple but effective measure to ensure that implementation matches planning, a crucial step for any manager.

Hardware

Duplicate data backup devices in case a backup or data restoration unit fails, forcing extensive work-arounds. The choice of the backup hardware should be predicated upon the choice of media, media reliability, media compatibility, and interchangeability. If disaster strikes and the backup media are unreadable, not only has a lot of time and effort been wasted, but the organization has been unduly risked.

The hardware selected for backup procedures should meet certain standards for reliability, speed, ease of use, and its ability to be repaired. Other concerns include storage density and dropout, recycling, and compatibility.

Certainly, a media that is specific to a single unit has marginal worth; should that unit ever fail, the media are useless. Therefore, media should be interchangeable from one machine to another. Also, consider that should a network catastrophe occur, it may be critical for the continuation of the organization that the data backups be accessible by another organization or another network site. Data backup compatibility, in media format, media density, track alignment, and physical accessibility, is an underlying criterion. Likewise, data density has some bearing. The higher the density at which information is stored, the higher the risk that it will erode, be damaged by time, or experience "dropout." Dropout is when information on media degrades from usage and time. Dropout is often seen on much-used videotape; it occurs with all magnetic media. Laser burned media are usually immune from such problems.

However, whatever media actually are selected, the speed raises secondary concerns. As the density of storage is increased, the media are more prone to dropout and media failure. At the same time, storage space is reduced, labor and media handling costs are reduced, and potentially, backup time is saved. Additionally, higher densities often place a higher transmission load on the network because the storage device services a faster rate of data transfer. The media transport mechanism is usually the limiting factor on speed. Thus, by increasing the media density, higher speeds and efficiencies are achieved. Common reel tape densities include 800 bits per inch, 1600 and 3200 bits per inch, and 6250 bits per inch. The media for each density are identical, although total information storage increases by nearly a factor of four from the lowest to the highest density.

Lack of expertise is a risk. When personnel is untrained, processes will be efficient, slow, or poorly administered. Problems that might be simple for trained personnel attain an air of catastrophe and confusion when handled by a staff that is too inexperienced. Expertise, both technical and managerial, smooths rough edges inherent in any network. Expertise is expensive. It gravitates to the most interesting jobs, the ones with the most salary or enjoyment. As elsewhere, assess the level of risk an organization is willing to assume uninsured.

Labor

A network administration team is generally employed where a network is large and distributed, where the problems are many, and complex, and where the network fulfills a critical role within the organization. In critical situations it is important to have backup for all key components. Not only does this mean software, data and node and network hardware, it also includes the people that maintain the network. Sickness, vacations, long days, job dissatisfaction, and other factors can mean that labor is not always available. If 24-hour network response and problem coverage are required, then extra resources must be available for around-the-clock coverage. If problems cannot wait for the system administrator and he or she is out of the office, then an assistant may be the appropriate solution. If only one person knows the answers, the crisis-level discomfort is increased, breeding mutual distrust. Adequate resources resolve such issues.

Redundancy

Elsewhere, maintaining equipment redundancy and a parts inventory were proposed as an operationally astute policy. The issue here is backup, and when parts fail it becomes important to have replacement units available to solve the problem. Media backups, in part, provide a measure of security. The storage equipment and the device drivers are equally liable to fail and require replacement. Redundant parts are suggested. In addition, the people who maintain the network will occasionally be at home, on vacation, out sick, or leaving for a new job. The expertise to complete a repair should be available in duplicate to prevent a knowledge shortage. The level of redundancy maintained should factor in the level of risk an organization is willing to assume uninsured, since redundancy of parts and labor is an expense.

Parts supposedly in inventory, backups prepared and saved, should be available and usable. Moreover, that inventory should be functional as well as available. Test the parts. Test the media.

Chapter 19

Human Factors

Network communication has become a sophisticated management role. An organization inexperienced in communications technology faces a credibility problem because so much of business and management is based upon rapid and effective communication. Therefore, qualified people who can design, plan, install, and maintain a communications network are very important. The role is a difficult one because a network manager is a vendor to the user community. The responsibilities include responding to user and network problems, enhancing the information flow and installing new applications, as well as maintaining network resources and costs within the established range.

There is never a lack of problems, always a lack of time to get things done, and a shortage of staff to do all that needs to be done. Frequently, this results in a poor image and puts undue stress on the staff. The solution is more people—unacceptable to upper management—or a reduction in the level of network service—unacceptable to everyone in the user community. Therefore, a significant part of any network management including Ethernet is a clear understanding of these stresses and a means to cope with this supportive role.

The charters for network management, whether issued formally or developed over time and never verbally expressed, are **compatibility**, **credibility**, **security**, and **stability**, or C_2S_2. Figure 19.1 reiterates these charters fulfilled with a network team, experienced management, and administrative control of the network resources.

- Compatibility
- Credibility
- Security
- Stability

Figure 19.1 The network management charter.

Network Management

While a manager cannot control certain types of events, a manager can respond to events beyond control. Failure to accept events and responsibility for their impact, or reluctance to act and compensate for detrimental affects is a clear sign of management problems. Action, concerted and focused, is a clear sign of acceptance and control, whereas a reluctance to finalize decisions is an indication of a technical vacuum, a lack of clear lines of authority, or a basic interpersonal communication weakness. On the other hand, frantic and undirected action imparts a disharmony to the user community. A network is a critical cog in the communications pathway; action and results in time of crisis are imperative.

Required Management Skills

The network manager's administrative abilities should encompass record-keeping, inventory-tracking, technical, diagnostic, interpersonal and analytical abilities. Little can overcome weak administrative control of resources. Figure 19.2 outlines these management needs.

- Administrative control
- Record-keeping skills
- Inventory-tracking skills
- Technical management skills
- Ability to make decisions
- Ability to establish priorities
- Means to cope with staff shortages and burnout
- Ability to provide recognition
- Skills to develop employees
- Team building skills
- Evaluation skills

Figure 19.2 Network management skill set.

Administrative Control

Administrative control is an important factor for a large, growing, or critical network. Otherwise, self-taught experts or members of an ad hoc committee provide such expertise. When a network provides development services, interorganization communications, or financial services such as accounting, the network requires backup, daily maintenance, and a reliable team to control its operations. The network administrator provides planning, network design and configuration expertise, maintenance and upgrade abilities, and also serves as the arbiter of file space, network access, and performance disputes. The most important role may be that of a clearing-house for information and liaison to the user community. Note, however, that responsiveness does not mean saying "yes" to everything. A negative reply is just as responsive as a positive one; no administrator can afford to forget this, nor the meaning of "yes" and "no."

Lone wolves, the ruthless, aggressive types, are not effective managers despite the long-standing stereotype. A good administrator must be a team player. The traditional, autonomous "chief" is not effective in a service environment, and is counterproductive in today's workplace. Team orientation, responsiveness to subordinates, and a service ethic are personality traits that people welcome in an administrator today.

Distance from peers and subordinates results in an inability to hear constructive gossip. The gap also undermines administrative authority which should be based upon the nonegalitarian principle of information sharing and coordination rather than rank and command. The principle of "we are all in the same boat" is not a farce if actual rather than "authoritative" control is desired.

Record-keeping and Inventory-tracking Skills

Since the network is composed of many parts—hardware, software, data, and personal node equipment—accounting and inventory skills are required to track components and maintain an adequate inventory of spare repair parts. Records should indicate the status of software and hardware, and node configurations of all network components. A manager must know how to blueprint the network and track the status of work orders and job completions.

Technical Skills

A serious issue for most organizations is finding a technical manager with the right mix of technical and organizational abilities. Often a skilled technician is elevated to a management role solely because of his demonstrated expertise, or a skilled manager will find his talents at odds with the culture of a technical organization. These mismatches need to be corrected quickly for the good of all. Sometimes, when a qualified administrator is placed in the position of managing highly qualified technical personnel, the troops test and bait the manager in order to evaluate the manager's technical skills. If they find the technical ability lacking, they generally assume that the manager will not be competent. Network administration is a bifurcated need requiring both clear and ordered administration abilities and well-honed technical skills.

In the case of the technically competent manager, the administrative and interpersonal skills will present a valid challenge. This challenge must be confronted squarely, not avoided. A technical manager will certainly resolve the technical problems with ease, the technical manager may often fail to meet the expectations of subordinates and peers for handling issues, or disappoint the high expectations of network users. The solution, as proposed by the copious managerial literature, is to map out the organizational interrelationships in order to understand the hidden needs, agendas, and expectations, and to build a power base within the organization. Listening to gossip is also suggested, although this implies a sufficiency of time to chat with and *listen to* people. Such a power base opens conduits of information, provides for both formal and informal sources of answers, help, and organizational support.

In the case of the skilled manager who lacks the necessary technical skills, the problems will be in locating resources to solve problems and gaining the respect of the troops. The skilled manager usually brings a power base and organizational contacts as a matter of course.

Technical Managing Skills

Part of any job is managing people. For the network team, this is a two-way process. Not only must the network manager manage the network team, all members of the network team must manage expectations company-wide, since the company is the team's client. Management is not only from the top down, but also from the bottom up. The required skill set comprises more than the technical skills to maintain the physical and operative well being of the network. Users must be satisfied that they are receiving adequate and equal (to any fee basis, if applicable) service. Because this skill set is so large, a single person might not succeed at the job. Perception of the workload usually determines who and how many people comprise the management team. If more than a single person is required—in fact, several might be required to provide hardware, software, maintenance, and administrative support—the intra-group dependence adds to the management demands.

A good manager knows how to manage and control a situation. This does not imply that a good manager controls his or her team; rather, it means that the manager is able to control the situation and derive *consensus* goals and communicate them clearly to the team for implementation. The manager might feel distinctly out of control because of a dependence on the network team for implementation and technical skills. Here, as elsewhere, success will depend upon building consensus.

Interpersonal Communication Skills

Organizations spend money on technology, not on the basic skills of how to be a good employee; this issue must be addressed. While technical skills are clearly necessary to resolve the technical network problems, a honed communication skill is a prerequisite. Reiterating an earlier point, there is a vendor/user relationship in the network maintenance role. A manager can do a top-notch job in the mechanical side of the network, but still fail if the targeted user community is ignored. People slated to use the system are often removed from the planning process and find that plans made for them really don't solve their problems.

Additionally, a manager should know how to prepare all the paperwork that goes with being a manager. Honed presentation skills help convince others that you know how to design, plan, implement, and manage.

Making Decisions

Think big: realize that the consequences of many decisions may not become apparent for a year or more. New administrators tend to err on the conservative side finding it difficult to leap from their petty circumstances to the big picture. The game could be lost on this relative inaction.

Often the network administration team will be constrained to repair only those items that show clear failures. While individual problems may be innocuous, a number of marginal problems may combine to produce a global effect. Because the network management role is a repair, replace, and restore role, forward thinking action is difficult to achieve. Upper management rarely encourages potentially disruptive risk-taking. Radical changes are frowned upon and network changes are filtered through a conservative screen of consensus. This policy can be the death of a network manager, because growth, technological change, and proliferating problems may undermine his or her authority, perceived competence, and ability to institute large-scale repairs. This tendency should be resisted. Not only will conservatism ultimately devalue the network manager and the team, but the organization as an entity may slip behind the competition, as new technology supersedes the old.

Conservatism boxes a manager into a suboptimal position and limits the options otherwise available. When decision making is indecisive and risk taking has been avoided as a matter of policy, taking even moderate chances raises eyebrows because others have become accustomed to the norm. Breach of the norm, no matter how risky or risk-adverse, will cause objections. Establish your credibility soon. The pattern of risk-taking is established early on and success with those risks builds a consistent confidence in the network administration team.

Setting Priorities

The best action is to *negotiate* with the user community. If users are denied a say in network management, you will have a poor user/vendor relationship. Users clearly will not get the type and level of service which they desire. It is erroneous to assume that you or your team can determine needs and priorities. Users feel slighted and out of control when decisions are made for them. Certain projects or certain users may be key to the organization. For example, their network welfare is more critical than the welfare of other users. Unless this circumstance is communicated to the user community, other user groups might feel short-changed when resources are applied to resolve problems not affecting them personally.

Working Around Staff Shortages

Extra staffing is always needed and difficult to obtain; staffing is always a real management issue. A high level of skill in small part counter-balances the paucity of staff. Good management, good organizational skills, and clear communication with the user community almost make up for thread-bare resources. Involve the user community in the planning process; users know what they want. If consulted and apprised of events, they will help the process. If users are uncomfortable, they will reflect and magnify this insecurity over time. The users will understand resource limitations if clearly expressed. Involve them, and they will be part of your team.

Burn-out and Recognition

"Burn-out" is a common result of understaffing. The level of network problems and the workload imposed are often beyond the control of the network team or the manager. Lack of control is a situation that can be rectified, but the daily pressures magnify the difficulty of the job. Without adequate recognition of accomplishments, the team members will feel frustrated, undervalued, and often, angry.

A manager who communicates well with the user community has solved part of this problem by explaining the limits of the resources within his control and the level of service that can be provided. This will lessen the daily pressures, thus diverting episodic burn-outs. More important, how-ever, is attributing credit where it is due. Provide positive feedback to the team members and be certain that the user community is aware of the value of the services rendered.

Employee Development Skills

Since staff shortages are a certainty, it is important to recognize the desires of the employees for technical achievement and accomplishment and help the employees to develop new skills. In order to construct an effective network management team it is important to provide a defined framework within which the group functions. Demonstrate policies by example and maintain a clear and concise model. Avoid sudden shifts in demands, needs, and policy. Practice and rehearse the policies until the group is competent and confident. By all means, provide feedback, demonstrate by example, reaffirm correct and incorrect procedures, reaf-firm the developing skill sets, and fine tune any newly acquired skills. Train on all levels. Role models acting differently will undermine any "positive" results. Figure 19.3 lists team development suggestions.

```
• Define a framework
• Demonstrate by example
• Practice for confidence and competence
• Provide feedback
```

Figure 19.3 Team development steps.

Team Building Skills

It is a given that there will be staff shortages and that the staff will experience burn-out. In order to cope with these problems it is imperative that the manager understand how to encourage the staff to develop new skills, and how to foster initiative and a team approach.

Evaluation Skills

Part of the job of manager includes hiring, firing, specifying the pay scale for each job, and evaluating the team members. Good evaluation skills are important for maintaining each team member's sense of fair pay for work performed. Effective evaluation encourages superior performance by outlining what the expected goals are, and how each team member has performed relative to these goals. Failure to present clear and concise goals will discourage good team spirit and confuse the team members and the user community. Additionally, inability to evaluate team performance will create disgruntled employees.

The Network Team

Crucial to any Ethernet is an experienced network team. A network team would not be needed if Ethernet were a simple hook-up-and-run type of network. Instead, the link requires shared resources that offer both load limitations and a complex architecture. The simplified wiring of Ethernet eases the burden of maintaining a network in contrast to the star-coupled mainframe environment. As a consequence, the skill set for the network team should be different from that of a mainframe support team. The network team must understand the diverse needs and varied equipment in use within the network community. A good team can make a crucial difference between a functioning network, and an unmitigated disaster.

Team Skill Requirements

Several skill sets are required to keep the link of that network up and running. Figure 19.4 lists some of these needs. The physical layers of Ethernet need to be maintained and the software link layers need management. The node equipment, nonspecialized computer hardware, needs physical maintenance. The node equipment can range from simple and reliable personal computers to more fragile and complex engineering workstations, file servers, and print servers. This application layer requires software, physical, and lubricative maintenance.

- Technical knowledge
- Diagnostic skills
- Analytic skills
- Interpersonal communication abilities

Figure 19.4 The network team skill set.

Technical Knowledge

The network team applies mechanical and computer knowledge to plan, design, implement, and repair the network. Alternatively, if the group has a firm organizational charter, hired outside experts ease the load when problems exceed the abilities of the in-house crew.

Diagnostic and Analytic Skills

As important as good technical skills for the success of a team member is the ability to uncover network problems in an Ethernet environment. Problems are not textbook knowledge, and often transcend the vendor manuals and the scope of any book. It is therefore important that each team member know how to think through a situation given the relevant facts, and apply his or her technical knowledge to solving the problem.

Interpersonal Communication Skills

Organizations spend money on the people who bring to the company technical skills but not necessarily the basic skills of how to be a good employee. However, although technical skills are clearly necessary to resolve the technical network problems, a honed communication skill is prerequisite, not only for managers, but for the technicians as well. A technician can do a top-notch job in developing and repairing or implementing the mechanical side of the network, but still fail if the targeted user community is ignored. People slated to use the system are often removed from the repair process and find that plans made for them really don't solve their problems, or negatively effect their work.

Squeaky Wheel versus Problem Resolution

Users shout and scream for their share of the pie. Each user will want more attention, faster service, and better results. Some shout louder than others, and clearly some users will have more political clout as a consequence of their position, length of service, or network of friendships. While it often is necessary to resolve problems within a political framework, this should be moderated by clearly stated policies. A network by its design is an interrelated organism; thus certain problems need solution as a prerequisite to repairing others. A service policy is a must.

Set up a policy. For example, respond to problems on global resources before those of user-specific workstations. Repair global failures that inhibit the work of a larger group before attending to a single user's complaint. Repairs or changes that are upgrades or minor modifications should command less priority than a total failure of a user workstation. Such a setting of priorities requires a clear policy from the network manager. Adhere to that policy.

The Effects of Change

There are two successful ways of organizing a company, centralized and decentralized. There are valid reasons for going either way. Most managers and consultants know the textbook reasons; a decentralized company focuses the power in the hands of those who can best apply that power, whereas a centralized organizational structure returns control to a select few. But reasons for choosing a particular structure are irrelevant when facing problems. What often counts is simply changing the organization from one structure to the other. Changes compel people to reconsider how they do things, indicate that performance is being evaluated, and also that their needs for attention are being fulfilled.

A network manager would do well to remember this concept when a situation seems out-of-hand: a simple change of organizational structure, policy, and reporting relationships may restore control.

Easier Said than Done. . .

Most plans are easily derailed, easily completed. Communication and negotiations with the user community establish a credible relationship, while priorities determine which problems will be resolved and when they will be resolved. Despite the best of intentions, the workload usually outstrips available resources and the complexity of network problems often taxes the technical expertise and time availability of the network team. Things just will not get done. As long as the user community is apprised of these delays and gets clear feedback, options for temporary solutions, and/or revised time schedules, the relationship will flourish. Communication is key to successful human interaction.

Part 6

Troubleshooting Reference

This part contains practical and concise information for the network manager to help him or her debug Ethernet network failures. Instead of text and graphics, this part uses charts to detail a methodology that progressively isolates the suspected component. The proscribed procedures encourage good work habits and help network managers develop a logical approach to solving network failures. Additionally, several chapters demonstrate the uses for several network tools and include cross-referenced tables to use as aids in resolving network problems.

Chapter 20 is a detailed troubleshooting manual that describes techniques to isolate hardware, software, and the common network overloading problems. Chapter 21 summarizes the contents of this book with an Ethernet tool usage manual. This chapter supplies ideas and information on when to use the multitester, the TDR, the transceiver tester, and a protocol analyzer to solve network problems. Chapter 22 iconically describes the network components and then, using tables with four different formats, matches symptoms of common network problems with the possible causes. This information is not generally available elsewhere.

Chapter 20

The LAN Troubleshooting Sequence

Isolation Techniques

The first step when network failure occurs is to eliminate the obvious and isolate the problem for diagnosis. Figure 20.1 illustrates a logical step-by-step search pattern. The first step is to determine if failure is network software, network hardware, or node-specific. Unfortunately, experience with the reader's specific network provides the best basis for categorizing the failure. The only rule-of-thumb is that hardware failures are intermittent or transient and generally inexplicable, whereas software failures are reproducible and more logical. In either event if a wrong assumption is made, the step-by-step isolation technique presented will eventually indicate that the reader incorrectly diagnosed the failure.

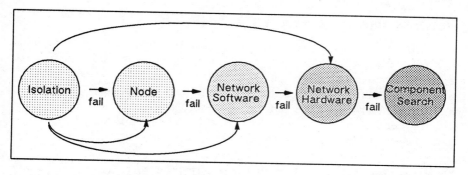

Figure 20.1 The logical LAN troubleshooting sequence.

Node Failures

If the failure has been isolated to a single node, follow the steps to accomplish repair. The node may have failed and this could cause network-wide failure. Assuming that the problem has been isolated to a failed node, follow the outlined steps in the tables. The sequence progresses with less likely causes of Ethernet failure.

Network Software Failures

If all checks succeed, the problem is probably global although individual nodes are more likely to fail than the entire Ethernet network and consequently they should be tested first. In fact, a failed node and an irate user are usually the first indicators of a global network problem. If the network fails as a unit, even though hardware is a more frequent cause of network loss than software, software should be explored first if at all possible because the diagnostic tools are more comprehensive.

If all nodes seem to be working independently, ascertain if network-level devices are suspect. While Ethernet and TCP/IP and many other upper-level communication software are supposed to be "state-less," some condition has likely occurred to lock the software into a perpetual waiting cycle. Assuming that the problem has been isolated to failed network software, follow the outlined steps in the accompanying tables. The sequence progresses with less likely causes of Ethernet failure. Should all software, both node-local and global, seem to be functioning correctly, it is probably a hardware malfunction causing the inconvenience.

The "server" side of a link shouldn't retain "state" before or after a transaction, although it frequently does. Therefore, every network transaction implies an open and close of a file and the network link. If state is maintained, the system is said to be *jammed*. Not only can this process halt the network, it also causes a degradation in normal network performance.

Network Hardware Failures

At this stage in the isolation process, the problem is probably a global network hardware problem. For example, a main connection is broken, or a crucial repeater or bridge has failed. Assuming that the problem has been isolated to a failed network hardware component, follow the outlined steps in the accompanying tables. The sequence progresses with less likely causes of Ethernet failure. If the network defies these standard debugging strategies, there may be a hidden component that is at fault.

Progressive Search for Hidden Component Failure

If all network components and devices appear to meet Ethernet specifications, the final alternative is to power down the network piece by piece, section by section, until the problem is uncovered. If the problem can't be resolved quickly and the user community is willing to endure a complete network shutdown, a sequential shutdown of the network in conjunction with a binary or sequential search pattern will ultimately uncover *any* network problem. Note that the binary search is more efficient on large networks. Follow the steps outlined. This is a last resort, and should only be performed with cooperation from the user community.

Isolation Techniques for Network Failures

For either hardware or software problems, isolate the location.

To isolate location:
- ☐ Apply binary search method or apply sequential search method
- ☐ Check for failed node/non-operation
- ☐ Check the software indicators
- ☐ Apply the multimeter
- ☐ Apply the transceiver tester
- ☐ Attach the time domain reflectometer
- ☐ Gather statistics and diagnose with the protocol analyzer

On location:
- ☐ Check to confirm that components are plugged in
- ☐ Jiggle components in case of short circuit
- ☐ Check for electrical shorts/breaks
- ☐ Replace failed components or interchange suspect components

For a software problem, isolate the location.

To isolate location:
- ☐ Gather statistics and diagnose with the protocol analyzer
- ☐ Analyze the network software
- ☐ Locate failed node/nonoperation
- ☐ Check the software indicators
- ☐ Root out nonfunctioning nodes

On location:
- ☐ Reboot system
- ☐ Restart software
- ☐ Replace software
- ☐ Debug/fix software
- ☐ Power cycle individual hardware components

Note: step through each check. If the test shows correct network operation, step to the next item. Each item is progressively less likely to occur. If all checks succeed, widen the search pattern to a larger subset of the network. If a node has failed without clear reason, check the network. If the network has failed without clear reason, check the network software.

Decreasing Likelihood Search: Node Failed

If a node has failed, check that:

- ☐ the workstation or node unit is plugged in
- ☐ the workstation has electrical power
- ☐ the workstation is functioning
- ☐ the workstation sees Ethernet and TCP/IP
- ☐ the transceiver drop cable connections are secure
- ☐ the transceiver drop cable is correct
- ☐ the transceiver electronics function
- ☐ the transceiver tap installation is to specification
- ☐ the Ethernet controller functions
- ☐ the Ethernet address is correct
- ☐ the Internet address is correct
- ☐ all other nodes are working
- ☐ some other nodes are working
- ☐ that Ethernet versions/variations match

If all checks succeed =>
.... you have a network software failure or
.... you have a network hardware failure or
.... you have a hidden component failure.

Note: step through each check. If the test shows correct network operation, step to the next item. Each item is progressively less likely to occur. If all checks succeed, widen the search pattern to a larger subset of the network. If a node has failed without clear reason, check the network. If the network has failed without clear reason, check the network software.

Decreasing Likelihood Search: Network Software Failed

If network software has failed, check that:

☐ the network software is correct
☐ the network is not overloaded with traffic
☐ the "state" of Ethernet is not jammed
☐ each software node is compatible
☐ Ethernet versions/variations match
☐ the network software is performing tasks
☐ the operating network software is not corrupted
☐ the software is compatible with physical devices

If all checks succeed =>
.... **you have a network hardware failure or**
.... **you have a hidden component failure.**

Note: step through each check. If the test shows correct network operation, step to the next item. Each item is progressively less likely to occur. If all checks succeed, widen the search pattern to a larger subset of the network. If a node has failed without clear reason, check the network. If the network has failed without clear reason, check the network software.

Decreasing Likelihood Search: Network Hardware Failed

If network hardware has failed, check that:

- ☐ the network software is correct
- ☐ the network print and file servers are online
- ☐ the network is not overloaded with traffic
- ☐ terminators are in place
- ☐ end connectors are correctly installed
- ☐ barrel connectors are tightly connecting
- ☐ no coaxial sections are broken
- ☐ there are no cable breaks, cuts, abrasions
- ☐ the "state" of Ethernet is not jammed
- ☐ the gateways and repeaters are functioning
- ☐ fan-out units are not jammed
- ☐ individual network segments function
- ☐ repeated segments are functioning
- ☐ gateway segments are functioning
- ☐ individual network cable sections are operational
- ☐ transceiver tap components are functioning
- ☐ transceivers are not jabbering/chattering
- ☐ transceiver electronics are operational
- ☐ there are no software node incompatibilities
- ☐ Ethernet versions/variations match
- ☐ there is no outside electrical or radio frequency interference

If all checks succeed =>
. . . . you have a hidden component failure.

Note: step through each check. If the test shows correct network operation, step to the next item. Each item is progressively less likely to occur. If all checks succeed, widen the search pattern to a larger subset of the network. If a node has failed without clear reason, check the network. If the network has failed without clear reason, check the network software.

Progressive Search for Hidden Component Failure

To shut down the entire network, follow these steps:

1. Power down all nodes.
2. Power down all bridges, fan-outs, gateways, and repeaters.
3. Power down all file servers, print servers and auxiliary devices.
4. Disconnect all network segments.
5. Terminate to specification all individual segments.
6. Electrically test coax components for electrical incompatibilities.
7. Electrically test transceivers for electrical incompatibilities.
8. Disconnect all network sections (institute binary search).
9. Electrically test coax components for electrical incompatibilities.
10. Electrically test transceivers for electrical incompatibilities.
11. Power up each individual network section.
12. Terminate to specification all individual segments.
13. Reconstitute segments from individual sections.
14. Power up each individual network segment.
15. Electrically test coax components for electrical incompatibilities.
16. Electrically test transceivers for electrical incompatibilities.
17. Power up all nodes on each individual segment.
18. Power up all file servers, print servers and auxiliary devices.
19. Power up fan-out units.
20. Power up gateways.
21. Power up bridges.
22. Power up repeaters.
23. Reconstitute network and reconnect all segments.
24. Power on all nodes.

If all checks succeed and the network remains dysfunctional =>
.... you have traffic overload
.... or an electrical problem
.... or vandalism

If all checks succeed and network now provides complete service =>
.... you have traffic overload
.... or a network "state" problem
.... or an electrical problem
.... or vandalism

Note: step through each check. If the test shows correct network operation, step to the next item. Each item is progressively less likely to occur. If all checks succeed, widen the search pattern to a larger subset of the network. If a node has failed without clear reason, check the network. If the network has failed without clear reason, check the network software.

Chapter 21

Tool Usage Reference

The four network tools—the multitester, the time domain reflectometer, the transceiver tester, and the protocol analyzer—have overlapping functionality. The accompanying tables coach the network management team in the hour(s) of crisis by suggesting appropriate uses for each tool. These uses and the listed sequences direct the reader to a careful investigation; the aim is to discover the causes of possible network malfunction. The ideal values are repeated here for the reader's convenience.

Additionally, there are two sections detailing the sequence of tools and the best tool to apply in cases of hardware or software failures. While hardware problems are often easier to locate and repair than software problems, search for problems at the highest, most comprehensive, level; this is often a statistical search with a protocol analyzer, or a software search. Note also that software-level searches are generally noninvasive.

As each test succeeds, select a more basic component until the problem is traced. Certain types of problems, including hardware malfunctions, may be clearly pinpointed with this software search and a software search with a protocol analyzer is apt to provide comprehensive diagnosis. In some serious cases network faults necessitate TDR or multitester testing because the network traffic is halted precluding the use of the protocol analyzer. Check the network globally first. Contrast any visible conditions with experienced events or network statistics. Check if any nodes are functioning in a stand-alone mode, or analyze any patterns of failed nodes. Check key servers for functionality. Localize the search to a common area, or common subset of possible problems and test accordingly.

If the problem cannot be localized, consider the possibility of a hardware malfunction and, as with the software tests, start with a major component and select progressively more basic components until the problem is traced. Unresolved problems may necessitate a complete shutdown and network restart as detailed in the preceding chapter.

Functionality of Network Tools

Multimeter
- [ ] Check network voltage   ± 2 volts
- [ ] Check network resistance   negligible
- [ ] Check network impedance   50 or 75 ohms
- [ ] Check connector conductivity
- [ ] Check network coaxial cable continuity
- [ ] Check transceiver tap probes for conductivity and pairwise isolation
- [ ] Check transceiver drop cable pinout continuity

Time Domain Reflectometer (TDR)
- [ ] Check network coaxial cable conductivity   50 or 75 ohms
- [ ] Check network coaxial cable continuity
- [ ] Check transceiver and connector installation
- [ ] Check transceiver busy signal acknowledgment

Transceiver Tester
- [ ] Check individual transceivers for functionality
- [ ] Check transceiver drop cables for correct pin-out

Protocol Analyzer
- [ ] Check for network traffic overload   >25% channel utilization
- [ ] Check for exceptionally busy nodes   >20% network load
- [ ] Check for chattering/jabbering transceivers
- [ ] Check for high collision rates   >8%
- [ ] Check for any failed transceivers/high CRC error rates
- [ ] Check for failed Ethernet controller/small or oversized packets
- [ ] Check for nonsense packets

Note: step through each check. If the test shows correct network operation, step to the next item. Each item is progressively less likely to occur. If all checks succeed, widen the search pattern to a larger subset of the network. If a node has failed without clear reason, check the network. If the network has failed without clear reason, check the network software.

Troubleshooting Sequence for Network Software Failures

If network functioning:

Protocol analyzer: partial network service

☐ perform a network-wide statistical evaluation:
.... traffic load
.... packet counts
.... packet defect rate
.... collision rates
.... missing packet addresses
.... jabbering transceivers
.... chattering transceivers
.... nonresponsive transceivers

Server software functioning with partial network service

☐ perform a network software and hardware evaluation:
.... check for any new changes
.... software functioning
.... version numbers
.... version compatibility
.... file service
.... memory levels
.... source
.... check for overloads

If node subset halted:

Protocol analyzer: partial network service

☐ perform network-wide statistical evaluation:
.... traffic load
.... packet counts
.... packet defect rate
.... collision rates
.... missing packet addresses
.... jabbering transceivers
.... chattering transceivers
.... nonresponsive transceivers

Node software functioning with partial network service

☐ perform a node software and hardware evaluation:
.... check for any new changes
.... software functioning
.... version numbers
.... version compatibility
.... file service
.... memory levels
.... source
.... overloads

Note: step through each check. If the test shows correct network operation, step to the next item. Each item is progressively less likely to occur. If all checks succeed, widen the search pattern to a larger subset of the network. If a node has failed without clear reason, check the network. If the network has failed without clear reason, check the network software.

Troubleshooting Sequence for Software Failures(continued)

If network halted and no network service is available:
☐ power down network and restart all nodes individually
☐ check hardware for proper installation and functionality
☐ or, as a last resort, apply a progressive search

Note: step through each check. If the test shows correct network operation, step to the next item. Each item is progressively less likely to occur. If all checks succeed, widen the search pattern to a larger subset of the network. If a node has failed without clear reason, check the network. If the network has failed without clear reason, check the network software.

Troubleshooting Sequence for Network Hardware Failures

If network functioning:

Protocol Analyzer: partial network service
☐ perform a network-wide statistical evaluation:
.... traffic load
.... packet counts
.... packet defect rate
.... collision rates
.... missing packet addresses
.... jabbering transceivers
.... chattering transceivers
.... nonresponsive transceivers

If node subset halted:

Protocol analyzer: partial network service
☐ perform statistical evaluation on suspect nodes if possible:
.... traffic load
.... packet counts
.... packet defect rate
.... collision rates
.... missing packet addresses
.... jabbering transceivers
.... chattering transceivers
.... nonresponsive transceivers

TDR: erratic or no network service
☐ check the coaxial cable for continuity in terms of:
.... breaks
.... shorts
.... abrasions
.... misspecified cable
.... excessive bends
.... impedance errors

☐ check the coaxial connectors for:
.... poor installation
.... shorts
.... breaks
.... unclean fittings

☐ view the transceivers for:
.... jabbering electronics
.... signal interference
.... poor installation

Note: step through each check. If the test shows correct network operation, step to the next item. Each item is progressively less likely to occur. If all checks succeed, widen the search pattern to a larger subset of the network. If a node has failed without clear reason, check the network. If the network has failed without clear reason, check the network software.

Troubleshooting Sequence for Network Hardware Failures
(continued)

If network halted:
TDR: no network service
☐ check the coaxial cable for continuity in terms of:
.... breaks
.... shorts
.... abrasions
.... misspecified cable
.... excessive bends
.... impedance errors

☐ check the coaxial connectors for:
.... poor installation
.... shorts
.... breaks
.... unclean fittings

☐ view the transceivers for:
.... jabbering electronics
.... poor installation

Transceiver tester: for node-specific hardware malfunctions
☐ check the transceivers for:
.... jabbering electronics
.... signal interference
.... poor installation
.... bad electronics
.... wrong Ethernet version
.... not functioning

☐ test the transceiver drop cables for:
.... bad pin-out
.... misspecified cable
.... impedance errors
.... shorts
.... breaks
.... unclean fittings
.... poor installation

Note: step through each check. If the test shows correct network operation, step to the next item. Each item is progressively less likely to occur. If all checks succeed, widen the search pattern to a larger subset of the network. If a node has failed without clear reason, check the network. If the network has failed without clear reason, check the network software.

Troubleshooting Sequence for Network Hardware Failures
(continued)

Multimeter: for serious cabling failures or isolated testing

☐ test the coaxial cable for:
.... breaks
.... shorts
.... abrasions
.... misspecified cable
.... impedance errors

☐ test the connectors for:
.... poorly installed
.... shorts
.... breaks
.... wrong connectors
.... unclean fittings

☐ test the transceiver taps for:
.... poor installation

Note: step through each check. If the test shows correct network operation, step to the next item. Each item is progressively less likely to occur. If all checks succeed, widen the search pattern to a larger subset of the network. If a node has failed without clear reason, check the network. If the network has failed without clear reason, check the network software.

Chapter 22

Troubleshooting Cross-Reference

This chapter presents five individual sections that cross-reference practical diagnostic information. Figure 22.1 lists these sections for the reader's benefit. They are useful both to provide diagnostic clues and to confirm that a hypothetical diagnosis does explain the observed symptoms of a network problem.

Components -> Typical Failures
Causes -> Symptoms
Possible Causes -> Symptoms
Transmission Problems -> Causes
Statistical Inferences

Figure 22.1 The troubleshooting reference tables.

The first section shows what can fail with each network component. Figure 22.2 illustrates the components included in the check list. Use it to narrow down a diagnosis when a problem has been localized to a specific component.

The second section lists common failures with each failure's characteristic symptoms. This table provides feedback that a repair solution has correctly addressed the situation. Use it to confirm your diagnosis.

The third section matches characteristic symptoms with the possible causes, therefore providing valuable ideas when a problem defies solution and has stumped the administration team. This section is a reorganization of the second section.

The fourth section defines transmission errors and offers insight into likely causes. While it is specific to network transmission-layer problems, the explanations do suggest hardware causes when pertinent.

The last section lists the prevalent network statistics trapped by protocol analyzers and system software. Also included is the range of the possible and the normally expected values. Explanations are listed for statistics that are skewed outside the normal range.

Check List of Typical Component Failures

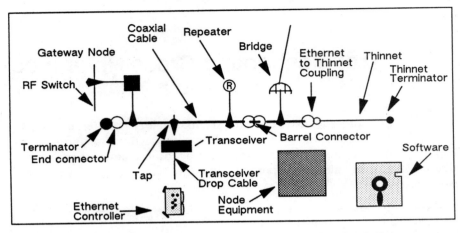

Figure 22.2 The Ethernet components included in the check list.

- **Coaxial Cable** .... RG-50. RG-52 (50 ohm)
- **Coaxial Cable** .... RG-6, RG-6a, RG-225 (75 ohm)
- **End Connectors** .... N-type
- **End Connectors** .... BNC
- **Barrel Connectors** .... all types
- **Terminators** .... all types
- **Ethernet-to-Thinnet Converter** .... all types
- **Tap Unit** .... "Vampire" type
- **Tap Unit** .... Screw connector
- **Transceiver** .... all types
- **Transceiver Drop Cable** .... all types
- **Ethernet Controller** .... Bus board
- **Ethernet Controller** .... Integrated
- **Fan-out Units** .... all types
- **Network Node** .... Hardware unit
- **Network Node** .... Workstation
- **Network Node** .... Server
- **Repeater** .... all types
- **Smart Repeater** .... all types
- **Gateway Node** .... all types
- **Bridge** .... all types
- **RF Switch** .... all types
- **Software** .... Generic

Note: the component failures are listed in decreasing likelihood of failure.

Coaxial Cable .... RG-50, RG-52 (50 ohm)
- ☐ Shorting at unused tap hole
- ☐ Excessive bend
- ☐ Inadvertent ground of shield
- ☐ Cut through jacket exposing shield
- ☐ Cut through to core conductor shorting core and shield
- ☐ Defective dielectric insulation (age)
- ☐ Break in core conductor
- ☐ Cable does not meet manufacturing specifications
- ☐ Segment too long
- ☐ Excessive number of sections in cable segment
- ☐ Defective cable
- ☐ Unsupported sections overstretched
- ☐ Radio interference through exposed tap
- ☐ Micro-fractures in core

Coaxial Cable .... RG-6, RG-6a, RG-225 (75 ohm)
- ☐ Shorting at unused tape hole
- ☐ Cable crushed
- ☐ Cable does not meet manufacturing specifications
- ☐ Inadvertent ground of shield
- ☐ Cut through jacket exposing shield
- ☐ Cut through to core conductor shorting core and shield
- ☐ Defective dielectric insulation (age)
- ☐ Break in core conductor
- ☐ Segment too long
- ☐ Excessive number of sections in cable segment
- ☐ Defective cable
- ☐ Radio interference through exposed tap
- ☐ Micro-fractures in core

End Connectors .... N-type
- ☐ Wrong size for cable diameter
- ☐ Short between shield and core
- ☐ Center probe improperly connected to core conductor
- ☐ Connector not screwed onto cable tightly enough
- ☐ Shield improperly secured to connector housing
- ☐ Improper assembly
- ☐ Unclean fittings

End Connectors .... BNC
- ☐ Wrong size for cable diameter
- ☐ Short between shield and core
- ☐ Center probe improperly connected to core conductor
- ☐ Connector not screwed onto cable tightly enough
- ☐ Shield improperly secured to connector housing
- ☐ Improper assembly—washer missing
- ☐ Unclean fittings

End Connectors .... all types
- ☐ Male prongs overextended
- ☐ Connector not screwed onto cable tightly enough
- ☐ Improper assembly
- ☐ Unclean fittings

Note: the component failures are listed in decreasing likelihood of failure.

Terminators .... **all types**
- ☐ Not screwed onto end connector tightly enough
- ☐ Not installed correctly
- ☐ Missing
- ☐ Fittings unclean
- ☐ Wrong type
- ☐ Defective unit

Ethernet-to-Thinnet Converter .... **Standard type**
- ☐ Not screwed onto end connector tightly enough
- ☐ Not installed correctly
- ☐ Missing
- ☐ Fittings unclean
- ☐ Wrong type

Tap Unit .... **"Vampire" type**
- ☐ Center probe not in contact with core conductor
- ☐ Ground probes not in contact with shield
- ☐ Stray shield braid wires shorting to core or tap body
- ☐ Broken probes
- ☐ Insufficient pressure applied with clamping mechanism
- ☐ Center probe access not drilled deeply enough
- ☐ Bent probes
- ☐ Wrong size of tap for cable diameter

Tap Unit .... **Screw connector**
- ☐ Not screwed onto end connector tightly enough
- ☐ Fittings unclean
- ☐ Insufficient pressure applied with clamping mechanism

Transceiver .... **all types**
- ☐ Bad tap
- ☐ Bent tap probes
- ☐ Incomplete connection to transceiver drop cable
- ☐ Wrong Ethernet version for network
- ☐ Defective electronics:
  - . Chatter
  - . Jabber
  - . Misframed packets
  - . Bad CRC
  - . Packets too long or too short
  - . Corrupted packets

Note: the component failures are listed in decreasing likelihood of failure.

Transceiver Drop Cable .... **all types**
- ☐ Poor connection with node equipment
- ☐ Poor connection with transceiver
- ☐ Worn-out slide latch connectors
- ☐ Transmit wires shorting to shield
- ☐ Wires internally shorting
- ☐ Defective dielectric insulation (age)
- ☐ Cut through jacket exposing shield
- ☐ Shield not grounded
- ☐ Cable does not meet manufacturing specifications
- ☐ Cable too long
- ☐ Not correctly grounded
- ☐ Bad wire pin-out

Ethernet Controller .... **Bus board**
- ☐ Mismatched with network Ethernet version
- ☐ Jumpers improperly selected
- ☐ Mismatched with node hardware
- ☐ Mismatched with other network equipment
- ☐ Not installed properly
- ☐ Not grounded
- ☐ Defective electronics

Ethernet Controller .... **Integrated**
- ☐ Mismatched with network Ethernet version
- ☐ Jumpers improperly selected
- ☐ Mismatched with other network equipment
- ☐ Not grounded
- ☐ Defective electronics

Fan-out Units .... **all types**
- ☐ Electronics jammed (power cycle)
- ☐ Defective electronics
- ☐ Transceiver drop cables not securely attached
- ☐ Transceiver drop cables exceed length specification
- ☐ Powered off
- ☐ Not correctly grounded
- ☐ Mismatched with network Ethernet version
- ☐ Cascaded too many deep
- ☐ Too many network addresses

Network Node .... **Hardware unit**
- ☐ Network node equipment not working
- ☐ Poor transceiver drop cable connection
- ☐ Defective transceiver
- ☐ Defective transceiver tap
- ☐ Defective Ethernet Controller
- ☐ mismatched version of Ethernet Controller
- ☐ mismatched version of transceiver
- ☐ Defective drop cable
- ☐ Network overloaded

Note: the component failures are listed in decreasing likelihood of failure.

Network Node .... **Workstation**
- ☐ Poor transceiver drop cable connection
- ☐ Defective transceiver
- ☐ Defective transceiver tap
- ☐ Defective Ethernet controller
- ☐ mismatched version of Ethernet controller
- ☐ mismatched version of transceiver
- ☐ Defective drop cable
- ☐ Network overloaded
- ☐ mismatched network software
- ☐ Overloaded workstation
- ☐ Workstation not working
- ☐ Workstation hardware component failure
- ☐ Software "wedged"
- ☐ Improper Ethernet address
- ☐ Improper Internet address
- ☐ Too many network addresses

Network Node .... **Server**
- ☐ Poor transceiver drop cable connection
- ☐ Defective transceiver
- ☐ Defective transceiver tap
- ☐ Defective Ethernet Controller
- ☐ mismatched version of Ethernet Controller
- ☐ mismatched version of transceiver
- ☐ Defective drop cable
- ☐ Network overloaded
- ☐ mismatched network software
- ☐ Overloaded server
- ☐ Server not working
- ☐ Server hardware component failure
- ☐ Software "wedged"
- ☐ Improper Ethernet address
- ☐ Improper Internet address
- ☐ Too many network addresses

Repeater .... **all types**
- ☐ Poor transceiver drop cable connection
- ☐ Defective transceiver
- ☐ Defective transceiver tap
- ☐ mismatched version of transceiver
- ☐ Network overloaded

Smart Repeater .... **all types**
- ☐ "Missing" nodes
- ☐ Fails to rout packets
- ☐ Poor transceiver drop cable connection
- ☐ Defective transceiver
- ☐ Defective transceiver tap
- ☐ mismatched version of transceiver
- ☐ Network overloaded

Note: the component failures are listed in decreasing likelihood of failure.

Gateway Node .... **all types**
- ☐ Poor transceiver drop cable connection
- ☐ Defective transceiver
- ☐ Defective transceiver tap
- ☐ mismatched version of transceiver
- ☐ Overloaded gateway server
- ☐ Defective software
- ☐ Network overloaded
- ☐ Software "wedged"
- ☐ Improper Ethernet address
- ☐ Improper Internet address
- ☐ Too many network addresses

Bridge .... **all types**
- ☐ Poor transfer connection
- ☐ Poor transmit connection
- ☐ Busy common carrier
- ☐ Line dead
- ☐ Overloaded destination network
- ☐ Defective software

RF Switch .... **all types**
- ☐ Unlubricated relay
- ☐ Defective mechanism
- ☐ Failed signal receiver
- ☐ Not screwed onto end connector tightly enough
- ☐ Bad fittings
- ☐ Not installed correctly
- ☐ Network coaxial cable severed

Software .... **Generic**
- ☐ Not applied correctly
- ☐ Not installed correctly
- ☐ Software bug
- ☐ Wrong software revision
- ☐ Out of memory
- ☐ Jammed into a nonfunctioning state
- ☐ Software version incompatible with node system software
- ☐ Software version incompatible with server software
- ☐ Software version incompatible with node hardware
- ☐ Software corrupted on source media
- ☐ Software overwritten in memory
- ☐ Software overloaded by demand requests for service

Note: the component failures are listed in decreasing likelihood of failure.

Causes ————————————————➤ Symptom

---

overloaded network .... network jammed
workstation jammed
slow reponse
partial network response
collisions
bad packets
retransmissions
no network service
poor performance
no remote file service
slow file service
erratic file service
partial system boot
"software" problems

---

network terminator missing .... network jammed

---

open break on network .... network jammed
node dead
nodes missing
no network service
partial network response
erratic file service
no file service
"software" problem

---

open short on network .... network jammed
node dead
terminator missing
no network service
partial network response
erratic file service
no file service
"software" problem

---

improper shielding from noise .... network jammed
collisions
files corrupted
bad packets
nodes missing
poor performance
"software" problems

---

in excess of 100 taps on a coax segment .... network jammed
collisions
slow response

---

improper coaxial grounding .... collisions
slow response
networks jammed

Note: the symptoms are in decreasing likelihood of occurrence.

Causes ─────────────────────────────► Symptom

---

faulty transceiver . . . . files corrupted
collisions
no network service
bad packets
workstation jammed
no answer from a node

---

transceiver with improper frequency . . . . network jammed

---

transceiver with improper voltage . . . . network jammed

---

transceiver edge connector broken . . . . node dead
partial network response
bad packets
no remote boot
no remote file service
network jammed
no answer from a node

---

transceiver tap probes broken . . . . node dead
partial network response
bad packets
no remote boot
no remote file service
no answer from a node

---

drop cable not properly connected . . . . network jammed
workstation jammed
collisions
files corrupted
bad packets
retransmissions
partial system boot
no remote system boot
no answer from a node

---

drop cable not properly connected . . . . network jammed
workstation jammed
collisions
files corrupted
bad packets
retransmissions
partial system boot
no remote system boot
no answer from a node

Note: the symptoms are in decreasing likelihood of occurrence.

Causes ─────────────────────────────▶ Symptom

defective drop cable . . . . network jammed
workstation jammed
collisions
files corrupted
bad packets
retransmissions
no remote system boot
partial system boot
partial system boot
no answer from a node

bad tap . . . . files corrupted
collisions
no network service
bad packets
partial system boot

tap probe not in contact with coax . . . . network jammed
partial network response
poor performance
no network service

no transceiver heartbeat . . . . workstation jammed
no remote file service
poor performance
slow response
intermittent slowdowns

Fan-out jammed . . . . workstation jammed

malfunctioning repeater . . . . network jammed
partial network response
no answer from a node
nodes missing

malfunctioning gateway . . . . network jammed
partial network response
bad packets
no answer from a node
nodes missing

file server down . . . . no network service
no file service
slow file service
no remote system boot

Note: the symptoms are in decreasing likelihood of occurrence.

Causes ————————————————▶ Symptom

file server overloaded . . . . no network service
no file service
slow file service
erratic file service

defective system software . . . . workstation jammed
no network service
no file service
slow file service
erratic file service

corrupted system files . . . . partial system boot
no remote system boot

user files corrupted . . . . erratic file service

mismatched hardware . . . . network jammed
workstation jammed
no file service
erratic file service
no remote system boot
partial system boot
slow file service
collisions
files corrupted
bad packets
node dead
partial network response
"software" problems

coaxial cable metal fatigue . . . . network jammed
workstation jammed
slow response
partial response
collisions
bad packets
no network service
no file service

Note: the symptoms are in decreasing likelihood of occurrence.

Possible Causes ————————————➤ Symptom

---

overloaded network .... network jammed
network terminator missing
open break on network
open short on network
Improper shielding from noise
in excess of 100 taps on a coax segment
improper coaxial grounding
transceiver with improper frequency
transceiver with improper voltage
transceiver edge connector broken
drop cable not properly connected
defective drop cable
tap probe not in contact with coax
fan-out jammed
malfunctioning repeater
malfunctioning gateway
mismatched hardware

---

overloaded network .... workstation jammed
drop cable not properly connected
defective drop cable
no transceiver heartbeat
bad transceiver
defective system software
mismatched hardware

---

overloaded network .... slow response
in excess of 100 taps on a coax segment
improper coaxial grounding

---

overloaded network .... partial network response
open break on network
open short on network
transceiver edge connector broken
transceiver tap probes broken
malfunctioning repeater
malfunctioning gateway
tap probe not in contact with coax
mismatched hardware

---

overloaded network .... collisions
improper coaxial grounding
Improper shielding from noise
in excess of 100 taps on a coax segment
bad transceiver
drop cable not properly connected
defective drop cable
bad tap
mismatched hardware

Note: the symptoms are in decreasing likelihood of occurrence.

Possible Causes ————————————➤ Symptom

Improper shielding from noise .... files corrupted
bad transceiver
drop cable not properly connected
defective drop cable
bad tap
defective system software
mismatched hardware

---

overloaded network .... bad packets
Improper shielding from noise
bad transceiver
transceiver edge connector broken
transceiver tap probes broken
drop cable not properly connected
defective drop cable
bad tap
malfunctioning gateway
mismatched hardware

---

transceiver edge connector broken .... no remote system boot
transceiver tap probes broken
defective drop cable
file server down
corrupted system files
mismatched hardware

---

drop cable not properly connected .... partial system boot
defective drop cable
bad tap
mismatched hardware

---

overloaded network .... no remote file service
transceiver tap probes broken
transceiver edge connector broken
no transceiver heartbeat
file server down
file server overloaded

---

overloaded network .... retransmissions
drop cable not properly connected
defective drop cable

---

overloaded network .... partial system boot
drop cable not properly connected
defective drop cable

Note: the symptoms are in decreasing likelihood of occurrence.

Possible Causes ━━━━━━━━━━━━━━━━━━▶ Symptom

---

overloaded network .... no network service
open break on network
open short on network
bad tap
tap probe not in contact with coax
file server down
file server overloaded
defective system software

---

overloaded network .... poor performance
tap probe not in contact with coax
no transceiver heartbeat
Improper shielding from noise

---

no transceiver heartbeat .... intermittent slowdowns

---

open break on network .... nodes missing
open short on network
malfunctioning repeater
malfunctioning gateway
Improper shielding from noise

---

open break on network .... node dead
open short on network
transceiver edge connector broken
transceiver tap probes broken
mismatched hardware

---

bad transceiver .... no answer from a node
transceiver edge connector broken
transceiver tap probes broken
drop cable not properly connected
defective drop cable
malfunctioning repeater
malfunctioning gateway

---

open break on network .... no file service
open short on network
file server down
file server overloaded
defective network software
mismatched hardware

---

overloaded network .... slow file service
file server down
file server overloaded
defective network software
mismatched hardware

Note: the symptoms are in decreasing likelihood of occurrence.

Possible Causes ———————————►Symptom

---

overloaded network .... erratic file service
open break on network
open short on network
file server overloaded
defective network
user files corrupted
mismatched hardware

---

overloaded network .... "software" problems
mismatched hardware
open break on network
open short on network
improper shielding from noise

Note: the symptoms are in decreasing likelihood of occurrence.

Transmission Problem  Definition

Likely causes for observed transmission problem

Abnormal Preamble .... **frame start not identified**
1. The preamble pattern doesn't match the legal eight byte Ethernet synchronization pattern because a transmitter is non-spec, or a receiver is non-spec.

Runt Frame .... **frame less than minimum 60 bytes**
1. Collisions cause runt frames. Fragments of colliding packets are runt frame by Ethernet definition, since collisions occur within the first 56 bytes transmitted.
2. A late collision cause runt frames. If a node is not transmitting according to specification.
3. The network is too large, and the return delay is insuffcient for the CSMA/CD mechanism to properly identify colllisions.
4. The transmitting station purposely transmitted a runt frame.

Jabber Frame .... **frame greater than maximum 1518 bytes**
1. If a node is not transmitting according to specification.
2. A transceiver has failed and is transmitting garbage packets.

Mis-aligned Frame .... **uneven frame size and FCS error**
1. A transceiver has failed and is transmitting garbage packets.
2. Hardware impedance mismatches is causing coaxial noise and internal reflection.

Corrupt Data .... **hardware failure**
1. An Ethernet transceiver or controller is not transmitting according to specification.
2. There are an excessive number of jabber frames on the network.
3. A repeater, smart repeater, gateway or bridge is not performing correctly.

FCS Error .... **late collision**
1. A transceiver has failed and is transmitting garbage packets.
2. Signal interference disrupted communications.
3. An Ethernet transceiver or controller is not transmitting according to specification.
4. The network coaxial cable is improperly grounded.
5. Network segment exceeds length limitations.

No Backoff Error .... **late collision**
1. A transceiver has failed and is transmitting garbage packets.
2. An Ethernet transceiver or controller is not transmitting according to specification.

Address Error .... **packets not received**
1. Improper node address initialization.
2. Signal interference is disrupting communications.
3. An Ethernet controller is not transmitting according to specification.

Note: the symptoms are in decreasing likelihood of occurrence.

Transmission Problem ──────────▶ Definition

Likely causes for observed transmission problem

Type Error .... packet misinterpretation
   1. A transceiver has failed and is transmitting garbage packets.
   2. System software error.
   3. Operator or network administration error.
   4. Mis-matched IEEE 802.3 or Ethernet standards.

Interface Problem .... no Ethernet access
   1. Improper transceiver type for transmitting characteristics.
   2. Mis-matched hardware.
   3. Mis-matched communication software.
   4. A transceiver has failed and is transmitting garbage packets.
   5. The network coaxial cable is improperly grounded or connected.
   6. An Ethernet controller is not transmitting according to specification.
   7. TCP/IP specification infraction.

No Synchronization .... packets garbled
   1. Invalid type.
   2. Mis-specified LLC.
   3. Link initialization problems.
   4. Link disconnection.
   5. No message acknowledgement.
   6. TCP/IP specification infraction or TCP/IP controller timing error.

No Response .... transmission confirmation not received
   1. Node not online.
   2. Node failed.
   3. Node overloaded.
   4. Improper Internet address.
   5. TCP/IP specification infraction or TCP/IP error.
   6. Protocol mismatched.

IncompleteTransmission .... indicative of non-specific problem
   1. Node not online.
   2. Node failed.
   3. Node overloaded.
   4. Improper Internet address.
   5. TCP/IP error.
   6. Protocol mismatched.
   7. Software failure.
   8. Network overloaded.
   9. Global network "state" lockup, software or hardware.
   10. Application failure.
   11. Interface problem.
   12. Synchronization error.

"Transmission Error" .... indicative of non-specific problems

---

Note: the symptoms are in decreasing likelihood of occurrence.

Statistical Inference

This section explores statistical information for   isolating and understanding network problems. The first column, the actual statistic, is shown with a range if applicable and a "normal" value. When the statistic exceeds the normal range, an inference is listed in the last column.

Packet Counts

Statistic ➤ Range ➤ Norm ────────➤ Inference			
packets transmitted	0–3571	*	statistical overloads
packets received	0–3571	*	statistical overloads
collision rate	0–100%	1–2%	malfunctions, overloads
			faulty transceivers
			defective hardware
packets deferred	0–100%	1–2%	faulty transceivers
packets per node	prorated capacity		faulty transceiver, overloads
source	prorated capacity		faulty transceiver, overloads
destination	prorated capacity		improper segmentation
source to destination	prorated capacity		improper segmentation
size distribution	64–1518	64–1518	design violations
			faulty software
network period peaks	0–3571	*	statistical overloads
			improper segmentation
node period peaks	0–3571	*	statistical overloads
			improper segmentation

Packet Errors

Statistic ➤ Range ➤ Norm ────────➤ Inference			
alignment errors	*	0	defective hardware
CRC errors	*	0	statistical overloads
			defective hardware
			defective software
short packets	*	0	statistical overloads
			defective hardware
			defective software
long packets	˘	o	statistical overloads
			defective hardware
			defective software
"invisible" packets	*	0	faulty transceiver
incompatible packets	*	*	mismatched hardware
misaddressed packets	*	*	defective hardware
			defective software

legend: all figures are packets per second.
        percentages are a fraction of theoretical capacity.

Channel Utilization

Statistic	Range	Norm	Inference
throughput	0–3571	800	statistical overloads
peak rate	692–3571	varies	overloads
			defective transceiver
utilization rate	0–100%	<35%	statistical overloads

Performance Statistics

Statistic	Range	Norm	Inference
interarrival time	96 μs or greater		statistical overloads
			software error
			user perpetrated
latency time		96 μs or less	timing errors
			defective transceivers
packet size	64–1518	*	defective software
			statistical overloads
channel utilization rate	0–100%	<35%	statistical overloads
			improper network segmentation
node usage rate	*	*	statistical overloads
			improper network segmentation

legend: all figures are packets per second.
    percentages are a fraction of theoretical capacity.

Part 7

Appendix

Appendix A is a glossary with local area network and Ethernet terms defined and cross-referenced by the all-too-common acronyms.

Appendix B is a bibliography of reference materials and some suggested additional readings.

The index is a page index of key words and concepts.

Appendix A

Glossary of Networking Terms

AUI Cable: Attachment Unit Interface cable that connects a workstation to a transceiver or fan-out box. Often called a **drop cable.**

Abnormal Preamble: A packet error that occurs when the preamble doesn't match the legal eight-byte Ethernet synchronization pattern.

Address Error: A packet is improperly labeled with either source or destination information.

Alignment Error: A packet that has not been synchronized correctly. It usually is uncovered as a packet that is not a multiple of eight bits.

Analog: Something that bears a similarity to something else.

Analog Signal: A transmission in which information is represented as physical magnitudes of electrical signals.

Application Level: The seventh layer of the OSI network model design which supports identification of communicating partners, establishes the authority to communicate, transfers information, applies privacy mechanisms and cost allocations. It may be a complex layer. The application layer supports file services, print services, and electronic mail.

BPS: Rate at which data is transmitted over a communications channel. See **Bits Per Second.**

Bandwidth: The range (band) of frequencies that are transmitted on a channel. The difference between the highest and lowest frequencies is expressed in hertz.

Barrel Connectors: A double-sided male coupling that interconnects co-axial sections.

Baseband: A transmission channel which carries a single communications channel, on which only one signal can transmit at a given time.

Bend Radius: The minimum bend allowable for Ethernet coaxial cable. PVC cable is 10 inches. The minimum bend for teflon cable is 18 inches.

Bits Per Second (bps): Rate at which data is transmitted over a channel.

Bridge: A device that interconnects local area networks using similar protocols.

Broadband: A transmission coaxial cable with a wider frequency range (than baseband) that carries individual multiplexed communications channels.

Broadcast: The transmission from one node on a LAN to all other nodes on a LAN.

Bus: A network topology in which nodes are connected to a linear configuration of cable.

CSMA: See **Carrier Sense Multiple Access.**

CSMA/CD: See **Carrier Sense Multiple Access with Collision Detection.**

CRC: See **Cyclic Redundancy Check.**

CRC Error: See **Cyclic Redundancy Check Error.**

Capacitance: The electrical properties of the coaxial cable and network hardware.

Carrier Sense: A signal provided by the Physical Layer to the Data Link Layer indicating that one or more nodes are transmitting on the channel.

Carrier Sense Multiple Access: A communication protocol in which nodes contend for a shared communication channel and all nodes have equal access to the network. It is a channel access control protocol for multiple access transmissions. Each node monitors the channel and transmits only if the channel is idle.

Carrier Sense Multiple Access with Collision Detection (CSMA/CD): A communications protocol in which nodes contend for a shared communications channel and all nodes have equal access to the network. Simultaneous transmissions from two or more nodes results in random restart of those transmissions. It is a refinement of CSMA because transmitting nodes cease transmission when a collision is detected.

Channel: An individual path that carries signals.

Channel Logic: The logical functions between the transceiver cable and the Data Link Layer which support the defined interface between the system and the hardware,

Chatter: The condition resulting when transceiver electronics fail to shut down after a transmission, and the transceiver floods the network with random signals.

Cheapernet: A version of Ethernet that is limited to 200 meters. It uses less expensive connectors, less expensive 75-ohm coaxial cable, and often needs no separate transceiver hardware for transmission.

Client: A network "user," often a **device** or **workstation**.

Client Layer: The collective term that is used to refer to the **Data Link** and **Physical Layers** of the OSI networking model.

Coax: See **Coaxial Cable**.

Coaxial Cable: An insulated, tinned copper conducting wire surrounded by foamed **PVC** or **Teflon**, and shielded by tinned copper braid or an aluminum sleeve. It can carry data transmissions at very high data rates with little loss of information and with a high immunity to outside interference.

Coaxial Cable Section: An unbroken piece of coaxial cable fitted with end connectors and used to build up coaxial cable segments.

Coaxial Cable Segment: A length of coaxial cable consisting of one or more coaxial cable sections and connectors, properly terminated at each end. A 500-meter segment is the longest configuration possible without repeaters.

Collision: The event occurring when two or more nodes contend for the network at the same time. This is usually caused by the time delay that the signal requires to travel the length of the network.

Collision (Error): This network event is not an error in and of itself. It is an indication that two or more nodes attempted to transmit within the same slot. Unless the number of collisions is excessive, this is a "normal" condition.

Collision Detect: A signal provided by the Physical Layer to the Data Link Layer to indicate that one or more other nodes are contending with a node's transmission.

Collision Detection (CD): A node's ability to detect when two or more nodes are transmitting simultaneously on a shared network.

Collision Enforcement: The transmission of extra "jam" bits, after a collision is detected, to insure that all other transmitting nodes detect the collision.

Common Carrier: Companies which provide communication networks (like AT&T).

Contention: The condition occurring when two or more more nodes access the channel at the same time, resulting in a collision.

Core: The central conductor element in a coaxial cable, a large diameter wire usually constructed of copper. See **Coaxial Cable**.

Corrupt Data Error: Condition resulting when hardware components fail.

Cyclic Redundancy Check: A check sum—an error checking algorithm—that the transmitting station includes within a packet. The receiving station generates its own CRC to check against the transmitted CRC. If the results are different, the receiver usually requests a retransmission of the packet. This encoded value is appended to each frame by the Data Link Layer to allow receiving Ethernet controllers to detect transmission errors in the physical channel. This is also called a **Frame Check Sequence.**

Cyclic Redundancy Check Error: An error caused by alignment errors, under- or over-sized packets.

DECnet: Digital Equipment Corporation's vendor implementation of Ethernet.

DTE: Acronym for Data Terminal Equipment. A computer terminal.

Data Compression: A method of reducing the space required to represent data, either as bits, characters, or as graphic images.

Data Link Layer: The second layer OSI network model design. It manages transmissions and error acknowledgment and recovery. Technically, the mechanical devices map data units to data link units, and provide physical error detection and notification, and link activation and de-activation.

Deference: The process by which an ethernet controller delays its transmission when the channel is busy to avoid contention with an ongoing network transmission.

Delni Unit: A type of fan-out box.

Destination Address: The receiving station's **Ethernet Address.** See **Ethernet Address.**

Device: Any item on the network, both logical as in an address that refers to software or hardware and a physical node.

Digital: A representation of information by a unit of length or size.

Digital Transmission: A transmission of information represented by electrical units.

Drop Cable: See **Transceiver Cable** and **AIU Cable.**

Duplex: The method in which communication occurs, either two-way as in **full duplex,** or unidirectional as in **half duplex.**

EMI: See **Electro-Magnetic Interference.**

Electro-Magnetic Interference: Signal noise pollution from radio, radar, or electronic instruments.

End Connector: A female coupling that attaches to the ends of a coaxial cable section to interconnect sections or to accept segment terminators.

Enet: See **Ethernet**.

Ethernet: A popular example of a Local Area Network from which the IEEE 802.3 standard was derived. Ethernet uses the **CSMA/CD** protocol on a **BUS** topology.

Ethernet Address: A coded value indicating the manufacturer, machine type, and a unique identifying number. There are source and destination addresses.

Ethernet Controller: An interface device that provides protocol access for computer equipment to a network. Each node on the network must have an Ethernet controller.

Ethernet PROM: A computer chip containing an **Ethernet Address** that uniquely defines each item of Ethernet-compatible equipment and enables the accurate delivery of packets to the proper destinations.

FCS: See **Frame Check Sequence**.

FCS Error: See **Frame Check Sequence Error**.

FEP: Fluorinated Ethylene Propylene better known as Teflon®. This high temperature insulator is used in cable coatings and foam compositions where building codes specify fire-resistant, high temperature applications.

Fan-out Box: A device that provides the capability to connect multiple workstations to a single transceiver. It also allows the construction of local area networks without coaxial cable, or the construction of concentrated clusters on a coaxial cable. It is often referred to as a **delni**, a **multi-port**, or as a **multi-tap**.

Fiber Optics: Thin glass or plastic cables that transmit data by modulating light pulses.

File Server: A device that provides file services for other nodes. It is a shared resource often with higher speed, larger capacity or better economies of scale than remote data storage.

Forced Collision: A collision that occurs when a packet is transmitted even if traffic (carrier sense) is detected on the network, that is, if the packet will collide with other packets already on the network. When a packet is transmitted and collides, it is received at the destination node with either a **CRC error** or an **alignment error**, if it is received at all.

Frame: See **Packet**.

Frame Check Sequence: Cyclic Redundancy Check. The encoded value appended to each frame by the Data Link Layer to allow receiving Ethernet controllers to detect transmission errors in the physical channel. Also called a Cyclic Redundancy Check.

Frame Check Sequence Error: The condition occurring when the encoded value appended to each frame specifies the received frame as corrupt. See also **Cyclic Redundancy Check Error.**

Full Duplex: A two-way transmission method that echoes characters to insure proper reception.

Gateway: A device that routes information from one network to another. It often interfaces between dissimilar networks and provides protocol translation between the networks. A gateway is also a software connection between different networks; this meaning is not implied in this book.

HPnet: Hewlett-Packard Corporation's vendor version of Ethernet.

Half-Duplex: A one-way transmission method that does not support characters echo.

Handshaking: The exchange of signals between transmitting and receiving devices or their associated modems to establish that each is working and ready to communicate, and to synchronize timing.

Heartbeat: See **Signal Quality Error Heartbeat.**

Hertz: A unit of frequency that is one cycle per second. Ethernet is 10 million hertz, or 10 million cycles per second.

Hunt Group: A series of telephone numbers in sequence that allows the calling party to connect with the first available line.

IEEE: The Institute for Electrical and Electronic Engineering.

IEEE 802: An Institute for Electrical Engineering standard for interconnection of local area networking computer equipment. The IEEE 802 standard describes the physical and link layers of the OSI reference model.

IEEE 802.3: An Ethernet specification derived from the original Xerox Ethernet specifications. It describes the CSMA/CD protocol on a bus topology using baseband transmissions.

ISO: International Standards Organization which created the OSI reference model.

ISN: See **Information System Network.**

Impedance: The mathematical combination of **Resistance** and **Capacitance** that is used as a measurement to describe the electrical properties of the coaxial cable and network hardware.

OLD FORGE LIBRARY

P.O. Box 128
Crosby Blvd.
Old Forge, NY 13420

Librarian
Isabella Worthen
Assistant
Frances Fulton

SERVICES OFFERED:

Special Adirondack
Collection
Job Information Center
Used Books for Sale
Programs for All Ages
Throughout the Year

Parking in Rear
HANDICAP ACCESS

LIBRARY HOURS

Monday	2:00 - 5:00
	7:00 - 9:00
Wednesday	2:00 - 5:00
	7:00 - 9:00
Friday	10:00 - 1:00
	2:00 - 5:00
	7:00 - 9:00

~~SATURDAY   10:00 - 1:00~~

Sat   10 am   1 pm

Phone: (315) 369-6008

Inductance; The property of electrical fields to *induce* a voltage to flow on the coaxial cable and network hardware. It is usually a disruptive signal that interferes with normal network transmissions.

Information System Network: An AT&T-built multipurpose network connectivity device providing bridging and protocol conversions, gateway services, smart repeater performance, and single-node concentration for multiple modems or terminals. It can be repaired while still functioning.

Interface: A device that connects equipment of different types for mutual access. Generally, this refers to computer software and hardware that enable disks and other storage devices to communicate with a computer. In networking, an interface translates different protocols so that different types of computers can communicate together. In the OSI model, the interface is the method of passing data between layers on one device.

Interface Error: A condition indicative of hardware or software incompatibilities.

Interframe Spacing: The 96-millisecond waiting time between transmissions to allow receiving Ethernet controllers to recover.

Internet Address: An address applied at the TCP/IP protocol layer to differentiate network nodes from each other. This is in addition to the **Ethernet Address.**

Internet Protocol: See **Transaction Control Protocol/Internet Protocol.**

Internetworking: Communication between two or more different networks through a **bridge,** a **gateway,** a **modem,** or other routing equipment.

Jabber: To talk without making sense. The condition when a transceiver's carrier sense electronics malfunction, and the transceiver broadcasts in excess of the specified 150-Msec time limit and creates an over-sized frame.

Jabber Frame: A frame that exceeds 1518 bytes in the data field and violates the IEEE 802.3 specifications.

Jam: A short encoded sequence emitted by the transmitting node to ensure that all other nodes have detected a collision, and used for collision enforcement.

LAN: Acronym for Local Area Network.

Late Collision: A collision, indicated by an oversized runt frame, usually indicative of a network exceeding length or size specifications.

Learning Bridge: A smart device that interconnects two local area networks using similar protocols. It learns what nodes are on each connecting segment and routes only that information which is destined for the other segment, therefore improving network performance.

Link Control Field: A data field contained with an an Ethernet packet as part of the **Internet Protocol.**.

Linkage Produc: Any unit that provides an interface between network segments. This includes gateways, bridges, and other specialty components.

Local Area Network: Also referred to by the acronym, LAN. A network limited in size to a floor, building, or city block.

Logical Device: A description that lists how the network references **Physical Devices.**

Logical Link Control: A data link control field occupying the first few bytes of the Ethernet frame data field that initiates, maintains, and terminates any communication.

Long Packet: A packet that exceeds 1518 bytes including address, length, and CRC fields.

Loopback Test: A test for faults over a transmission medium where received data is returned to the sending point (thus traveling a loop) and compared with the data sent.

MAU: See **Media Access Unit.**

MPS: Megabits (1,000,000 decimal units) per second. This is a channel bandwidth. See also **Bandwidth** and **BPS.**

Manchester Encoding: A digital encoding technique in which there is a transition in the middle of each bit time period. A "1" is represented by a high level during the first half of the bit time period whereas a "0" is represented by a low level during the first half of the bit time period.

Media Access Unit: Media Access Unit connects directly to a coaxial cable and broadcasts and receives information over that cable. It is often called a **transceiver.**

Meter: Unit of measurement equivalent to 39.25 inches, or 3.27 feet.

Misaligned Frame: A frame that trails a fragmentary byte (1–7 residual bits), and has an **FCS Error,** or an Ethernet packet that was framed improperly by the receiving station, therefore a **Synchronization Error.**

Modem: A device which converts digital to analog signals and reconverts analog signals back into digital signals for transmission over a network.

Monitor: See **Protocol Analyzer.**

Multicast: The ability to broadcast to a select subset of nodes.

Multimeter: A test tool that measures electrical voltages and resistances. It is also called **Multitester.** Sometimes called an ohmmeter.

Multiport: See **Multi-tap.**

Multi-tap: Fan-out box. A multiple-socket box that provides for a multiple number of workstations to connect to a single node.

Multitester: A test tool that measures electrical voltages and resistances.

NAU: Network Access Unit. See **Ethernet Controller.**

NIDL: See **Network Interface Definition Language.**

NIU: Network Interface Unit. See **Ethernet Controller.**

N-type: A connector designation compatible with 50-ohm, RG-50, and RG-52 coaxial cables.

Network: Hardware and software that allow computers to transmit data over both local and long distances.

Network Computing: The ability of underutilized workstations to broadcast their status and provide automatic parallel compute power.

Network Interface Definition Language: IEEE proposed model for parallel processing and logical process partitioning across a distributed network. See also **Network Computing.**

Network Layer: The third layer of the OSI network model design which activates the routing with network address resolution, flow control in terms of segmentation and blocking, and in the case of Ethernet, collision handling. Also, this layer provides service selection, connection resets, and expedited data transfers. The **Internet Protocol** (IP), a common Ethernet software, runs at this level.

Network Monitor: See **Protocol Analyzer.**

No Backoff Error: A transmission state that results if a transceiver transmits when there is no carrier, but does not wait for the necessary 9.6-microsecond delay.

Node: A logical, nonphysical interconnection to the network that supports computer workstations or other types of physical devices on a network. Alternatively, a node may connect to a **fan-out** unit providing network access for many devices. A device might be a terminal server, a shared peripheral like a file server, printer, or plotter.

Noise: Electrical signal interference on a communication channel that can distort or disrupt data signals. Generally, this refers to **EMI** or **RFI.**

OSI Reference Model: Open Systems Interconnection reference model defined by the International Standards Organization (ISO) which has determined a data communication architectural model for networking.

Ohmmeter: See **Multimeter.**

Optical Fiber: A glass or plastic material drawn into a cable that carries data communications via light modulation.

Over-sized Packet: A packet that exceeds 1518 bytes including address, length, and CRC fields.

PBX: See **Private Branch Exchange.**

PVC: Polyvinyl Chloride. An extensively used insulator in cable coatings and coaxial cable foam compositions.

Packet: A self-contained group of bits representing data and control information. The control information usually includes source and destination addressing, sequencing, flow control, error control information at different protocol levels. Packet length can be fixed or variable depending upon the protocol.

Packet Switching Network: A network transmission methodology that uses data to define a start and length of a transmission for digital communications. A process of sending data in discrete blocks.

Peer-to-Peer Exchange: The ability of computer workstations from the same or different vendors to interconnect and communicate.

Physical Address: The unique address associated with each workstation on a network. An Ethernet physical address is designed to be distinct from *all* other physical addresses on *all* Ethernet networks. A worldwide designation unique to each unit. See **Ethernet Address.**

Physical Channel: The actual wiring and transmission hardware required to implement networking.

Physical Device: Any item of hardware on the network.

Physical Layer: Level 1 of the OSI networking model which insulates the Data Link Layer from the medium-dependent physical characteristics.

Polling: An access method involving a central node asking each node in a predetermined order if it has data to send. This is often used in mainframe environments, and the order is often determined as a function of priority.

Preamble: The 64-bit encoded sequence which the Physical Layer transmits before each frame to synchronize clocks and other Physical Layer circuitry at other nodes on the Ethernet channel.

Presentation Layer: This is the sixth layer of the OSI network model design which transfers information from the application software to the network session layer of the operating system. At this level, software performs data transformations, data formatting, syntax selection (including ascii, ebcdic, or other numeric or graphic formats), device selection and control, and last, data compression or encryption.

Print Server: A device that provides print services for other nodes. It is a shared resource often with higher speed, larger capacity, or better economies-of-scale than local printers.

Private Branch Exchange: Also called a **PBX**. A telephone system used to connect calls between offices in the same complex, and to switch calls between the site and a larger phone network.

Protocol: A formal set of rules by which computers can communicate including session initiation, transmission maintenance, and termination.

Protocol Analyzer: Test equipment that transmits, receives, and captures Ethernet packets to verify proper network operation.

RF: Acronym for radio frequency. Refers to a **Radio Frequency Switch**.

RFI: Acronym for **Radio Frequency Interference**.

RS-232: A standard for interfacing data communications between peripheral devices and the computer.

Radio Frequency Interference: Electronically propogated noise from radar, radio, or electronic sources. See **Electro-Magnetic Interference**.

Radio Frequency Switch: A remote radio frequency trigger relay that electrically switches sections of Ethernet coax and alters network topology.

Repeater: A device that boosts a signal from one network segment and continuing transmission to another similar network segment. Protocols must match on both segments.

Resistance: The measurement of the electrical properties of the coaxial cable and network hardware that describes their ability to hinder the passage of electrons.

Ring: A network topology that has nodes in a circular configuration.

Round-trip Propagation Time: The worst case bit time required for the transmitting node's collision detect jam signal to propagate throughout the network. It is the two-way travel time because the transmitting node needs to receive acknowledgment from all the contending nodes. This delay is the primary component of slot time.

Runt Frame: An Ethernet frame that is too short. A runt frame has fewer than the 60 bytes in the data fields required by the IEEE 802.3. If the frame length is less than 53 bytes, a runt frame indicates a normal collision. A frame less than 60 bytes, but at least 53 bytes, indicates a **late collision**.

SQE: See **Signal Quality Error Heartbeat**.

Section: A length of coaxial cable that forms the transmission medium for a network. Sections are interconnected to form a complete **Segment**. See **Coaxial Cable Section**.

Segment: One or more sections of coaxial cable that forms the transmission medium for a network. A segment is a complete, stand-alone network. Several segments can be interconnected with bridges or repeaters to extend network coverage geographically or for improved performance. See **Coaxial Cable Segment.**

Server: A dedicated processor performing a function such as printing, file storage, or tape storage. See also **File Server** and **Print Server.**

Session Layer: The fifth layer of the OSI network model design. It recognizes the nodes on the LAN and sets up the tables of source and destination addresses. It also establishes, quite literally, a hand-shaking for each session between different nodes. Technically, these services are called session connection, exception reporting, coordination of send/receive modes, and of course, the actual data exchange.

Service Address Point: A data link status value contained within the logical **link control field** of each Ethernet frame data field that initiates, maintains, and terminates any communication.

Shield: A barrier, usually metallic, within a coaxial cable that is designed to contain the high-powered broadcast signal within the cable. The shield reduces **EMI** and **RFI,** and signal loss.

Short Packet: A packet that contains less than 64 bytes, including address, length, and CRC fields.

Signal: A transmission broadcast. The electrical pulse that conveys information.

Signal Interphasing: A technique of overlapping multiple transmission signals simultaneously to achieve higher transmission rates.

Signal Quality Error Heartbeat: A signal from the transceiver to the node peripheral indicating that the transceiver is functioning correctly.

Simplex: A transmission standard that does not echo characters.

Slot Time: A multipurpose parameter to describe the contention behavior of the **Data Link Layer.** It is defined in Ethernet as the propagation delay of the network for a minimum size packet (66 bytes). Slot time provides an upper limit on the collision vulnerability of a given transmission, an upper limit on the size of the frame fragment produced by the collision **runt frame,** and the scheduling time for collision retransmission.

Source Address: The transmitting station's **Ethernet Address.**

Star: A network topology that has all nodes joined at a central location.

Starlan: A TCP/IP and Ethernet version that uses twisted pair or telco wiring in place of coaxial cable. It operates at transmission speeds of 1MPS although 3MPS or 10MPS are possible.

Station: A single addressable **Node** on Ethernet, generally implemented as a stand-alone computer or a peripheral device such as a printer or plotter, connected to Ethernet with a **transceiver** and **Ethernet Controller.** Also termed a **Workstation.**

Stochastic: A process that is random, or probabilistic.

Sub-net: A terminated Ethernet segment that is a portion of a larger network.

Synchronization: The event occurring when transmitting and receiving stations operate in unison for very efficient (or inefficient) utilization of the communications channel.

Synchronization Error: An Ethernet packet that was framed improperly by the receiving station.

TCP/IP: Acronym for **transaction control protocol/internet protocol.** Although commonly referred to as TCP/IP, a complete implementation of this networking protocol includes Transmission Control Protocol (TCP), Internet Protocol (IP), Internetwork Control Message Protocol (ICMP), User Datagram Protocol (UDP), and Address Resolution Protocol (ARP). Standard applications are File Transfer Protocol (FTP), Simple Mail Transfer Protocol (SMTP), and TELNET which provide virtual terminal on any remote network system.

TDR: See **Time Domain Reflectometer.**

Teflon: Trade name for fluorinated ethylene propylene. A nonflammable material used for cable foam and jacketing.

Telco: A reference to modular telephone wiring.

10BASE2: An uncommon reference to the Ethernet standard, specifically **Cheapernet** and **Thinnet** variations. The number scheme designates that these networks are baseband networks with transmission rates of 10 Mbits per second with maximum contiguous coaxial segment lengths of 2×10^2 meters (200 meters).

10BASE5: An uncommon reference to the Ethernet standard. The number scheme designates that these networks are baseband networks with transmission rates of 10 Mbits per second with maximum contiguous coaxial segment lengths of 5×10^2 (500 meters).

10BASE-T: An uncommon reference to the Ethernet standard, specifically to telco wiring and connectors and twisted pair variations. The number scheme designates that these networks are baseband networks with transmission rates of 10 Mbits per second. The maximum contiguous cable segment lengths is usually limited to 100 meters due to the extreme signal interference on the unshielded cabling. There are two versions. One supports bi-directional signaling with dual pair telco wiring thus allowing hardware to see collisions. The other version uses single pair to support daisy-chaining of multiple workstations. Note that duplicate repeaters are required for the dual pair telco.

Terminal Server: A computer device that provides low-speed DTE network access. A device for connecting terminals to a network.

Terminator: A resistor that absorbs spent broadcast signals at the ends of each coaxial cable segment. A terminator must be properly installed at each segment endpoint for Ethernet to operate.

Thicknet: An Ethernet variation utilizing standard 50-ohm coaxial cable. It is IEEE 802.3 and Ethernet standard.

Thinnet: An Ethernet variation utilizing 75-ohm coaxial cable rather than the 50-ohm standard.

Time Division Multiplexer: A method using specific time slots to access a communication link. This is accomplished by combining data from several devices into one transmission.

Time Domain Reflectometer: Test equipment that verifies proper functioning of the physical components of the network with a sequence of time delayed electrical pulses. Primarily, this tool checks for contiguity and isolation of coaxial cable.

Time Domain Reflectometry: The process of testing transmission lines for proper electrical functioning.

Topology: Layout of a network. This describes how the nodes are physically joined to each other.

Traffic: A measure of Ethernet network load which refers to the packet transmission rate (frames/second or frames/hour).

Transaction Control Protocol/Internet Protocol: Common communication protocol conforming to the Network and Transport Layers that provides transmission routing control and data transfer.

Transceiver: The Physical Layer electronics that connect directly to the coaxial cable. See **Media Access Unit**.

Transceiver Cable: A four pair, shielded cable that interconnects a workstation to a transceiver or fan-out box. Often called a **Drop Cable** or **AUI Cable**.

Transceiver Chatter: See **Chatter**.

Transmission Deferred: The act of not transmitting when such transmission would create a **Collision**. This is sometimes called an avoidance of contention. See also **Deference**.

Transceiver Exerciser: see **Transceiver Tester**.

Transceiver Jabber: See **Jabber Frame**.

Transceiver Tester: Test equipment that exercises the full functionality of an Ethernet transceiver and verifies its correct operation.

Transmission Error: Catch-all term for a **CRC Error**. Such errors are caused by **Alignment Errors, Under-** or **Over-sized Packets**, plus a variety of application, system software, or hardware failures.

Transport Layer: The fourth layer of the OSI network model design which controls data transfer and transmission control. This software level is called **Transaction Control Protocol** (TCP), the common Ethernet software.

Twisted Pair: Telephone wire twisted over its length to preserve signal strength and minimize **Electro-Magnetic Interference**.

Type Error: A packet that is improperly labeled with protocol information.

UDP: User Datagram Protocol. A simplified version of the **Transmission Control Protocol** for application level data.

Undercarpet Ribbon: A specialized coaxial cable designed for installation in walkways and undercarpet applications, as its name implies. This cable is best used for lengths not too exceed five feet.

Under-sized Packet: A packet that contains less than 64 bytes, including address, length, and CRC fields.

WAN: Wide Area Network. A network that spans cities, states, countries, or oceans. **PBX** services usually supply the network links.

Workstation: A single addressable site on Ethernet, generally implemented as a stand-alone computer or a peripheral device, connected to Ethernet with a **Transceiver** and **Ethernet Controller**. Also termed a **Station**.

XNS: Xerox Network System. This is a vendor implementation of Ethernet.

Appendix B

Bibliography

1. DEC–INTEL–XEROX, *The Ethernet, A Local Computer Network, Data Link Layer and Physical Layer, Version 1.0*, September 30, 1980.

2. John F. Shoch and Jon A. Hupp, *Performance of an Ethernet Local Network—A Preliminary Report, Local Area Communications Symposium*, Mitre and NBS, Boston Massachusetts, May 1979.

3. *Internet Protocol Transition Workbook*, March 1981, SRI International, Menlo Park, California, 94025.

4. Frederich S. Hiller and Gerald J. Lieberman, *Operations Research*, Holden-Day, Inc. 1974.

5. Peter J. Bickel and Kjell A. Doksum, *Mathematical Statistics: Basic Ideas and Selected Topics*, Holden-Day, Inc. 1977.

6. P. T. Wang and Michael McGinn, Mitre Corporation, *Performance of a Stochastically Optimized CMSA Network*, /0742/1303/85/000/0061 IEEE. 1979.

7. American National Standards Institute (ANSI), *Advanced Data Communications Control Procedures* (ADCCP), ANSI X3.66. New York, 1979.

8. *IEEE Standards for Local Area Networks: Logical Link Control Procedures*, IEEE, New York, 1985.

9. Jeannie Hammond, Spider Systems Limited, Edinborough EH6 5JQ, United Kingdom.

10. James Fetterolf, AMP Incorporated. Valley Forge, Pennsylvania, 01776.

11. National Security Decisions Directive (issued September 17, 1984, #14 unclassified).

12. SST Company, PO Box 771, Brookline, Massachusetts, 02146–0771.

13. Kathleen Babcock, Hewlett-Packard Corporation, Boulder CO.

14. Kevin MacLean, Cabletron Systems, Incorporated, East Rochester, NH 03867.

15. C. E. Shannon, *The Mathematical Theory of Communications,* University of Illinois Press, Urbana, Illinois, 1964.

16. John Campbell, *Grammatical Man,* Simon and Schuster. New York, 1982.

17. Elizabeth Grieser, Triplett Corporation, Bluffton, OH 45817

Index